Volvo V70
Owners Workshop Manual
Chris Randall

Models covered *(5557 - 304)*

V70 Estate with 1.6 litre (1560cc), 2.0 litre (1998cc & 1984cc) & 2.4 litre (2400cc) 4-cyl & 5-cyl turbo-diesel engines

*Does NOT cover 2.4 litre twin-turbo diesel engine, models with petrol engines,
'FlexiFuel' models, or vehicles with AWD or 'Powershift' transmission*

© Haynes Publishing 2012

ABCDE
FGHIJ
KLMNO
PQRST

A book in the **Haynes Owners Workshop Manual Series**

ISBN 978 0 85733 557 9

British Library Cataloguing in Publication Data
A catalogue record for this book is available from the British Library.

Printed in the USA

Haynes Publishing
Sparkford, Yeovil, Somerset BA22 7JJ, England

Haynes North America, Inc
861 Lawrence Drive, Newbury Park, California 91320, USA

Haynes Publishing Nordiska AB
Box 1504, 751 45 UPPSALA, Sverige

Contents

Contents

REPAIRS AND OVERHAUL

The Volvo V70 Estate models were originally introduced in 2000, being based on the platform of the S80 model introduced a year earlier. Following a facelift in 2004, a new model (the subject of this manual) was introduced in 2007. Although visually quite similar to the old V70, the new model introduced a range of improved diesel engines including, from 2009, an economy-focused 'DRIVe' unit and from 2010 the replacement of the 4-cylinder 2.0 litre unit with a 5-cylinder version of the same capacity. Also new for this model were redesigned interiors, and a range of new comfort and safety features.

This manual covers the full range of diesel engines on offer, the only exception being the twin-turbo version of the 2.4 litre engine that was introduced for the 2011 model year.

Transmissions are either 5- or 6-speed manual, or 6-speed 'Geartronic' automatic with computer control. The automatic transmission features mode control selection, allowing the driver to alter the transmission characteristics to suit normal or winter driving requirements.

Braking is by discs all round with anti-lock braking (ABS) and power-assisted steering standard on all models.

A wide range of standard and optional equipment is available within the range to suit virtually all tastes. As with all Volvo models, safety features are of paramount importance, and the comprehensive airbag system and Side Impact Protection System (SIPS) offer an exceptional level of driver and passenger protection throughout the vehicle.

Provided that regular servicing is carried out in accordance with the manufacturer's recommendations, the Volvo V70 should provide many years of reliable service. Despite the engine's complexity, the engine compartment is relatively spacious, and most of the items requiring frequent attention are easily accessible.

Your Volvo manual

The aim of this manual is to help you get the best value from your vehicle. It can do so in several ways. It can help you decide what work must be done (even should you choose to get it done by a garage). It will also provide information on routine maintenance and servicing, and give a logical course of action and diagnosis when random faults occur. However, it is hoped that you will use the manual by tackling the work yourself. On simpler jobs it may even be quicker than booking the car into a garage and going there twice, to leave and collect it. Perhaps most important, a lot of money can be saved by avoiding the costs a garage must charge to cover its labour and overheads.

The manual has drawings and descriptions to show the function of the various components so that their layout can be understood. Tasks are described and photographed in a clear step-by-step sequence. The illustrations are numbered by the Section number and paragraph number to which they relate – if there is more than one illustration per paragraph, the sequence is denoted alphabetically.

References to the 'left' or 'right' of the vehicle are in the sense of a person in the driver's seat, facing forwards.

Acknowledgements

Certain illustrations are the copyright of Volvo Car Corporation, and are used with their permission. Thanks are due to Draper Tools Limited, who provided some of the workshop tools, and to all those people at Sparkford who helped in the production of this manual.

We take great pride in the accuracy of information given in this manual, but vehicle manufacturers make alterations and design changes during the production run of a particular vehicle of which they do not inform us. No liability can be accepted by the authors or publishers for loss, damage or injury caused by any errors in, or omissions from the information given.

Project vehicles

The main vehicle used in the preparation of this manual, and which appears in many of the photographic sequences, was a 2009 Volvo V70 fitted with the 5-cylinder 2.4 litre D5 diesel engine.

Working on your car can be dangerous. This page shows just some of the potential risks and hazards, with the aim of creating a safety-conscious attitude.

General hazards

Scalding

• Don't remove the radiator or expansion tank cap while the engine is hot.

• Engine oil, transmission fluid or power steering fluid may also be dangerously hot if the engine has recently been running.

Burning

• Beware of burns from the exhaust system and from any part of the engine. Brake discs and drums can also be extremely hot immediately after use.

Crushing

• When working under or near a raised vehicle, always supplement the jack with axle stands, or use drive-on ramps.

Never venture under a car which is only supported by a jack.

• Take care if loosening or tightening high-torque nuts when the vehicle is on stands. Initial loosening and final tightening should be done with the wheels on the ground.

Fire

• Fuel is highly flammable; fuel vapour is explosive.

• Don't let fuel spill onto a hot engine.

• Do not smoke or allow naked lights (including pilot lights) anywhere near a vehicle being worked on. Also beware of creating sparks (electrically or by use of tools).

• Fuel vapour is heavier than air, so don't work on the fuel system with the vehicle over an inspection pit.

• Another cause of fire is an electrical overload or short-circuit. Take care when repairing or modifying the vehicle wiring.

• Keep a fire extinguisher handy, of a type suitable for use on fuel and electrical fires.

Electric shock

• Ignition HT and Xenon headlight voltages can be dangerous, especially to people with heart problems or a pacemaker. Don't work on or near these systems with the engine running or the ignition switched on.

• Mains voltage is also dangerous. Make sure that any mains-operated equipment is correctly earthed. Mains power points should be protected by a residual current device (RCD) circuit breaker.

Fume or gas intoxication

• Exhaust fumes are poisonous; they can contain carbon monoxide, which is rapidly fatal if inhaled. Never run the engine in a confined space such as a garage with the doors shut.

• Fuel vapour is also poisonous, as are the vapours from some cleaning solvents and paint thinners.

Poisonous or irritant substances

• Avoid skin contact with battery acid and with any fuel, fluid or lubricant, especially antifreeze, brake hydraulic fluid and Diesel fuel. Don't syphon them by mouth. If such a substance is swallowed or gets into the eyes, seek medical advice.

• Prolonged contact with used engine oil can cause skin cancer. Wear gloves or use a barrier cream if necessary. Change out of oil-soaked clothes and do not keep oily rags in your pocket.

• Air conditioning refrigerant forms a poisonous gas if exposed to a naked flame (including a cigarette). It can also cause skin burns on contact.

Asbestos

• Asbestos dust can cause cancer if inhaled or swallowed. Asbestos may be found in gaskets and in brake and clutch linings. When dealing with such components it is safest to assume that they contain asbestos.

Special hazards

Hydrofluoric acid

• This extremely corrosive acid is formed when certain types of synthetic rubber, found in some O-rings, oil seals, fuel hoses etc, are exposed to temperatures above 4000C. The rubber changes into a charred or sticky substance containing the acid. *Once formed, the acid remains dangerous for years. If it gets onto the skin, it may be necessary to amputate the limb concerned.*

• When dealing with a vehicle which has suffered a fire, or with components salvaged from such a vehicle, wear protective gloves and discard them after use.

The battery

• Batteries contain sulphuric acid, which attacks clothing, eyes and skin. Take care when topping-up or carrying the battery.

• The hydrogen gas given off by the battery is highly explosive. Never cause a spark or allow a naked light nearby. Be careful when connecting and disconnecting battery chargers or jump leads.

Air bags

• Air bags can cause injury if they go off accidentally. Take care when removing the steering wheel and trim panels. Special storage instructions may apply.

Diesel injection equipment

• Diesel injection pumps supply fuel at very high pressure. Take care when working on the fuel injectors and fuel pipes.

Warning: Never expose the hands, face or any other part of the body to injector spray; the fuel can penetrate the skin with potentially fatal results.

Remember...

DO

• Do use eye protection when using power tools, and when working under the vehicle.

• Do wear gloves or use barrier cream to protect your hands when necessary.

• Do get someone to check periodically that all is well when working alone on the vehicle.

• Do keep loose clothing and long hair well out of the way of moving mechanical parts.

• Do remove rings, wristwatch etc, before working on the vehicle – especially the electrical system.

• Do ensure that any lifting or jacking equipment has a safe working load rating adequate for the job.

DON'T

• Don't attempt to lift a heavy component which may be beyond your capability – get assistance.

• Don't rush to finish a job, or take unverified short cuts.

• Don't use ill-fitting tools which may slip and cause injury.

• Don't leave tools or parts lying around where someone can trip over them. Mop up oil and fuel spills at once.

• Don't allow children or pets to play in or near a vehicle being worked on.

The following pages are intended to help in dealing with common roadside emergencies and breakdowns. You will find more detailed fault finding information at the back of the manual, and repair information in the main chapters.

If your car won't start and the starter motor doesn't turn

☐ If it's a model with automatic transmission, make sure the selector is in P or N.
☐ Open the bonnet and make sure that the battery terminals are clean and tight.
☐ Switch on the headlights and try to start the engine. If the headlights go very dim when you're trying to start, the battery is probably flat. Get out of trouble by jump starting using a friend's car.

If your car won't start even though the starter motor turns as normal

☐ Is there fuel in the tank?
☐ Is there moisture on electrical components under the bonnet? Switch off the ignition, then wipe off any obvious dampness with a dry cloth. Spray a water-repellent aerosol product (WD-40 or equivalent) on fuel system electrical connectors like those shown in the photos.

A Check the fuel injection system airflow meter wiring is secure.

B Check the condition and security of the battery connections.

C Check the fuses in the panel under the bonnet.

Check that electrical connections are secure (with the ignition switched off) and spray them with a water dispersant spray like WD-40 if you suspect a problem due to damp.

Jump starting

Jump starting will get you out of trouble, but you must correct whatever made the battery go flat in the first place. There are three possibilities:

1 *The battery has been drained by repeated attempts to start, or by leaving the lights on.*

2 *The charging system is not working properly (alternator drivebelt slack or broken, alternator wiring fault or alternator itself faulty).*

3 *The battery itself is at fault (electrolyte low, or battery worn out).*

When jump-starting a car, observe the following precautions:

✓ Before connecting the booster battery, make sure that the ignition is switched off.

Caution: Remove the key in case the central locking engages when the jump leads are connected

✓ Ensure that all electrical equipment (lights, heater, wipers, etc) is switched off.

✓ Take note of any special precautions printed on the battery case.

✓ Make sure that the booster battery is the same voltage as the discharged one in the vehicle.

✓ If the battery is being jump-started from the battery in another vehicle, the two vehicles MUST NOT TOUCH each other.

✓ Make sure that the transmission is in neutral (or PARK, in the case of automatic transmission).

Budget jump leads can be a false economy, as they often do not pass enough current to start large capacity or diesel engines. They can also get hot.

1 Connect one end of the red jump lead to the positive (+) terminal of the flat battery

2 Connect the other end of the red lead to the positive (+) terminal of the booster battery.

3 Connect one end of the black jump lead to the negative (-) terminal of the booster battery

4 Connect the other end of the black jump lead to a bolt or bracket on the engine block, well away from the battery, on the vehicle to be started.

5 Make sure that the jump leads will not come into contact with the fan, drive-belts or other moving parts of the engine.

6 Start the engine using the booster battery and run it at idle speed. Switch on the lights, rear window demister and heater blower motor, then disconnect the jump leads in the reverse order of connection. Turn off the lights etc.

Wheel changing

Some of the details shown here will vary according to model. For instance, some models may have steel wheels with plastic covers rather than the alloy wheels shown.

⚠️ *Warning: Do not change a wheel in a situation where you risk being hit by another vehicle. On busy roads, try to stop in a lay-by or a gateway. Be wary of passing traffic while changing the wheel – it is easy to become distracted by the job in hand.*

Preparation

☐ When a puncture occurs, stop as soon as it is safe to do so.
☐ Park on firm level ground, if possible, and well out of the way of other traffic.
☐ Use hazard warning lights if necessary.
☐ If you have one, use a warning triangle to alert other drivers of your presence.
☐ Apply the handbrake and engage first or reverse gear (or Park on models with automatic transmission).
☐ If the ground is soft, use a flat piece of wood to spread the load under the jack.

Changing the wheel

1 The spare is stored beneath the luggage compartment floor covering. The jack and toolkit are located in a tray within the spare wheel. Lift out the tray, undo the plastic nut and lift the spare wheel from the well in the floor.

2 Chock a front or rear wheel as appropriate.

3 On models with alloy wheels, a Volvo socket may be needed to remove the security bolt – the socket should be in the glovebox or toolkit.

4 Slacken each wheel bolt half a turn using the wheel brace. If the bolts are too tight DON'T stand on the brace to undo them – call for assistance.

5 Engage the jack head with the reinforced bracket located in the sill on each side of the car (don't jack the vehicle at any other point on the sill).

6 Turn the handle clockwise until the wheel is raised clear of the ground, then unscrew the wheel bolts and remove the wheel.

7 Once the wheel has been removed it should be placed beneath the sill as a precaution against the jack falling.

Finally...
☐ Remove the wheel chocks.
☐ Stow the jack and tools in the correct locations in the car.
☐ Check the tyre pressure on the wheel just fitted. If it is low, or if you don't have a pressure gauge with you, drive slowly to the nearest garage and inflate the tyre to the right pressure.
☐ Have the damaged tyre or wheel repaired as soon as possible.

8 Fit the spare wheel, ensuring it locates correctly on the hub.

9 With the spare wheel fitted, tighten the bolts moderately with the wheel brace. Lower the vehicle to the ground then finally tighten the wheel bolts in a diagonal sequence. Refit the wheel cover/bolt caps as applicable. Note that the wheel bolts should be tightened to the specified torque at the earliest opportunity.

Note: *If a temporary 'space-saver' spare wheel has been fitted, special conditions apply to its use. This type of spare wheel is only intended for use in an emergency, and should not remain fitted any longer than it takes to get the punctured wheel repaired. While the temporary wheel is in use, do not exceed 50 mph, and avoid harsh acceleration, braking or cornering. Note that, besides being narrower than a normal roadwheel, the temporary spare wheel is of smaller diameter; therefore, since ground clearance will be slightly reduced with the temporary spare in use, take care when travelling over rough ground.*

Towing

When all else fails, you may find yourself having to get a tow home – or of course you may be helping somebody else. Long-distance recovery should only be done by a garage or breakdown service. For shorter distances, DIY towing using another car is easy enough, but observe the following points:
☐ Use a proper tow-rope or solid towing bar – they are not expensive. The vehicle being towed must display an ON TOW sign in its rear window.
☐ Always insert the remote unit when the vehicle is being towed, so that the steering lock is released, and that the direction indicator and brake lights will work.
☐ A rear towing eye is provided below the right-hand side of the bumper. The front towing eye is provided behind the cover on the right-hand side of the front bumper – pull the cover from the bumper and screw in the towing hook supplied with the vehicle **(see illustrations)**.
☐ Before being towed, release the handbrake and select neutral on the transmission. On models with automatic transmission, do

not exceed 30 mph or tow for more than 30 miles. In doubt, do not tow, or transmission damage may result.
☐ Note that greater-than-usual pedal pressure will be required to operate the brakes, since the vacuum servo unit is only operational with the engine running.
☐ Greater-than-usual steering effort will also be required.

☐ The driver of the car being towed must keep the tow-rope taut at all times to avoid snatching.
☐ Make sure that both drivers know the route before setting off.
☐ Only drive at moderate speeds and keep the distance towed to a minimum. Drive smoothly and allow plenty of time for slowing down at junctions.

Identifying leaks

Puddles on the garage floor or drive, or obvious wetness under the bonnet or underneath the car, suggest a leak that needs investigating. It can sometimes be difficult to decide where the leak is coming from, especially if an engine undershield is fitted. Leaking oil or fluid can also be blown rearwards by the passage of air under the car, giving a false impression of where the problem lies.

 Warning: Most automotive oils and fluids are poisonous. Wash them off skin, and change out of contaminated clothing, without delay.

 The smell of a fluid leaking from the car may provide a clue to what's leaking. Some fluids are distinctively coloured. It may help to remove the engine undershield, clean the car carefully and to park it over some clean paper overnight as an aid to locating the source of the leak.
Remember that some leaks may only occur while the engine is running.

Sump oil

Engine oil may leak from the drain plug...

Oil from filter

...or from the base of the oil filter.

Gearbox oil

Gearbox oil can leak from the seals at the inboard ends of the driveshafts.

Antifreeze

Leaking antifreeze often leaves a crystalline deposit like this.

Brake fluid

A leak occurring at a wheel is almost certainly brake fluid.

Power steering fluid

Power steering fluid may leak from the pipe connectors on the steering rack.

Introduction

There are some very simple checks which need only take a few minutes to carry out, but which could save you a lot of inconvenience and expense.

These checks require no great skill or special tools, and the small amount of time they take to perform could prove to be very well spent, for example;

☐ Keeping an eye on tyre condition and pressures, will not only help to stop them wearing out prematurely, but could also save your life.

☐ Many breakdowns are caused by electrical problems. Battery-related faults are particularly common, and a quick check on a regular basis will often prevent the majority of these.

☐ If your car develops a brake fluid leak, the first time you might know about it is when your brakes don't work properly. Checking the level regularly will give advance warning of this kind of problem.

☐ If the oil or coolant levels run low, the cost of repairing any engine damage will be far greater than fixing the leak, for example.

Underbonnet check points

◀ **2.4 litre engine shown, other models are similar**

A *Engine oil level dipstick*

B *Engine oil filler cap*

C *Coolant expansion tank*

D *Washer fluid reservoir*

E *Brake fluid reservoir*

F *Power steering fluid reservoir*

Coolant level

 Warning: DO NOT attempt to remove the expansion tank pressure cap when the engine is hot, as there is a very great risk of scalding. Do not leave open containers of coolant about, as it is poisonous.

Car care

● With a sealed-type cooling system, adding coolant should not be necessary on a regular basis. If frequent topping-up is required, it is likely there is a leak. Check the radiator, all hoses and joint faces for signs of staining or wetness, and rectify as necessary.

● It is important that antifreeze is used in the cooling system all year round, not just during the winter months, as it helps to prevent corrosion in the cooling system. Don't top-up with water alone, as the antifreeze will become too diluted.

1 The coolant level varies with the temperature of the engine. When the engine is cold, the coolant level should be between the MIN and MAX marks.

2 If topping-up is necessary, wait until the engine is cold. Slowly unbolt the cap to release any pressure present in the cooling system, and remove the cap.

3 Add a mixture of water and antifreeze to the expansion tank until the coolant level is on the MAX mark.

Engine oil level

Before you start

✔ Make sure that your car is on level ground.
✔ Check the oil level before the car is driven, or at least 5 minutes after the engine has been switched off.

 HAYNES HiNT *If the oil is checked immediately after driving the vehicle, some of the oil will remain in the upper engine components, resulting in an inaccurate reading on the dipstick.*

The correct oil

Modern engines place great demands on their oil. It is very important that the correct oil for your car is used (see *Lubricants and fluids*).

Car care

● If you have to add oil frequently, you should check whether you have any oil leaks. Place some clean paper under the car overnight, and check for stains in the morning. If there are no leaks, the engine may be burning oil.
● Always maintain the level between the upper and lower dipstick marks. If the level is too low severe engine damage may occur. Oil seal failure may result if the engine is overfilled by adding too much oil.

1 The dipstick is located on the front of the engine (see *Underbonnet check points* for exact location). Withdraw the dipstick.

2 Using a clean rag or paper towel, wipe all oil from the dipstick. Insert the clean dipstick into the tube as far as it will go, then withdraw it again.

3 Note the oil level on the end of the dipstick, which should be between the upper and lower mark. Approximately 1.0 litre of oil will raise the level from the lower mark to the upper mark.

4 Oil is added through the filler cap on top of the engine. Turn the cap through a quarter-turn anti-clockwise and withdraw it.

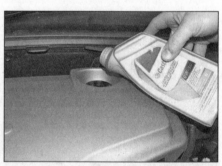

5 Top-up the level. A funnel may help to reduce spillage. Add the oil slowly, checking the level on the dipstick often. Do not overfill.

Brake (and clutch) fluid level

Warning:
● *Brake fluid can harm your eyes and damage painted surfaces, so use extreme caution when handling and pouring it.*
● *Do not use fluid that has been standing open for some time, as it absorbs moisture from the air, which can cause a dangerous loss of braking effectiveness.*

● *The fluid level in the reservoir will drop slightly as the brake pads wear down, but the fluid level must never be allowed to drop below the MIN mark.*

HAYNES HINT *Make sure that your car is on level ground.*

Safety first!

● If the reservoir requires repeated topping-up this is an indication of a fluid leak somewhere in the system, which should be investigated immediately.
● If a leak is suspected, the car should not be driven until the braking/clutch system has been checked. Never take any risks where brakes are concerned.

1 The MAX and MIN marks are indicated on the reservoir. The fluid level must be kept within the marks at all times.

2 Unscrew the cover on the right-hand side of the plenum cover. Clean the area around the filler cap to prevent dirt entering the hydraulic system.

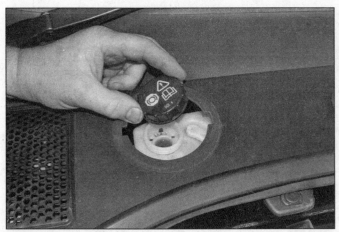

3 Unscrew the cap and inspect the reservoir – if the fluid is dirty the hydraulic system should be drained and refilled (see Chapter 1).

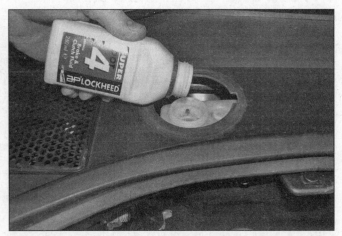

4 Carefully add fluid, taking care not to spill it onto the surrounding areas. Use only the specified fluid as mixing different types can cause damage to the system. After topping-up to the correct level, securely refit the cap and wipe off any spilt fluid.

Tyre condition and pressure

It is very important that tyres are in good condition, and at the correct pressure - having a tyre failure at any speed is highly dangerous. Tyre wear is influenced by driving style - harsh braking and acceleration, or fast cornering, will all produce more rapid tyre wear. As a general rule, the front tyres wear out faster than the rears. Interchanging the tyres from front to rear ("rotating" the tyres) may result in more even wear. However, if this is completely effective, you may have the expense of replacing all four tyres at once!

Remove any nails or stones embedded in the tread before they penetrate the tyre to cause deflation. If removal of a nail does reveal that the tyre has been punctured, refit the nail so that its point of penetration is marked. Then immediately change the wheel, and have the tyre repaired by a tyre dealer.

Regularly check the tyres for damage in the form of cuts or bulges, especially in the sidewalls. Periodically remove the wheels, and clean any dirt or mud from the inside and outside surfaces. Examine the wheel rims for signs of rusting, corrosion or other damage. Light alloy wheels are easily damaged by "kerbing" whilst parking; steel wheels may also become dented or buckled. A new wheel is very often the only way to overcome severe damage.

New tyres should be balanced when they are fitted, but it may become necessary to re-balance them as they wear, or if the balance weights fitted to the wheel rim should fall off. Unbalanced tyres will wear more quickly, as will the steering and suspension components. Wheel imbalance is normally signified by vibration, particularly at a certain speed (typically around 50 mph). If this vibration is felt only through the steering, then it is likely that just the front wheels need balancing. If, however, the vibration is felt through the whole car, the rear wheels could be out of balance. Wheel balancing should be carried out by a tyre dealer or garage.

1 ***Tread Depth - visual check***
The original tyres have tread wear safety bands (B), which will appear when the tread depth reaches approximately 1.6 mm. The band positions are indicated by a triangular mark on the tyre sidewall (A).

2 ***Tread Depth - manual check***
Alternatively, tread wear can be monitored with a simple, inexpensive device known as a tread depth indicator gauge.

3 ***Tyre Pressure Check***
Check the tyre pressures regularly with the tyres cold. Do not adjust the tyre pressures immediately after the vehicle has been used, or an inaccurate setting will result.

Tyre tread wear patterns

Shoulder Wear

Underinflation (wear on both sides)
Under-inflation will cause overheating of the tyre, because the tyre will flex too much, and the tread will not sit correctly on the road surface. This will cause a loss of grip and excessive wear, not to mention the danger of sudden tyre failure due to heat build-up.
Check and adjust pressures
Incorrect wheel camber (wear on one side)
Repair or renew suspension parts
Hard cornering
Reduce speed!

Centre Wear

Overinflation
Over-inflation will cause rapid wear of the centre part of the tyre tread, coupled with reduced grip, harsher ride, and the danger of shock damage occurring in the tyre casing.
Check and adjust pressures

If you sometimes have to inflate your car's tyres to the higher pressures specified for maximum load or sustained high speed, don't forget to reduce the pressures to normal afterwards.

Uneven Wear

Front tyres may wear unevenly as a result of wheel misalignment. Most tyre dealers and garages can check and adjust the wheel alignment (or "tracking") for a modest charge.
Incorrect camber or castor
Repair or renew suspension parts
Malfunctioning suspension
Repair or renew suspension parts
Unbalanced wheel
Balance tyres
Incorrect toe setting
Adjust front wheel alignment
Note: *The feathered edge of the tread which typifies toe wear is best checked by feel.*

Power steering fluid level

Before you start
✔ Park the vehicle on level ground.
✔ Set the steering wheel straight-ahead.
✔ The engine should be cold and turned off.

Safety first!
● The power steering fluid reservoir is located on the right-hand side of the engine compartment, just in front of the coolant expansion tank.

● Check for leaks if frequent topping-up is required. Do not run the engine without fluid in the reservoir.

1 The MAX and MIN marks are indicated on the reservoir. The fluid level must be kept within the marks at all times.

2 If topping-up is necessary, wipe clean the area around the reservoir filler neck, and unscrew the filler cap from the reservoir. Use clean fluid of the specified type (see *Lubricants and fluids*).

Washer fluid level

● Screenwash additives not only keep the windscreen clean during foul weather, they also prevent the washer system freezing in cold weather – which is when you are likely to need it most. Don't top-up using plain water as the screenwash will become too diluted, and will freeze during cold weather.

⚠ *Warning: On no account use coolant antifreeze in the washer system – this could discolour or damage paintwork.*

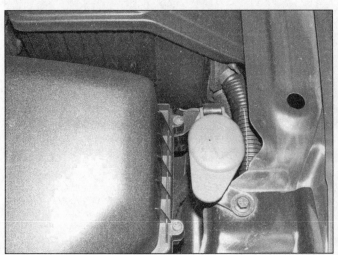

1 The washer fluid reservoir filler is located at the front left-hand side of the engine compartment (the reservoir itself is located behind the front bumper).

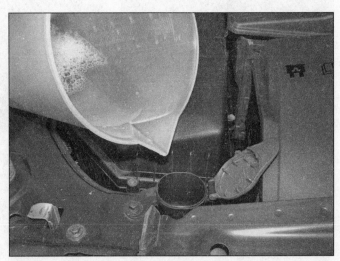

2 When topping-up the reservoir, a screenwash additive should be added in the quantities recommended on the bottle.

Battery

Caution: Before carrying out any work on the vehicle battery, read the precautions given in Safety first! at the start of this manual.

✔ Make sure that the battery tray is in good condition, and that the clamp is tight. Corrosion on the tray, retaining clamp and the battery itself can be removed with a solution of water and baking soda. Thoroughly rinse all cleaned areas with water. Any metal parts damaged by corrosion should be covered with a zinc-based primer, then painted.

✔ Periodically (approximately every three months), check the charge condition of the battery as described in Chapter 5A.

✔ If the battery is flat, and you need to jump start your vehicle, see *Roadside repairs*.

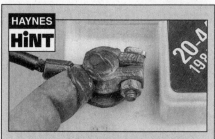

HAYNES HiNT

Battery corrosion can be kept to a minimum by applying a layer of petroleum jelly to the clamps and terminals after they are reconnected.

1 The battery is located under a cover on the left-hand side of the engine compartment.

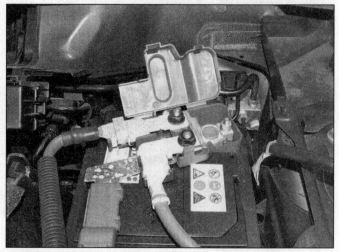

2 Check the tightness of the positive (+) terminal clamps . . .

3 . . . and the negative (-) terminal clamp. You should not be able to move them. Also check each cable for cracks and frayed conductors.

4 If corrosion (white, fluffy deposits) is evident, remove the cables from the battery terminals, clean them with a small wire brush, then refit them. Automotive stores sell a tool for cleaning the battery post . . .

5 . . . as well as the battery cable clamps.

Electrical systems

✔ Check all external lights and the horn. Refer to the appropriate Sections of Chapter 12 for details if any of the circuits are found to be inoperative.
✔ Visually check all accessible wiring connectors, harnesses and retaining clips for security, and for signs of chafing or damage.

HAYNES HINT *If you need to check your brake lights and indicators unaided, back up to a wall or garage door and operate the lights. The reflected light should show if they are working properly.*

1 If a single indicator light, brake light or headlight has failed, it is likely that a bulb has blown and will need to be renewed. Refer to Chapter 12 for details. If both brake lights have failed, it is possible that the brake light switch operated by the brake pedal has failed. Refer to Chapter 9 for details.

2 The fuses are located in the fusebox on the left-hand side of the engine compartment.

3 To renew a blown fuse, simply pull it out using the plastic tweezers provided. Fit a new fuse of the same rating (see Chapter 12). If the fuse blows again, it is important that you find out why – a complete checking procedure is given in Chapter 12.

4 Additional fuses are located in the luggage compartment behind the side trim panel on the left-hand side.

Wiper blades

1 Check the condition of the wiper blades; if they are cracked or show any signs of deterioration, or if the glass swept area is smeared, renew them. Wiper blades should be renewed annually.

2 Depending on the type of wiper blade fitted, swivel the blade through 90 degrees, press the locking tab with your finger and slide the blade out of the arm's hooked end.

3 Alternatively, pull the arm fully away from the glass until it locks. Squeeze together the retaining clips and pull them away from the blade, then slide the blade from the end of the arm. Push the blade firmly home to refit.

Lubricants and fluids

Engine . . . .   Multigrade engine oil, viscosity SAE 0W-30

Cooling system. . . . .   Refer to dealer

Transmission
   Manual gearbox . . . .   Volvo oil MTF 97309
   Automatic transmission. . . . .   Volvo automatic transmission fluid JWS 3309

Braking and clutch systems . . . .   Hydraulic fluid to DOT 4+

Power steering system . . . .   Volvo power steering fluid M2C204-A

Tyre pressures

Note: *The recommended tyre pressures for each vehicle are given on a sticker attached to the driver's door pillar. The pressures given are for the original equipment tyres – the recommended pressures may vary if any other make or type of tyre is fitted; check with the tyre manufacturer or supplier for latest recommendations.*

Chapter 1
Routine maintenance and servicing

Contents

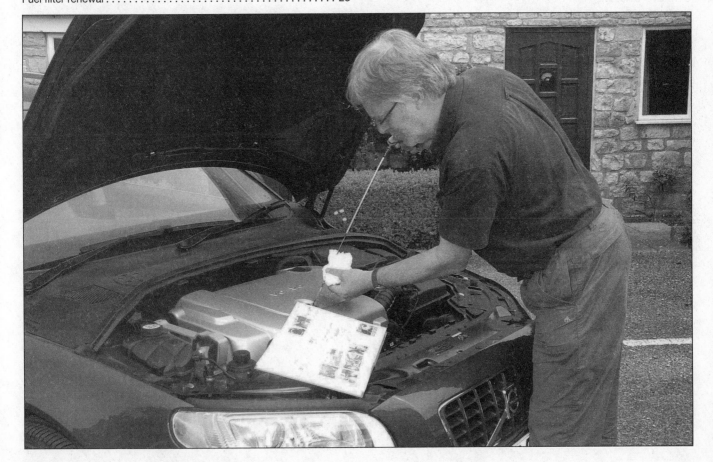

Degrees of difficulty

Easy, suitable for novice with little experience	**Fairly easy,** suitable for beginner with some experience	**Fairly difficult,** suitable for competent DIY mechanic	**Difficult,** suitable for experienced DIY mechanic	**Very difficult,** suitable for expert DIY or professional

Lubricants and fluids

Refer to end of *Lubricants and fluids*.

Capacities

Engine oil
Drain and refill including filter change:

1.6 litre (D4164T)	4.0 litres
2.0 litre:	
4-cylinder (D4204T)	4.3 litres
5-cylinder (D5204T2)	5.9 litres
2.4 litre (D5244T4 to T19)	5.5 litres

Cooling system
All models. . . . .   12.5 litres

Fuel tank
All models. . . . .   70 litres

Manual transmission

MTX75	2.1 litres
M66	1.9 litres
MMT6	1.65 litres

Automatic transmission
Drain and refill . . . .   7.0 litres (approx)

Cooling system

Specified antifreeze mixture. . . . .   50% antifreeze/50% water
Note: *Refer to Chapter 3 for further details.*

Brakes

Brake pad minimum lining thickness . . . .   2.0 mm

Remote control battery

Type . . . .   CR 2032 3V

Torque wrench settings

	Nm	lbf ft
Automatic transmission:		
Drain plug.	35	26
Filler plug	35	26
Plug	8	6
Auxiliary drivebelt tensioner	24	18
Engine oil drain plug:		
1.6 litre	34	25
All other engines.	38	28
Oil filter cover	25	18
Roadwheel bolts.	140	103

The maintenance intervals in this manual are provided with the assumption that you, not the dealer, will be carrying out the work. These are the average maintenance intervals recommended by the manufacturer for vehicles driven daily under normal conditions. Obviously some variation of these intervals may be expected depending on territory of use, and conditions encountered. If you wish to keep your vehicle in peak condition at all times, you may wish to perform some of these procedures more often. We encourage frequent maintenance because it enhances the efficiency, performance and resale value of your vehicle.

When the vehicle is new, it should be serviced by a dealer service department (or other workshop recognised by the vehicle manufacturer as providing the same standard of service) in order to preserve the warranty. The vehicle manufacturer may reject warranty claims if you are unable to prove that servicing has been carried out as and when specified, using only original equipment parts or parts certified to be of equivalent quality.

If the vehicle is driven in dusty areas, used to tow a trailer, driven frequently at slow speeds (idling in traffic) or on short journeys, more frequent maintenance intervals are recommended.

Every 250 miles or weekly
☐ Refer to *Weekly checks*.

Every 9000 miles or 6 months, whichever comes first
☐ Renew the engine oil and filter – models up to 2010 (Section 3).
Note: *Although Volvo recommend that the engine oil and filter are changed at 18 000 miles or every 12 months, frequent oil and filter changes are good for the engine. We therefore recommend changing the oil more frequently.*
Note: *On later models this procedure requires the use of specialist tools to check the oil temperature and level.*

Every 18 000 miles or 12 months, whichever comes first
In addition to the items listed above, carry out the following:
☐ Check the condition of the brake pads (Section 4).
☐ Thoroughly inspect the engine compartment for fluid leaks (Section 5).
☐ Check the condition and security of the steering and suspension components (Section 6).
☐ Check the condition of the driveshaft gaiters (Section 7).
☐ Inspect the clutch components (Section 8).
☐ Renew the pollen filter (Section 9).
☐ Check the battery electrolyte level (Section 10).
☐ Inspect the underbody, brake hydraulic pipes and hoses, and fuel lines (Section 11).

Every 18 000 miles or 12 months, whichever comes first (continued)
☐ Check the condition and security of the exhaust system (Section 12).
☐ Check the handbrake (Section 13).
☐ Check the condition of the seat belts (Section 14).
☐ Lubricate the locks and hinges (Section 15).
☐ Check the headlight beam alignment (Section 16).
☐ Check the coolant antifreeze concentration (Section 17).
☐ Reset the service reminder indicator (Section 18).
☐ Road test (Section 19).
☐ Check the operation of the air conditioning system (Section 20).
☐ Drain fuel filter of water (Section 21).
☐ Renew the remote battery (Section 22).

Every 36 000 miles or 2 years, whichever comes first
In addition to the items listed above, carry out the following:
☐ Renew the air cleaner element (Section 23).
☐ Check the automatic transmission fluid level (Section 24).
☐ Renew the fuel filter (Section 25).

Every 90 000 miles or 5 years, whichever comes first
In addition to the items listed above, carry out the following:
☐ Renew the timing belt and tensioner (Section 26).
Note: *It is recommended that this interval is reduced on vehicles which are subjected to intensive use, ie, mainly short journeys or a lot of stop-start driving. The actual belt renewal interval is very much up to the individual owner, but bear in mind that severe engine damage will result if the belt breaks.*
☐ Renew the auxiliary drivebelt (Section 27).

Every 2 years, regardless of mileage
☐ Renew the brake fluid (Section 28).

Every 3 years, regardless of mileage
☐ Renew the coolant (Section 29).
Note: *This work is not included in the Volvo schedule, and should not be required if the recommended Volvo antifreeze/inhibitor is used.*

Front underbody view

1 Engine oil drain plug
2 Engine oil level sensor
3 Air conditioning compressor
4 Engine oil cooler
5 Lower control arm
6 Steering track rod

Rear underbody view

1 Fuel filter
2 Fuel tank
3 Rear silencer
4 Lower arm
5 Anti-roll bar
6 Track control arm

Underbonnet view of a 2.4 litre model. Other models are similar

1 Engine oil level dipstick
2 Engine oil filler cap
3 Air filter
4 Coolant reservoir

5 Brake fluid reservoir
6 Power steering fluid reservoir
7 Screen washer fluid reservoir

8 Fusebox
9 Battery
10 Mass airflow meter

Maintenance procedures

1 Introduction

This chapter is designed to help the home mechanic maintain his/her vehicle for safety, economy, long life and peak performance.

This chapter contains a master maintenance schedule, followed by Sections dealing specifically with each task in the schedule. Visual checks, adjustments, component renewal and other helpful items are included. Refer to the accompanying illustrations of the engine compartment and the underside of the vehicle for the locations of the various components.

Servicing your vehicle in accordance with the mileage/time maintenance schedule and the following Sections will provide a planned maintenance programme which should result in a long and reliable service life. This is a

comprehensive plan, so maintaining some items but not others at the specified service intervals will not produce the same results.

As you service your vehicle, you will discover that many of the procedures can – and should – be grouped together, because of the particular procedure being performed, or because of the close proximity of two otherwise-unrelated components to one another. For example, if the vehicle is raised for any reason, the exhaust should be inspected at the same time as the suspension and steering components.

The first step of this maintenance programme is to prepare yourself before the actual work begins. Read through all the Sections relevant to the work to be carried out, then make a list and gather together all the parts and tools required. If a problem is encountered, seek advice from a parts specialist or a dealer service department.

Service interval display

All models are equipped with a service interval display indicator in the instrument panel. When a predetermined mileage, time period, or number of hours of engine operation has elapsed since the display was last reset, the service light will illuminate, providing a handy reminder of when the next service is required.

The display should not necessarily be used as a definitive guide to the servicing needs of your Volvo, but it is useful as a reminder, to ensure that servicing is not accidentally overlooked. Owners of older cars, or those covering a small annual mileage, may feel inclined to service their car more often, in which case the service interval display is perhaps less relevant.

Refer to Section 18 for the resetting procedure.

2 Regular maintenance

1 If, from the time the vehicle is new, the routine maintenance schedule is followed closely, and frequent checks are made of fluid levels and high-wear items, as suggested throughout this manual, the engine will be kept in relatively good running condition, and the need for additional work will be minimised.

2 It is possible that there will be some times when the engine is running poorly due to the lack of regular maintenance. This is even more likely if a used vehicle, which has not received regular and frequent maintenance checks, is purchased. In such cases, additional work may need to be carried out, outside of the regular maintenance intervals.

3 If engine wear is suspected, a compression test (refer to Part 2 of Chapters 2A, 2B and 2C) will provide valuable information regarding the overall performance of the main internal components. Such a test can be used as a basis to decide on the extent of the work to be carried out. If, for example, a compression test indicates serious internal engine wear, conventional maintenance as described in this Chapter will not greatly improve the performance of the engine, and may prove a waste of time and money, unless extensive overhaul work (Chapter 2D) is carried out first.

4 The following series of operations are those often required to improve the performance of a generally poor-running engine:

Primary operations

a) *Clean, inspect and test the battery (See 'Weekly checks' and Section 10).*

b) *Check all the engine-related fluids (See 'Weekly checks').*

c) *Renew the auxiliary drivebelt (Section 27).*

d) *Check the condition of the air cleaner filter element and renew if necessary (Section 23).*

e) *Renew the fuel filter (Section 25).*

f) *Check the condition of all hoses, and check for fluid leaks (Section 5).*

5 If the above operations do not prove fully effective, carry out the following operations:

Secondary operations

All the items listed under *Primary operations*, plus the following:

a) *Check the charging system (Chapter 5A).*

b) *Check the fuel system (Chapter 4A).*

c) *Check the preheating system (Chapter 5B).*

Every 9000 miles or 6 months

3 Engine oil and filter renewal (up to 2010 model year)

Note: *On later models this procedure requires the use of specialist diagnostic tools to check the oil temperature and level; no further information was available at time of printing.*

1 Make sure that you have all the necessary tools before you begin this procedure. You should also have plenty of rags or newspapers handy, for mopping-up any spills. The oil should preferably be changed when the engine is still fully warmed-up to normal operating temperature, just after a run; warm oil and sludge will flow out more easily. Take care, however, not to touch the exhaust or any other hot parts of the engine when working under the vehicle. To avoid any possibility of scalding, and to protect yourself from possible skin irritants and other harmful contaminants in used engine oils, it is advisable to wear gloves when carrying out this work.

2 Access to the underside of the vehicle is greatly improved if the vehicle can be lifted on a hoist, driven onto ramps, or supported by axle stands (see *Jacking and vehicle support*). Whichever method is chosen, make sure that the vehicle remains level, or if it is at an angle, that the drain point is at the lowest point. Release the screws and remove the engine undershield **(see illustration)** for access to the sump and drain plug.

3 Position the draining container under the drain plug, and unscrew the plug **(see illustration)**. If possible, try to keep the plug pressed into the sump while unscrewing it by hand the last couple of turns.

4 Allow the oil to drain into the container, and discard the drain plug sealing washer. A new one must be fitted.

5 Allow some time for the old oil to drain, noting that it may be necessary to reposition the container as the oil flow slows to a trickle; when the oil has completely drained, wipe clean the drain plug and its threads in the sump and refit the plug with a new sealing washer, tightening it to the specified torque.

6 Remove the old oil and all tools from under the vehicle, then lower the vehicle to the ground.

7 Renew the oil filter as described below.

8 Remove the dipstick and the oil filler cap from the engine. Fill the engine with oil, using the correct grade and type of oil (see

3.2 Undo the screws (arrowed) and remove the engine undershield

3.3 Undo the engine oil drain plug (arrowed)

Lubricants and fluids and Specifications). Pour in half the specified quantity of oil first, then wait a few minutes for the oil to run to the sump. Continue adding oil a small quantity at a time, until the level is up to the lower mark on the dipstick. Adding approximately 1.2 litres will raise the level to the upper mark on the dipstick (see illustration).

9 Start the engine. The oil pressure warning light will take a few seconds to go out while the new filter fills with oil; do not race the engine while the light is on. Run the engine for a few minutes, while checking for leaks around the oil filter seal and the drain plug. Refit the engine undershield.

10 Switch off the engine, and wait a few minutes for the oil to settle in the sump once more. With the new oil circulated and the filter now completely full, recheck the level on the dipstick, and add more oil as necessary.

11 Dispose of the used engine oil safely and in accordance with environmental regulations (see *General repair procedures*).

Oil filter renewal

1.6 litre engine

12 The oil filter is located on the front, left-hand end of the engine, accessible from above. Remove the plastic cover on top of the engine.

3.8 The maximum and minimum level markings are at the end of the hatched section on the dipstick

13 Undo the clamps and remove the air pipe between the air cleaner assembly and the turbocharger. Undo the securing bolt for the air pipe bracket, adjacent to the oil filter housing, and move the pipe to one side.

14 Using a socket on an extension bar, undo the oil filter housing cap. Lift the cap up, with the filter element inside it. Discard the filter and the O-ring seal around the circumference of the cap.

2.0 and 2.4 litre engines

15 The oil filter is located at the front of the engine, accessible from above. Pull the plastic

3.16 Use a socket or adjustable spanner to undo the oil filter cover (arrowed)

cover over the engine straight up to release it from the mountings.

16 Using a socket or adjustable spanner, undo the filter cover and remove it (see illustration), followed by the old filter element. Discard the filter cover O-ring seal, a new one must be fitted.

17 Using a clean, lint-free rag, wipe clean the inside of the filter housing and cover.

18 Apply a light coating of clean engine oil to the new O-ring seal and fit it to the filter cover. Insert the filter element into the cover, then screw the filter cover into position on the engine until it seats, then tighten it to the specified torque.

Every 18 000 miles or 12 months

4 Brake pad wear check

1 Jack up the front or rear of the vehicle in turn, and support it on axle stands (see *Jacking and vehicle support*).

2 For better access to the brake calipers, remove the roadwheels.

3 Check that the thickness of the friction lining material on each of the pads is not less than the recommended minimum thickness

given in the Specifications (see illustration). If any one of the brake pads has worn down to, or below, the specified limit, *all four* pads at that end of the car must be renewed as a set (ie, all the front pads or all the rear pads).

4 For a comprehensive check, the brake pads should be removed and cleaned. The operation of the brake calipers can then be checked, and the brake discs can be fully examined. Refer to Chapter 9 for details.

A leak in the cooling system will usually show up as white- or antifreeze-coloured deposits on the areas adjoining the leak.

4.3 Check the thickness of the brake pad friction material by removing a front wheel

5 Underbonnet check for fluid leaks and hose condition

Caution: Renewal of air conditioning hoses must be left to a dealer service department or air conditioning specialist who has the equipment to depressurise the system safely. Never remove air conditioning components or hoses until the system has been depressurised.

General

1 High temperatures in the engine compartment can cause the deterioration of the rubber and plastic hoses used for engine, accessory and emission systems operation. Periodic inspection should be made for cracks, loose clamps, material hardening and leaks.

2 Carefully check the large top and bottom radiator hoses (see Haynes Hint), along with the other smaller-diameter cooling system hoses and metal pipes; do not forget the heater hoses/pipes which run from the engine to the bulkhead. Inspect each hose along its entire length, renewing any that are cracked, swollen or shows signs of deterioration. Cracks may become more apparent if the hose is squeezed.

5.4 Check all hose connections for tightness and signs of leakage

6.2 Check the condition of the steering rack rubber gaiters

6.5 Check for wear in the wheel bearing by grasping the wheel and trying to rock it

3 Make sure that all hose connections are tight. If the spring clamps that are used to secure some of the hoses appear to be slackening, they should be updated with screw-type clips to prevent the possibility of leaks.

4 Some other hoses are secured to their fittings with screw-type clips. Where screw-type clips are used, check to be sure they haven't slackened, allowing the hose to leak. If clamps or screw-type clips aren't used, make sure the hose has not expanded and/or hardened where it slips over the fitting, allowing it to leak **(see illustration)**.

5 Check all fluid reservoirs, filler caps, drain plugs and fittings, etc, looking for any signs of leakage of oil, transmission and/or brake hydraulic fluid, coolant and power steering fluid. If the vehicle is regularly parked in the same place, close inspection of the ground underneath will soon show any leaks; ignore the puddle of water which will be left if the air conditioning system is in use. As soon as a leak is detected, its source must be traced and rectified. Where oil has been leaking for some time, it is usually necessary to use a steam cleaner, pressure washer or similar, to clean away the accumulated dirt, so that the exact source of the leak can be identified.

Vacuum hoses

6 It's quite common for vacuum hoses, especially those in the emissions system, to be numbered or colour-coded, or to be identified by coloured stripes moulded into them. Various systems require hoses with different wall thicknesses, collapse resistance and temperature resistance. When renewing hoses, be sure the new ones are made of the same material.

7 Often the only effective way to check a hose is to remove it completely from the vehicle. If more than one hose is removed, be sure to label the hoses and fittings to ensure correct installation.

8 When checking vacuum hoses, be sure to include any plastic T-fittings in the check. Inspect the fittings for cracks, and check the hose where it fits over the fitting for distortion, which could cause leakage.

9 A small piece of vacuum hose can be used as a stethoscope to detect vacuum leaks.

Hold one end of the hose near to your ear, and probe around vacuum hoses and fittings, listening for the hissing sound characteristic of a vacuum leak.

 Warning: When probing with the vacuum hose stethoscope, be very careful not to come into contact with moving engine components such as the auxiliary drivebelt, radiator electric cooling fan, etc.

Fuel hoses

 Warning: Before carrying out the following operation, refer to the precautions given in 'Safety first!' at the beginning of this manual, and follow them implicitly. Fuel is a highly dangerous and volatile liquid, and the precautions necessary when handling it cannot be overstressed.

10 Check all fuel hoses for deterioration and chafing. Check especially for cracks in areas where the hose bends, and also just before fittings, such as where a hose attaches to the fuel filter.

11 High-quality fuel line, usually identified by the word 'Fluoroelastomer' printed on the hose, should be used for fuel line renewal. Never, under any circumstances, use unreinforced vacuum line, clear plastic tubing or water hose for fuel lines.

12 Spring-type clamps are commonly used on fuel lines. These clamps often lose their tension over a period of time, and can be 'sprung' during removal. Update all spring-type clamps with screw clips whenever a hose is renewed.

13 If a fuel leak is suspected, remember that any leak will be more obvious with the system at full pressure, such as when the engine is running, or shortly after switching off.

Metal lines

14 Sections of metal piping are often used for fuel line between the fuel filter and the engine. Check carefully to be sure the piping has not been bent or crimped, and that cracks have not started in the line.

15 If a section of metal fuel line must be renewed, only seamless steel piping should be used, since copper and aluminium piping don't have the strength necessary to withstand normal engine vibration.

16 Check the metal brake lines where they enter the master cylinder and ABS hydraulic unit for cracks in the lines or loose fittings. Any sign of brake fluid leakage calls for an immediate and thorough inspection of the brake system.

---

6   Steering and suspension check

Front suspension and steering

1 Apply the handbrake, then jack up the front of the vehicle and support it on axle stands (see *Jacking and vehicle support*).

2 Visually inspect the balljoint dust covers and the steering gear gaiters for splits, chafing or deterioration **(see illustration)**. Any wear of these components will cause loss of lubricant, together with dirt and water entry, resulting in rapid deterioration of the balljoints or steering gear.

3 Check the power steering fluid hoses for chafing or deterioration, and the pipe and hose unions for fluid leaks. Also check for signs of fluid leakage under pressure from the steering gear rubber gaiters, which would indicate failed fluid seals within the steering gear.

4 Check for signs of fluid leakage around the suspension strut body, or from the rubber boot around the piston rod (where fitted). Should any fluid be noticed, the shock absorber is defective internally, and renewal is necessary.

5 Grasp the roadwheel at the 12 o'clock and 6 o'clock positions, and try to rock it **(see illustration)**. Very slight free play may be felt, but if the movement is appreciable, further investigation is necessary to determine the source. Continue rocking the wheel while an assistant depresses the footbrake. If the movement is now eliminated or significantly reduced, it is likely that the wheel bearings are at fault. If the free play is still evident with the footbrake depressed, then there is wear in the suspension joints or mountings.

6 Now grasp the wheel at the 9 o'clock and 3 o'clock positions, and try to rock it as before. Any movement felt now may again be caused by wear in the wheel bearings or the steering

7.1 Inspect the condition of the driveshaft gaiters

track rod end balljoints. If the outer track rod end is worn, the visual movement will be obvious. If the inner joint is suspect, it can be felt by placing a hand over the rack-and-pinion rubber gaiter, and gripping the track rod. If the wheel is now rocked, movement will be felt at the inner joint if wear has taken place.

7 Using a large screwdriver or flat bar, check for wear in the suspension mounting bushes by levering between the relevant suspension component and its attachment point. Some movement is to be expected as the mountings are made of rubber, but excessive wear should be obvious. Also check the condition of any visible rubber bushes, looking for splits, cracks or contamination of the rubber.

8 With the vehicle standing on its wheels, have an assistant turn the steering wheel back-and-forth, about an eighth of a turn each way. There should be very little, if any, lost movement between the steering wheel and roadwheels. If this is not the case, closely observe the joints and mountings previously described, but in addition, check the steering column universal joints for wear, and also check the rack-and-pinion steering gear itself.

9 The efficiency of the shock absorber may be checked by bouncing the car at each front corner. Generally speaking, the body

will return to its normal position and stop after being depressed. If it rises and returns on a rebound, the shock absorber is probably suspect. Examine also the shock absorber upper and lower mountings for any signs of wear or fluid leakage.

Rear suspension

10 Chock the front wheels, then raise the rear of the vehicle and support it on axle stands (see *Jacking and vehicle support*).

11 Check the rear hub bearings for wear, using the method described for the front hub bearings (paragraph 5).

12 Using a large screwdriver or flat bar, check for wear in the suspension mounting bushes by levering between the relevant suspension component and its attachment point. Some movement is to be expected as the mountings are made of rubber, but excessive wear should be obvious. Check the condition of the shock absorbers as described previously.

7 Driveshaft gaiter check

1 With the vehicle raised and securely supported on axle stands (see *Jacking and vehicle support*), turn the steering onto full lock, then slowly rotate the roadwheel. Inspect the condition of the outer constant velocity (CV) joint rubber gaiters, squeezing the gaiters to open out the folds **(see illustration)**. Check for signs of cracking, splits or deterioration of the rubber, which may allow the grease to escape, and lead to water and grit entry into the joint. Also check the security and condition of the retaining clips. Repeat these checks on the inner CV joints. If any damage or deterioration is found, the gaiters should be renewed as described in Chapter 8.

2 At the same time, check the general condition of the CV joints themselves by first holding the driveshaft and attempting to rotate the wheel. Repeat this check by holding the inner joint and attempting to rotate the driveshaft. Any appreciable movement indicates wear in the joints, wear in the driveshaft splines, or a loose driveshaft retaining bolt/nut.

8 Clutch check

1 Check that the clutch pedal moves smoothly and easily through its full travel, and that the clutch itself functions correctly, with no trace of slip or drag.

2 Undo the two screws and remove the lower facia panel above the pedals for access to the clutch pedal, and apply a few drops of light oil to the pedal pivot. Refit the panel.

3 From within the engine compartment, check the condition of the fluid lines and hoses.

9 Pollen filter renewal

1 Undo the two screws and remove the lower facia panel from above the passenger's footwell.

2 Remove the front section of the left-hand side centre console side panel as shown in Chapter 11.

3 Pull back the carpet slightly and unclip the cover for the pollen filter. Withdraw the filter **(see illustrations)**. This operation is shown with the heater unit removed for clarity.

4 Slide the new filter into place, refit the cover, and refit the lower facia panel and console side panel.

9.3a Unclip the cover . . .

9.3b . . . and withdraw the pollen filter

11.4a Check the condition of the fuel hoses looking for signs of leaks

11.4b Check the condition of the rubber brake hoses by bending them slightly and looking for cracks

10 Battery electrolyte level check

⚠ **Warning: The electrolyte inside a battery is diluted acid – it is a good idea to wear suitable rubber gloves. When topping-up, don't overfill the cells so that the electrolyte overflows. In the event of any spillage, rinse the electrolyte off without delay. Refit the cell covers and rinse the battery with copious quantities of clean water. Don't attempt to siphon out any excess electrolyte.**

1 The battery is located on the left-hand side of the engine compartment.

2 Some models covered by this manual are fitted with a maintenance-free battery as standard equipment, or may have had one fitted. If the battery in your vehicle is marked Freedom, Maintenance-Free or similar, no electrolyte level checking is required (the battery is often completely sealed, preventing any topping-up).

3 Batteries which require their electrolyte level to be checked can be recognised by the presence of removable covers over the six battery cells – the battery casing is also sometimes translucent, so that the electrolyte level can be more easily checked.

4 Remove the cell caps or covers, and either look down inside the battery to see the level web, or check the level using any markings provided on the battery casing. The electrolyte should cover the battery plates by approximately 15 mm.

5 If necessary, top-up a little at a time with distilled (de-ionised) water until the level in all six cells is correct – don't fill the cells up to the brim. Wipe up any spillage, then refit the cell covers.

6 Further information on the battery, charging and jump starting can be found at the start of this manual and in Chapter 5A.

11 Underbody and fuel/brake line check

1 With the vehicle raised and supported on axle stands (see *Jacking and vehicle support*), or over an inspection pit, thoroughly inspect the underbody and wheel arches for signs of damage and corrosion. In particular, examine the bottom of the side sills, and any concealed areas where mud can collect.

2 Where corrosion and rust is evident, press and tap firmly on the panel with a screwdriver, and check for any serious corrosion which would necessitate repairs. If the panel is not seriously corroded, clean away the rust, and apply a new coating of underseal. Refer to Chapter 11 for more details of body repairs.

3 At the same time, inspect the treated lower body panels for stone damage and general condition.

4 Inspect all of the fuel and brake lines on the underbody for damage, rust, corrosion and leakage. Also make sure that they are correctly supported in their clips. Where applicable, check the PVC coating on the lines for damage **(see illustrations)**.

5 Inspect the flexible brake hoses in the vicinity of the front calipers and rear axle, where they are subjected to most movement. Bend them between the fingers (but do not actually bend them double, or the casing may be damaged) and check that this does not reveal previously-hidden cracks, cuts or splits.

12 Exhaust system check

1 With the engine cold (at least three hours after the vehicle has been driven), check the complete exhaust system, from its starting point at the engine to the end of the tailpipe. Ideally, this should be done on a hoist, where unrestricted access is available; if a hoist is not available, raise and support the vehicle on axle stands (see *Jacking and vehicle support*).

2 Check the pipes and connections for evidence of leaks, severe corrosion, or damage. Make sure that all brackets and rubber mountings are in good condition, and tight; if any of the mountings are to be renewed, ensure that the new ones are of the correct type **(see illustration)**. Leakage at any of the joints or in other parts of the system will usually show up as a black sooty stain in the vicinity of the leak.

3 At the same time, inspect the underside of the body for holes, corrosion, open seams, etc, which may allow exhaust gases to enter the passenger compartment. Seal all body openings with silicone or body putty, with due consideration given to the heat generated by the exhaust system and gases.

4 Rattles and other noises can often be traced to the exhaust system, especially the rubber mountings. Try to move the system, silencer(s) and catalytic converter. If any components can touch the body or suspension parts, secure the exhaust system with new mountings.

12.2 Make sure the rubber exhaust mountings are in good condition

13 Handbrake check and adjustment

Adjustment of the handbrake is carried out using the Volvo diagnostic system. This task should be entrusted to a Volvo dealer or suitably-equipped specialist.

14 Seat belt check

1 Check the seat belts for satisfactory operation and condition. Inspect the webbing for fraying and cuts. Check that they retract smoothly and without binding into their reels.
2 Check the seat belt mountings, ensuring that all the bolts are securely tightened.

15 Door, tailgate and bonnet check and lubrication

1 Check that the doors, bonnet and tailgate close securely. Check that the bonnet safety catch operates correctly. Check the operation of the door check straps.
2 Lubricate the hinges, door check straps, the striker plates and the bonnet catch sparingly with a little oil or grease.
3 If any of the doors, bonnet or tailgate do not close effectively, or appear not to be flush with the surrounding panels, carry out the relevant adjustment procedures contained in Chapter 11.

16 Headlight beam alignment check

Accurate adjustment of the headlight beam is only possible using optical beam-setting equipment, and this work should therefore be carried out by a Volvo dealer or service station with the necessary facilities.

Basic adjustments can be carried out in an emergency, and further details are given in Chapter 12.

17 Coolant antifreeze concentration check

1 The cooling system should be filled with the recommended antifreeze and corrosion protection fluid. Over a period of time, the concentration of fluid may be reduced due to topping-up (this can be avoided by topping-up with the correct antifreeze mixture) or fluid loss. If loss of coolant has been evident, it is important to make the necessary repair before adding fresh fluid. The exact mixture of antifreeze-to-water which you should use

depends on the relative weather conditions. The mixture should contain at least 40% antifreeze, but not more than 70%. Consult the mixture ratio chart on the antifreeze container before adding coolant. Use antifreeze which meets the vehicle manufacturer's specifications.
2 With the engine cold, carefully remove the cap from the expansion tank. If the engine is not completely cold, place a cloth rag over the cap before removing it, and remove it slowly to allow any pressure to escape.
3 Antifreeze checkers are available from car accessory shops. Draw some coolant from the expansion tank and observe how many plastic balls are floating in the checker. Usually, 2 or 3 balls must be floating for the correct concentration of antifreeze, but follow the manufacturer's instructions.
4 If the concentration is incorrect, it will be necessary to either withdraw some coolant and add antifreeze, or alternatively drain the old coolant and add fresh coolant of the correct concentration.

18 Service reminder indicator – resetting

1 Insert the remote control into its slot in the facia (ignition position I) (see illustration).
2 Press and hold the mileage trip reset button, then briefly press the start/stop button (ignition position II) (see illustration).
3 Wait for approximately 10 seconds, and when the information lamp starts to flash release the trip reset button.

19 Road test

Braking system

1 Make sure that the vehicle does not pull to one side when braking, and that the wheels do not lock when braking hard.
2 Check that there is no vibration through the steering when braking. Note that, under heavy braking, some vibration may be felt through the brake pedal – this is a normal feature of

the anti-lock braking system (ABS) operation, and does not normally indicate a fault.
3 Check that the handbrake operates correctly and that it holds the vehicle stationary on a slope.
4 With the engine switched off, test the operation of the brake servo unit as follows. Depress the footbrake four or five times to exhaust the vacuum, then start the engine. As the engine starts, there should be a noticeable give in the brake pedal as vacuum builds-up. Allow the engine to run for at least two minutes, and then switch it off. If the brake pedal is now depressed again, it should be possible to detect a hiss from the servo as the pedal is depressed. After about four or five applications, no further hissing should be heard, and the pedal should feel considerably harder.

Steering and suspension

5 Check for any abnormalities in the steering, suspension, handling or road feel.
6 Drive the vehicle, and check that there are no unusual vibrations or noises.
7 Check that the steering feels positive, with no excessive sloppiness or roughness, and check for any suspension noises when cornering and driving over bumps.

Drivetrain

8 Check the performance of the engine, transmission and driveline.
9 Check that the engine starts correctly, both when cold and hot.
10 Listen for any unusual noises from the engine and transmission.
11 Make sure that the engine runs smoothly when idling, and that there is no hesitation when accelerating.
12 On manual transmission models, check that all gears can be engaged smoothly without noise, and that the gear lever action is smooth and not abnormally vague or notchy.
13 On automatic transmission models, make sure that the drive seems smooth – there should be no jerks or 'flaring' of engine speed as gearchanges are made. Check that all the gear positions can be selected with the vehicle at rest.

Clutch

14 Check that the clutch pedal moves smoothly and easily through its full travel,

18.1 Insert the remote unit into its slot in the facia

18.2 Press and hold the trip reset button

and that the clutch itself functions correctly, with no trace of slip or drag. If the movement is uneven or stiff in places, check the system components with reference to Chapter 6.

Instruments and electrical equipment

15 Check the operation of all instruments and electrical equipment.
16 Make sure that all instruments read correctly, and switch on all electrical equipment in turn, to check that it functions properly.

20 Air conditioning system check

⚠ **Warning: The air conditioning system is under high pressure. Do not loosen any fittings or remove any components until after the system has been discharged. Air conditioning refrigerant must be properly discharged into an approved type of container, at a dealer service department or an automotive air conditioning repair facility capable of handling the refrigerant safely. Always wear eye protection when disconnecting air conditioning system fittings.**

1 The following maintenance checks should be performed on a regular basis, to ensure that the system continues to operate at peak efficiency:

a) Check the auxiliary drivebelt. If it's worn or deteriorated, renew it (see Section 27).
b) Check the system hoses. Look for cracks, bubbles, hard spots and deterioration. Inspect the hoses and all fittings for oil bubbles and seepage. If there's any evidence of wear, damage or leaks, renew the hose(s).
c) Inspect the condenser fins for leaves, insects and other debris. Use a 'fin comb' or compressed air to clean the condenser.
d) Check that the drain tube from the front of the evaporator is clear – note that it is normal to have clear fluid (water) dripping from this while the system is in operation, to the extent that quite a large puddle can be left under the vehicle when it is parked.

⚠ **Warning: Wear eye protection when using compressed air.**

2 It's a good idea to operate the system for about 30 minutes at least once a month, particularly during the winter. Long term non-use can cause hardening, and subsequent failure, of the seals.
3 Because of the complexity of the air conditioning system and the special equipment necessary to service it, in-depth repairs are not included in this manual, apart from those procedures covered in Chapter 3.
4 The most common cause of poor cooling is simply a low system refrigerant charge. If a noticeable drop in cool air output occurs, the following quick check will help you determine if the refrigerant level is low.
5 Warm the engine up to normal operating temperature.

6 Place the air conditioning temperature selector at the coldest setting, and put the blower at the highest setting. Open the doors – to make sure the air conditioning system doesn't cycle off as soon as it cools the passenger compartment.
7 With the compressor engaged – the compressor clutch will make an audible click, and the centre of the clutch will rotate – feel the inlet and outlet pipes at the compressor. One side should be cold, and one hot. If there's no perceptible difference between the two pipes, there's something wrong with the compressor or the system. It might be a low charge – it might be something else. Take the vehicle to a dealer service department or an automotive air conditioning specialist.

21 Fuel filter water draining

1 The fuel filter is located near the right-hand side rear roadwheel, within the rear suspension subframe. Connect a length of hose to the drain screw and place the open end in a container. Slacken the drain screw on the underside of the filter by no more than 4 turns **(see illustration)**.
2 Drain off approximately 100 cc of fluid and tighten the drain screw.
3 Start the engine and check for leaks.

22 Remote control battery renewal

1 Remove the plastic emergency key from the end of the control, then use a small, flat-bladed screwdriver to gently prise up the rear edge of the cover on the remote **(see illustrations)**. Remove the cover.
2 Remove he battery from the control, noting its orientation **(see illustrations)**. Avoid touching the battery and contacts with bare fingers.
3 Fit the new battery into the control, refit the cover, and refit the emergency key.

21.1 Attach a length of hose and slacken the fuel filter drain screw (arrowed)

22.1a Remove the plastic emergency key from the remote unit

22.1b Use a screwdriver to prise up the rear edge of the cover

22.2a Remove the battery from the cover, noting its orientation

22.2b Fit the new battery into the cover

Every 36 000 miles or 2 years

23 Air cleaner element renewal

Note: *The 2.4 litre engine was used for photographic purposes, but the process is similar for all engines.*

1 Undo the securing screws and lift up the air cleaner housing cover **(see illustration)**.
2 Lift the air cleaner element from place, noting which way around it's fitted **(see illustration)**.
3 Fit the new element, refit the cover and tighten the securing screws.

24 Automatic transmission fluid level check

Note: *If the 'Gearbox oil change' indicator illuminates, this can only be reset using dedicated Volvo test equipment. Entrust this task to a Volvo dealer or suitably-equipped specialist.*

General

1 The need for regular topping-up of the transmission fluid indicates a leak, which should be found and rectified without delay.
2 The condition of the fluid should also be checked along with the level. If the fluid at the end of the dipstick is black or a dark reddish-brown colour, or if it has a burned smell, the fluid should be changed. If you are in doubt about the condition of the fluid, purchase some new fluid, and compare the two for colour and smell.
3 If the car is used regularly for short trips, taxi work, or does a lot of towing, the transmission fluid should be renewed on a regular basis. Likewise, if a high mileage has been completed, or the history of the car is unknown, it might be worth renewing the fluid

23.1 Undo the screws securing the air cleaner housing cover

for peace of mind. Normally, however, renewal of the fluid is not a service requirement.

Fluid level check

4 The level of the automatic transmission fluid should be carefully maintained. Low fluid level can lead to slipping or loss of drive, while overfilling can cause foaming, loss of fluid and transmission damage.
5 Ideally, the transmission fluid level should be checked when the transmission is hot (50° to 60°C).
6 Park the vehicle on level ground, firmly apply the handbrake, and remove the engine transmission undershield.
7 Remove the air cleaner housing as described in Chapter 4A.
8 Clean the area on the top of the transmission around the filler plug, then using a T55 Torx bit, unscrew the filler plug **(see illustration)**.
9 Position the end of a hose in the filler aperture, and attach a funnel to the other end. Temporarily refit the air cleaner housing.
10 Start the engine. While the engine is idling, depress the brake pedal and move the selector lever through all gear positions (pausing in each position for 2 seconds), returning finally to the P position.
11 With the engine still running, unscrew the level plug from the centre of the transmission

23.2 Lift up the cover and remove the air cleaner element

drain plug using a T40 Torx bit **(see illustration)**. If no fluid emerges from the level aperture, add the specified fluid (see *Lubricants and fluids*) through the funnel and hose until it does emerge. Refit the level plug and tighten it to the specified torque, using a new sealing washer.
12 Stop the engine, remove the air cleaner housing, and tighten the fluid filler plug to the specified torque, using a new sealing washer.
13 Refit the air cleaner housing as described in Chapter 4A, then refit the engine/ transmission undershield.

Fluid renewal

Note: *The automatic transmission fluid does not normally require changing. It's only necessary on vehicles which are used predominantly for towing or as taxis.*

14 Ideally, the transmission fluid level should be drained when the transmission is hot (at its normal operating temperature). Note that the fluid temperature must not be allowed to exceed 60°C, or an incorrect fluid level will result.
15 Jack up the front and rear of the vehicle and support it securely on axle stands (see *Jacking and vehicle support*). The vehicle should be level.
16 Release the screws and remove the engine undershield.
17 Position a container beneath the transmission and unscrew the level plug from the centre of the drain plug using a T40 Torx bit **(see illustration 24.11)**.
18 Unscrew the drain plug from the transmission and allow the fluid to drain. Refit

24.8 Unscrew the transmission filler plug

24.11 Transmission level plug (1), drain plug (3) and sealing washer (2)

the drain plug with a new seal and tighten it to the specified torque.

19 Refit the level plug, but only finger-tighten it at this stage.

20 Remove the air cleaner housing as described in Chapter 4A.

21 Clean the area on the top of the transmission around the filler plug, then using a T55 Torx bit, unscrew the filler plug (see illustration 24.8).

22 Disconnect the fluid return hose from the cooler adjacent to the radiator, and attach a length of clear hose to the cooler outlet. Volvo special tool No 999 7363 may be available for this purpose. Place the end of the hose into a container.

23 Using a funnel, add 4.0 litres of the specified fluid into the transmission casing through the filler hole.

24 Temporarily refit the air cleaner assembly. Fully apply the handbrake, and check the selector lever is in position P.

25 Start the engine, and allow it to idle. Shift through all the selector positions, pausing for 2 seconds at each position. Switch the engine off when air bubbles are visible in the clear hose attached to the cooler.

26 Add 2.0 litres of the specified fluid, then start the engine again and allow it to idle. Switch the engine off when air bubbles are visible in the clear hose.

27 Disconnect the clear hose from the cooler, and reconnect the fluid return hose.

28 Unscrew the level plug from the centre of the drain plug, and add fluid through the filler hole until It begins to run out of the level plug hole. Refit the level and filler plugs and tighten them to their specified torques.

29 Refit the air cleaner housing.

25 Fuel filter renewal

Note: Ensure the fuel tank level is less than 3/4 full before renewing the filter.

1 The fuel filter is located near the right-hand side rear roadwheel, within the rear suspension subframe (see illustration).

2 Place a container under the filter, then slacken the drain screw on the filter underside and allow the fluid to drain.

3 Use a strap wench or filter removal tool

25.1 The fuel filter is located under the right-hand side of the vehicle within the rear suspension subframe

to unscrew the filter from the housing. Be prepared for fluid spillage.

4 Ensure the small O-ring seal is fitted to the top of the element, then fit the large O-ring seal to the filter housing. Fit the new element into the filter holder, then fit the assembly to the housing, ensuring the top of the element locates in the housing. Tighten the filter by hand until the seal contacts the holder, then tighten it a further 1/2 to 3/4 of a turn.

5 Start the engine and check for leaks.

Every 90 000 miles or 5 years

26 Timing belt and tensioner renewal

Refer to Chapter 2A, 2B or 2C.

27.2 Undo the securing screws and remove the right-hand front wheel arch liner

27.4 Use a 15mm open-ended spanner to rotate the tensioner clockwise

27 Auxiliary drivebelt renewal

1 The auxiliary drivebelt transmits power from the crankshaft pulley to the alternator, steering pump and air conditioning compressor (as applicable).

2 To remove the drivebelt, first raise the front of the vehicle and support on axle stands (see Jacking and vehicle support). Undo the fasteners and remove the engine undershield. Remove the right-hand front wheel and the wheel arch liner (see illustration). Remove the plastic cover on top of the engine.

3 The correct drivebelt tension is maintained by an automatic adjuster and tensioner assembly. This device is bolted to the front of the engine, and incorporates a spring-loaded idler pulley.

27.5 Insert a 5mm drill bit/rod into the hole (arrowed) in the tensioner housing

1.6 litre engine

4 Use a 15 mm spanner to rotate the tensioner, while an assistant lifts the belt from the pulleys (see illustration).

5 Fit the tool or spanner to the tensioner arm and rotate the tensioner clockwise until the tensioner arm passes the hole in the housing, and a 5.0 mm drill bit can be inserted, locking the tensioner in position (see illustration).

6 Note how the belt is routed, then remove the belt from the pulleys (see illustration).

J46790

27.6 Auxiliary belt routing – 1.6 litre engine

1 Alternator pulley
2 Air conditioning compressor pulley
3 Crankshaft pulley
4 Tensioner

27.8 Rotate the tensioner pulley bolt anti-clockwise, then insert a 5 mm drill bit/rod through the locking holes once they align (arrowed)

7 Fit the new drivebelt onto the crankshaft, air conditioning compressor, alternator and tensioner/idler pulleys. Hold the tensioner stationary with the spanner and remove the locking drill bit. Slowly allow the tensioner arm to rotate and tension the belt. Remove the spanner.

2.0 litre 4-cylinder engine

8 Using a spanner on the tensioner centre bolt, turn the tensioner clockwise to release the drivebelt tension, then insert a 5 mm drill bit or rod through the holes in the arm/body when they align to lock the tensioner in this position (see illustration).

9 Note how the drivebelt is routed, then remove the belt from the pulleys (see illustration).

27.12a Use a spanner (arrowed) . . .

27.9 Auxiliary drivebelt routing – 2.0 litre 4-cylinder engine

1 Crankshaft pulley
2 Air conditioning compressor pulley
3 Alternator pulley
4 Tensioner

10 Fit the new drivebelt onto the crankshaft, air conditioning compressor, alternator, and tensioner pulleys. Use a spanner to hold the tensioner centre bolt, then remove the locking drill bit/rod, and allow the tensioner to rotate anti-clockwise and gently tension the belt.

5-cylinder engines

11 Unclip the power steering hose from the bracket, then undo the 2 Torx bolts and remove the auxiliary belt cover.

27.12b . . . on a T60 torx bit to rotate the tensioner clockwise

27.14 Auxiliary drivebelt routing – 5-cylinder engines

1 Power steering pump pulley
2 Alternator pulley
3 Air conditioning compressor pulley
4 Crankshaft pulley
5 Idler pulley
6 Tensioner

12 Use Volvo tool No 999 7109, or a T60 Torx bit and spanner, to rotate the tensioner clockwise, thereby relieving the belt tension. Slip the belt off all the pulleys, then release the tensioner and remove the belt (see illustrations).

13 Check the tensioner and idler pulleys for any roughness or damage. Renew as necessary.

14 Fit the new belt loosely over the pulleys and the tensioner, ensuring that it is properly seated – leave the belt off the top (power steering pump) pulley, however (see illustration).

15 Rotate the tensioner clockwise, then work the drivebelt over the top pulley. Release the tensioner, which will now automatically take up the adjustment.

All engines

16 If removed, refit the inner wheel arch panel, then refit the wheel and lower the car to the ground. Tighten the wheel bolts to the specified torque.

Every 2 years, regardless of mileage

28 Brake fluid renewal

⚠ **Warning: Brake hydraulic fluid can harm your eyes and damage painted surfaces, so use extreme**

caution when handling and pouring it. Do not use fluid that has been standing open for some time, as it absorbs moisture from the air. Excess moisture can cause a dangerous loss of braking effectiveness.

The procedure is similar to that for bleeding the hydraulic system as described in Chapter 9, except that the brake fluid reservoir should

be emptied by siphoning, and allowance should be made for the old fluid to be expelled when bleeding each section of the circuit.

Since the clutch hydraulic system uses the same fluid and reservoir as the braking system, it will probably be necessary to bleed the clutch system also (see Chapter 6).

Every 3 years, regardless of mileage

29 Coolant renewal

Note: *If genuine Volvo coolant, in the specified ratio, has been continuously maintained in the system, then coolant renewal will not normally be necessary. However, to be absolutely sure about the integrity of the antifreeze and anti-corrosion properties of the coolant, periodic renewal is to be recommended.*

⚠ **Warning: Wait until the engine is cold before starting this procedure. Do not allow antifreeze to come into contact with your skin, or with painted surfaces of the vehicle. Rinse off spills immediately with plenty of water. Never leave antifreeze lying around in an open container, or in a puddle in the driveway or on the garage floor. Children and pets are attracted by its sweet smell, but antifreeze can be fatal if ingested.**

Coolant draining

1 To drain the system, first remove the expansion tank filler cap (see *Weekly checks*).
2 If the additional working clearance is required, raise the front of the vehicle and support it securely on axle stands (see *Jacking and vehicle support*).
3 Undo the screws and remove the engine undershield, then place a large drain tray underneath the radiator.
4 Slacken the drain tap at the bottom left-hand corner of the radiator, attach a length of hose to the pipe stub, and allow the coolant to drain into the tray. If no drain tap is fitted, carefully loosen the clamp and disconnect the radiator bottom hose **(see illustration)**.

System flushing

5 With time, the cooling system may gradually lose its efficiency, as the radiator core becomes choked with rust, scale deposits from the water, and other sediment. This is especially likely if an inferior grade of antifreeze has been used. To minimise this, as well as using only the specified type of antifreeze and clean soft

29.4 Radiator drain tap (arrowed)

water, the system should be flushed as follows whenever any part of it is disturbed, and/or when the coolant is renewed.
6 With the coolant drained, close the drain taps and refill the system with fresh water. Refit the expansion tank filler cap, start the engine and warm it up to normal operating temperature, then stop it and (after allowing it to cool down completely) drain the system again. Repeat as necessary until only clean water can be seen to emerge, then refill finally with the specified coolant mixture.
7 If only clean, soft water and good-quality antifreeze has been used, and the coolant has been renewed at the specified intervals, the above procedure will be sufficient to keep the system clean for a considerable length of time. If, however, the system has been neglected, a more thorough operation will be required, as follows.
8 First drain the coolant, then disconnect the radiator top and bottom hoses. Insert a garden hose into the top hose, and allow water to circulate through the radiator until it runs clean from the bottom outlet.
9 To flush the engine, remove the thermostat (see Chapter 3), insert the garden hose into the thermostat housing, and allow water to circulate until it runs clear from the bottom hose. If, after a reasonable period, the water still does not run clear, the radiator should be flushed with a good proprietary cleaning agent.
10 In severe cases of contamination, reverse-flushing of the radiator may be necessary. To do this, remove the radiator (see Chapter 3), invert it, and insert the garden hose into the bottom outlet. Continue flushing until clear water runs from the top hose outlet. A similar procedure can be used to flush the heater matrix.
11 The use of chemical cleaners should be necessary only as a last resort. Normally, use of the correct coolant will prevent excessive contamination of the system.

Coolant filling

12 With the cooling system drained and flushed, ensure that all disturbed components or hose unions are correctly fitted, and that the drain tap is securely tightened. Refit the engine undershield removed for access. If it was raised, lower the vehicle to the ground.
13 Prepare a sufficient quantity of the specified coolant mixture (see Specifications); allow for a surplus, so as to have a reserve supply for topping-up.
14 Slowly fill the system through the expansion tank; since the tank is the highest point in the system, all the air in the system should be displaced into the tank by the rising liquid. Slow pouring reduces the possibility of air being trapped and forming air-locks. It

helps also if the large radiator hoses are gently squeezed during the filling procedure.
15 Continue filling until the coolant level reaches the expansion tank MAX level line, then wait for a few minutes. During this time, continue to squeeze the radiator hoses. When the level stops falling, top-up to the MAX level and refit the expansion tank cap.
16 Start the engine and run it at idle speed, until it has warmed-up to normal operating temperature. If the level in the expansion tank drops significantly, top-up to the MAX level line, to minimise the amount of air circulating in the system.
17 Stop the engine, allow it to cool down **completely** (overnight, if possible), then remove the expansion tank filler cap and top-up the tank to the MAX level line. Refit the filler cap, tightening it securely, and wash off any spilt coolant from the engine compartment and bodywork.
18 After refilling, always check carefully all components of the system (but especially any unions disturbed during draining and flushing) for signs of coolant leaks. Fresh antifreeze has a searching action, which will rapidly expose any weak points in the system.

Air-locks

19 If, after draining and refilling the system, symptoms of overheating are found which did not occur previously, then the fault is almost certainly due to trapped air at some point in the system, causing an air-lock and restricting the flow of coolant; usually, the air is trapped because the system was refilled too quickly.
20 If an air-lock is suspected, first try gently squeezing all visible coolant hoses. A coolant hose which is full of air feels quite different to one full of coolant, when squeezed. After refilling the system, most air-locks will clear once the system has cooled, and been topped-up.
21 While the engine is running at operating temperature, switch on the heater and heater fan, and check for heat output. Provided there is sufficient coolant in the system, lack of heat output could be due to an air-lock in the system.
22 Air-locks can have more serious effects than simply reducing heater output – a severe air-lock could reduce coolant flow around the engine. Check that the radiator top hose is hot when the engine is at operating temperature – a top hose which stays cold could be the result of an air-lock (or a non-opening thermostat).
23 If the problem persists, stop the engine and allow it to cool down **completely**, before unscrewing the expansion tank filler cap or disconnecting hoses to bleed out the trapped air. In the worst case, the system will have to be at least partially drained (this time, the coolant can be saved for re-use) and flushed to clear the problem.

Chapter 2 Part A:
1.6 litre engine in-car repair procedures

Degrees of difficulty

Easy, suitable for novice with little experience	Fairly easy, suitable for beginner with some experience	Fairly difficult, suitable for competent DIY mechanic	Difficult, suitable for experienced DIY mechanic	Very difficult, suitable for expert DIY or professional

Specifications

General

Engine type..	Double-overhead camshaft (DOHC) 16-valve design. Direct injection and turbocharged with four-cylinders
Engine code*...	D4164T
Capacity	1560 cc
Bore	75.0 mm
Stroke	88.3 mm
Direction of crankshaft rotation	Clockwise (viewed from the right-hand side of vehicle)
No 1 cylinder location...............................	At the transmission end of block
Maximum power output.................................	80 kW @ 4000 rpm
Maximum torque output................................	240 Nm @ 1750 rpm
Compression ratio	18.0:1

The engine code is stamped on a plate attached to the front of the cylinder block, next to the oil filter

Cylinder head gasket identification

	Piston protrusion	Gasket thickness
1 notch	0.53 to 0.63 mm	1.35 mm
2 notches	0.63 to 0.68 mm	1.25 mm
3 notches	0.68 to 0.73 mm	1.30 mm
4 notches	0.73 to 0.78 mm	1.40 mm
5 notches	0.78 to 0.89 mm	1.45 mm

Camshaft

Drive..	Toothed belt to inlet camshaft and then chain to exhaust camshaft

Lubrication system

Oil pump type..	Gear-type, driven directly from the right-hand end of the crankshaft by two flats machined along the crankshaft journal

Oil pressure – minimum (engine at operating temperature):
At idle	1.0 to 2.0 bar
At 2000 rpm	2.3 to 3.7 bar

Valves

Valve clearances.....................................	Hydraulic compensators – no adjustment necessary

Torque wrench settings

	Nm	lbf ft
Ancillary drivebelt tensioner roller	24	18
Big-end bolts:*		
Stage 1	10	7
Stage 2	Slacken 180°	
Stage 3	10	7
Stage 4	Angle-tighten a further 130°	
Camshaft bearing caps	10	7
Camshaft cover/bearing ladder:		
Stage 1	5	4
Stage 2	10	7
Camshaft position sensor bolt	5	4
Camshaft sprocket	43	32
Coolant outlet housing bolts	8	6
Crankshaft position/speed sensor bolt	10	7
Crankshaft pulley/sprocket bolt:*		
Stage 1	30	22
Stage 2	Angle-tighten a further 180°	
Cylinder head bolts:*		
Stage 1	20	15
Stage 2	40	30
Stage 3	Angle-tighten a further 220°	
Cylinder head cover/manifold	10	7
EGR valve	10	7
Engine mountings:		
Left-hand engine/transmission mounting:		
Mounting-to-bracket centre nut	148	109
Upper bracket:		
M8	24	18
M12	80	59
Right-hand engine mounting:		
Upper bracket:		
M8	24	18
M12	80	59
Centre retaining bolt	130	96
Mounting to engine	80	59
Mounting to subframe	80	59
Lower torque rod		
Rod to engine	50	37
Centre link bolt	80	59
Rod to subframe	80	59
Engine-to-transmission fixing bolts	50	37
Flywheel bolts:*		
Stage 1	30	22
Stage 2	Angle-tighten a further 90°	
Fuel pump sprocket	50	37
Main bearing ladder outer seam bolts:		
Stage 1	6	4
Stage 2	8	6
Main bearing ladder to cylinder block:		
Stage 1	10	7
Stage 2	Slacken 180°	
Stage 3	30	22
Stage 4	Angle-tighten a further 140°	
Piston oil jet spray tube bolt	20	15
Oil cooler retaining bolts	10	7
Oil filter cover	25	18
Oil pick-up pipe	10	7
Oil pressure switch	30	22
Oil pump to cylinder block	10	7
Sump bolts/nuts	10	7
Sump drain plug	34	25
Timing belt cover bolts	5	4
Timing belt idler pulley	45	33
Timing belt tensioner pulley	30	22
Timing chain tensioner	10	7
Vacuum pump	20	15

* Do not re-use

1 General information

Introduction

The 1.6 litre 'DRIVe' engine is the result of development collaboration between Citroën/Peugeot and Ford. The engine is of double overhead camshaft (DOHC) 16-valve design. The direct injection, turbocharged, four-cylinder engine is mounted transversely, with the transmission mounted on the left-hand side.

A toothed timing belt drives the inlet camshaft, high-pressure fuel pump and coolant pump. The inlet camshaft drives the exhaust camshaft via a chain. The camshafts operate the inlet and exhaust valves via rocker arms which are supported at their pivot ends by hydraulic self-adjusting tappets. The camshafts are supported by bearings machined directly in the cylinder head and camshaft bearing housing.

The high-pressure fuel pump supplies fuel to the fuel rail, and subsequently to the electronically-controlled injectors which inject the fuel direct into the combustion chambers. This design differs from the previous type where an injection pump supplies the fuel at high pressure to each injector. The earlier, conventional type injection pump required fine calibration and timing, and these functions are now completed by the high-pressure pump, electronic injectors and engine management ECM.

The crankshaft runs in five main bearings of the usual shell type. Endfloat is controlled by thrustwashers either side of No 2 main bearing.

The pistons are selected to be of matching weight, and incorporate fully-floating gudgeon pins retained by circlips.

How to use this Chapter

This Chapter describes the repair procedures that can reasonably be carried out on the engine while it remains in the vehicle. If the engine has been removed from the vehicle and is being dismantled as described in Part D, any preliminary dismantling procedures can be ignored.

Note that, while it may be possible physically to overhaul items such as the piston/connecting rod assemblies while the engine is in the car, such tasks are not usually carried out as separate operations. Usually, several additional procedures are required (not to mention the cleaning of components and oilways); for this reason, all such tasks are classed as major overhaul procedures, and are described in Part D of this Chapter.

Part D describes the removal of the engine/transmission from the car, and the full overhaul procedures that can then be carried out.

Repair operations precaution

The engine is a complex unit with numerous accessories and ancillary components. The design of the engine compartment is such that every conceivable space has been utilised, and access to virtually all of the engine components is extremely limited. In many cases, ancillary components will have to be removed, or moved to one side, and wiring, pipes and hoses will have to be disconnected or removed from various cable clips and support brackets.

When working on this engine, read through the entire procedure first, look at the car and engine at the same time, and establish whether you have the necessary tools, equipment, skill and patience to proceed. Allow considerable time for any operation, and be prepared for the unexpected.

Because of the limited access, many of the engine photographs appearing in this Chapter were, by necessity, taken with the engine removed from the vehicle.

⚠ **Warning: It is essential to observe strict precautions when working on the fuel system components of the engine, particularly the high-pressure side of the system. Before carrying out any engine operations that entail working on, or near, any part of the fuel system, refer to the special information given in Chapter 4A.**

Operations with engine in vehicle

a) Compression pressure – testing.
b) Cylinder head cover – removal and refitting.
c) Crankshaft pulley – removal and refitting.
d) Timing belt covers – removal and refitting.
e) Timing belt – removal, refitting and adjustment.
f) Timing belt tensioner and sprockets – removal and refitting.
g) Camshaft oil seal – renewal.
h) Camshaft, rocker arms and hydraulic tappets – removal, inspection and refitting.
i) Sump – removal and refitting.
j) Oil pump – removal and refitting.
k) Crankshaft oil seals – renewal.
l) Engine/transmission mountings – inspection and renewal.
m) Flywheel – removal, inspection and refitting.

2 Compression and leakdown tests – description and interpretation

Compression test

Note: *A compression tester specifically designed for diesel engines must be used for this test.*

1 When engine performance is down, or if misfiring occurs which cannot be attributed to the fuel system, a compression test can provide diagnostic clues as to the engine's condition. If the test is performed regularly, it can give warning of trouble before any other symptoms become apparent.

2 A compression tester specifically intended for diesel engines must be used, because of the higher pressures involved. The tester is connected to an adapter which screws into the glow plug or injector hole. On this engine, an adapter suitable for use in the glow plug holes will be required, so as not to disturb the fuel system components. It is unlikely to be worthwhile buying such a tester for occasional use, but it may be possible to borrow or hire one – if not, have the test performed by a garage.

3 Unless specific instructions to the contrary are supplied with the tester, observe the following points:

a) *The battery must be in a good state of charge, the air filter must be clean, and the engine should be at normal operating temperature.*
b) *All the glow plugs should be removed as described in Chapter 5B before starting the test.*
c) *Disconnect the fuel injector wiring plugs.*

4 The compression pressures measured are not so important as the balance between cylinders. You should refer to a Volvo dealer for compression pressures.

5 The cause of poor compression is less easy to establish on a diesel engine than on a petrol one. The effect of introducing oil into the cylinders ('wet' testing) is not conclusive, because there is a risk that the oil will sit in the swirl chamber or in the recess on the piston crown instead of passing to the rings. However, the following can be used as a rough guide to diagnosis.

6 All cylinders should produce very similar pressures. Note that the compression should build-up quickly in a healthy engine; low compression on the first stroke, followed by gradually-increasing pressure on successive strokes, indicates worn piston rings. A low compression reading on the first stroke, which does not build-up during successive strokes, indicates leaking valves or a blown head gasket (a cracked head could also be the cause). Deposits on the undersides of the valve heads can also cause low compression.

7 A low reading from two adjacent cylinders is almost certainly due to the head gasket having blown between them; the presence of coolant in the engine oil will confirm this.

8 If the compression reading is unusually high, the cylinder head surfaces, valves and pistons are probably coated with carbon deposits. If this is the case, the cylinder head should be removed and decarbonised (see Part D). **Note:** *After performing this test, a fault code may be generated and stored in the ECM memory. Have the ECM self-diagnosis facility interrogated by a Volvo dealer or suitably-equipped specialist, and the fault code erased.*

Leakdown test

9 A leakdown test measures the rate at which compressed air fed into the cylinder is lost. It is an alternative to a compression test, and in many

3.9 Insert a 5 mm drill bit/rod through the round hole in the sprocket flange into the hole in the oil pump housing (lower timing belt cover removed for clarity)

3.10 Insert an 8 mm drill bit/rod through the hole in the camshaft sprocket into the corresponding hole in the cylinder head

3.11 Insert the Volvo tool or a 5 mm drill bit/rod through the hole in the fuel pump sprocket into the fuel pump mounting bracket

ways it is better, since the escaping air provides easy identification of where pressure loss is occurring (piston rings, valves or head gasket).

10 The equipment needed for leakdown testing is unlikely to be available to the home mechanic. If poor compression is suspected, have the test performed by a suitably-equipped garage.

3 Engine assembly/valve timing holes – general information and usage

Note: *Do not attempt to rotate the engine whilst the crankshaft and camshaft are locked in position. If the engine is to be left in this state for a long period of time, it is a good idea to place suitable warning notices inside the vehicle, and in the engine compartment. This will reduce the possibility of the engine being accidentally cranked on the starter motor, which is likely to cause damage with the locking pins in place.*

1 Timing holes or slots are located only in the crankshaft pulley flange and camshaft sprocket hub. The holes/slots are used to position the pistons halfway up the cylinder bores. This will ensure that the valve timing is maintained during operations that require removal and refitting of the timing belt. When the holes/slots are aligned with their corresponding holes in the cylinder block and cylinder head, suitable diameter bolts/pins can be inserted to lock the crankshaft and camshaft in position, preventing rotation.

2 Note that the fuel system used on these engines does not have a conventional diesel injection pump, but instead uses a high-pressure fuel pump. However, the fuel pump sprocket must be pegged in position in a similar fashion to the camshaft sprocket.

3 To align the engine assembly/valve timing holes, proceed as follows.

4 Apply the handbrake, then jack up the front of the vehicle and support it on axle stands (see *Jacking and vehicle support*). Remove the right-hand front roadwheel.

5 To gain access to the crankshaft pulley, to enable the engine to be turned, the wheel

arch plastic liner must be removed. The liner is secured by several plastic expanding rivets/ nut/bolts. To remove the rivets, push in the centre pins a little, then prise the clips from place. Remove the liner from under the front wing. The crankshaft can then be turned using a suitable socket and extension bar fitted to the pulley bolt.

6 Remove the upper and lower timing belt covers as described in Section 6.

7 Temporarily refit the crankshaft pulley bolt, remove the crankshaft locking tool, then turn the crankshaft until the timing hole in the camshaft sprocket hub is aligned with the corresponding hole in the cylinder head. Note that the crankshaft must always be turned in a clockwise direction (viewed from the right-hand side of vehicle). Use a small mirror so that the position of the sprocket hub timing slot can be observed. When the slot is aligned with the corresponding hole in the cylinder head the camshaft is positioned correctly.

8 Remove the crankshaft drivebelt pulley as described in Section 5.

9 Insert a 5 mm diameter bolt, rod or drill through the hole in crankshaft sprocket flange and into the corresponding hole in the oil pump (see illustration), if necessary, carefully turn the crankshaft either way until the rod enters the timing hole in the block.

10 Insert an 8 mm bolt, rod or drill through the hole in the camshaft sprocket hub and into engagement with the cylinder head (see illustration).

11 When refitting the timing belt, insert the

Volvo tool through the hole in the fuel pump sprocket and into the corresponding hole in the fuel pump mounting bracket (see illustration). In the absence of this tool use a 5 mm bolt or drill bit.

12 The crankshaft and camshaft are now locked in position, preventing unnecessary rotation.

4 Cylinder head cover/ manifold – removal and refitting

Removal

1 Disconnect the battery negative lead as described in Chapter 5A.

2 Pull the plastic cover (where fitted) upwards from the top of the engine.

3 Remove the EGR cooler (where fitted) as described in Chapter 4B.

4 Undo the 3 bolts and remove the engine cover mounting mounting bracket from the end of the cylinder head.

5 Disconnect the wiring plugs from the top of each injector, undo the guide bolts, then make sure all wiring harnesses are freed from any retaining brackets on the cylinder head cover/ inlet manifold (see illustrations). Disconnect any vacuum pipes as necessary, having first

4.5a Depress the clip (arrowed) and disconnect the wiring plug from the injector

4.5b Undo the bolts (arrowed) and remove the wiring harness guide

4.6 Depress the release buttons (arrowed) and disconnect the fuel hoses

4.8 Undo the bolts and remove the oil separator (arrowed)

4.9 Undo the 2 remaining bolts (arrowed) and pull the cover/manifold upwards

noted their fitted positions. Remove the fuel injectors as described in Chapter 4A.

6 Depress the release buttons and disconnect the fuel feed and return hoses at the right-hand end of the cylinder head, then disconnect the fuel temperature sensor wiring plug, and move the pipe assembly to the rear **(see illustration)**. Plug the openings to prevent contamination.

7 Undo the 3 bolts and disconnect the air inlet pipe at the right-hand end of the cylinder head cover, then undo the 2 Torx bolts securing the EGR pipe.

8 Undo the retaining bolts and remove the oil separator (where fitted) from the top of the cylinder head **(see illustration)**. Recover the rubber seal.

9 Undo the bolts securing the cylinder head cover/inlet manifold. Lift the assembly away **(see illustration)**. Recover the manifold rubber seals.

Refitting

10 Refitting is a reversal of removal, bearing in mind the following points:

a) *Examine the seals for signs of damage and deterioration, and renew if necessary. Smear a little clean engine oil on the manifold seals.*

b) *Renew the fuel injector high-pressure pipes – see Chapter 4A.*

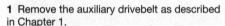

5 Crankshaft pulley – removal and refitting

Removal

1 Remove the auxiliary drivebelt as described in Chapter 1.

2 To lock the crankshaft, working underneath the engine, insert Volvo tool No 999 7169 into the

hole in the right-hand face of the engine block casting over the lower section of the flywheel. Rotate the crankshaft until the tool engages in the corresponding hole in the flywheel. In the absence of the Volvo tool, insert a 12 mm rod or drill into the hole **(see illustration)**. **Note:** *The hole in the casting and the hole in the flywheel are provided purely to lock the crankshaft whilst the pulley bolt is undone, it does **not** position the crankshaft at TDC.*

3 Using a suitable socket and extension bar, unscrew the retaining bolt, remove the washer, then slide the pulley off the end of the crankshaft **(see illustration)**. If the pulley is tight fit, it can be drawn off the crankshaft using a suitable puller. If a puller is being used, refit the pulley retaining bolt without the washer, to avoid damaging the crankshaft as the puller is tightened.

Refitting

4 Refit the pulley to the end of the crankshaft.

5 Thoroughly clean the threads of the pulley retaining bolt, then apply a coat of locking compound to the bolt threads.

6 Refit the crankshaft pulley retaining bolt and washer. Tighten the bolt to the specified torque, then through the specified angle, preventing the crankshaft from turning using the method employed on removal.

7 Refit and tension the auxiliary drivebelt as described in Chapter 1.

6 Timing belt covers – removal and refitting

> ⚠ **Warning: Refer to the precautionary information contained in Section 1 before proceeding.**

Removal

1 Remove the plastic cover from the top of the engine.

2 Remove the engine undershield.

3 Unclip the pipes from the bracket on the top of the upper cover.

4 Remove the crankshaft pulley as described in Section 5.

5 Undo the 5 bolts and remove the upper cover. Undo the 5 bolts and remove the lower cover **(see illustrations)**.

5.2 The locking pin/rod (arrowed) must be located in the hole in the flywheel (arrowed) to prevent rotation

5.3 Undo the crankshaft pulley retaining bolt (arrowed)

6.5a Upper timing cover bolts (arrowed)

6.5b Lower timing cover bolts (arrowed)

Refitting

6 Refitting of all the covers is a reversal of the relevant removal procedure, ensuring that each cover section is correctly located, and that the cover retaining bolts are securely tightened. Ensure that all disturbed hoses are reconnected and retained by their relevant clips.

7 Timing belt – removal, inspection, refitting and tensioning

General

1 The timing belt drives the inlet camshaft, high-pressure fuel pump, and coolant pump from a toothed sprocket on the end of the crankshaft. If the belt breaks or slips in service, the pistons are likely to hit the valve heads, resulting in expensive damage.

2 The timing belt should be renewed at the specified intervals, or earlier if it is contaminated with oil, or at all noisy in operation (a 'scraping' noise due to uneven wear).

3 If the timing belt is being removed, it is a wise precaution to check the condition of the coolant pump at the same time (check for signs of coolant leakage). This may avoid the need to remove the timing belt again at a later stage, should the coolant pump fail.

Removal

4 Apply the handbrake, then jack up the front of the vehicle and support it on axle stands (see *Jacking and vehicle support*). Remove the front right-hand roadwheel, wheel arch liner (to expose the crankshaft pulley), and the engine undershield. The wheel arch liner is secured by screws. The engine undershield is retained by several fasteners.

5 Remove the upper and lower timing belt covers, as described in Section 6.

6 Position a trolley/workshop jack under the engine. Place a block of wood on the jack head, then take the weight of the engine. Undo the nuts/bolts and remove the right-hand

7.7 Undo the bolt (arrowed) and remove the crankshaft position sensor

engine mounting as described in Chapter 2C.

7 Undo the bolt and remove the crankshaft position sensor adjacent to the crankshaft sprocket flange, and move it to one side **(see illustration)**.

8 Undo the 4 bolts and remove the plate below the camshaft sprocket.

9 Undo the retaining bolt and remove the timing belt protection bracket, again, adjacent to the crankshaft sprocket flange **(see illustration)**.

10 Lock the crankshaft and camshaft in the correct position as described in Section 3. If necessary, temporarily refit the crankshaft pulley bolt to enable the crankshaft to be rotated.

11 Insert a hexagon key into the belt tensioner pulley centre, slacken the pulley bolt, and allow the tensioner to rotate, relieving the belt tension **(see illustration)**. With belt slack, temporarily tighten the pulley bolt.

12 Note its routing, then remove the timing belt from the sprockets.

Inspection

13 Renew the belt as a matter of course, regardless of its apparent condition. The cost of a new belt is nothing compared with the cost of repairs should the belt break in service. If signs of oil contamination are found, trace the source of the oil leak and rectify it. Wash down the engine timing belt area and all related components, to remove all traces of oil. Check that the tensioner and idler pulleys rotate freely without any sign of roughness,

7.9 Remove the timing belt protection bracket

and also check that the coolant pump pulley rotates freely. If necessary, renew these items.

Refitting and tensioning

14 Commence refitting by ensuring that the crankshaft, camshaft and fuel pump sprocket timing pins are in position as described in Section 3.

15 Locate the timing belt on the crankshaft sprocket, then keeping it taut, locate it around the idler pulley, camshaft sprocket, high-pressure pump sprocket, coolant pump sprocket, and the tensioner roller **(see illustration)**.

16 Refit the timing belt protection bracket and tighten the retaining bolt securely.

17 Slacken the tensioner pulley bolt, and using a hexagonal key, rotate the tensioner anti-clockwise, which moves the index arm clockwise, until the index arm is aligned as shown **(see illustration)**.

18 Remove the camshaft, crankshaft and fuel pump sprocket (where applicable) timing pins and, using a socket on the crankshaft pulley bolt, rotate the crankshaft clockwise 10 complete revolutions. Refit the crankshaft and camshaft locking pins.

19 Check that the tensioner index arm is still aligned between the edges of the area shown. If it is not, remove the belt and begin the refitting process again, starting at Paragraph 14.

20 The remainder of refitting is a reversal of removal. Tighten all fasteners to the specified torque where given.

7.11 Slacken the bolt and allow the tensioner to rotate, relieving the tension on the belt

7.15 Timing belt routing

7.17 The index arm must align with the lug (arrowed)

TOOL TiP

A sprocket holding tool can be made from two lengths of steel strip bolted together to form a forked end. Drill holes and insert bolts in the ends of the fork to engage with the sprocket spokes.

8.5 Ensure the lug on the sprocket hub engages with the slot on the end of the camshaft (arrowed)

8.11a Slide the sprocket from the crankshaft . . .

8 Timing belt sprockets and tensioner – removal and refitting

Camshaft sprocket

1 Remove the timing belt as described in Section 7.

2 Remove the locking tool from the camshaft sprocket/hub. Slacken the sprocket hub retaining bolt. To prevent the camshaft rotating as the bolt is slackened, a sprocket holding tool will be required. In the absence of the special Volvo tool, an acceptable substitute can be fabricated at home **(see Tool Tip)**. *Do not* attempt to use the engine assembly/valve timing locking tool to prevent the sprocket from rotating whilst the bolt is slackened.

3 Remove the sprocket hub retaining bolt, and slide the sprocket and hub off the end of the camshaft.

4 Clean the camshaft sprocket thoroughly, and renew it if there are any signs of wear, damage or cracks.

5 Refit the camshaft sprocket to the camshaft **(see illustration)**.

6 Refit the sprocket hub retaining bolt. Tighten the bolt to the specified torque, preventing the camshaft from turning as during removal.

7 Align the engine assembly/valve timing slot in the camshaft sprocket hub with the hole in the cylinder head and refit the timing pin to lock the camshaft in position.

8 Fit the timing belt around the pump sprocket and camshaft sprocket, and tension the timing belt as described in Section 7.

Crankshaft sprocket

9 Remove the timing belt as described in Section 7.

10 Check that the engine assembly/valve timing holes are still aligned as described in Section 3, and the camshaft sprocket and flywheel are locked in position.

11 Slide the sprocket off the end of the

8.11b . . . and recover the woodruff key

crankshaft and collect the Woodruff key **(see illustrations)**.

12 Examine the crankshaft oil seal for signs of oil leakage and, if necessary, renew it as described in Section 14.

13 Clean the crankshaft sprocket thoroughly, and renew it if there are any signs of wear, damage or cracks. Recover the crankshaft locating key.

14 Refit the key to the end of the crankshaft, then refit the crankshaft sprocket (with the flange facing the crankshaft pulley).

15 Fit the timing belt around the crankshaft sprocket, and tension the timing belt as described in Section 7.

Fuel pump sprocket

16 Remove the timing belt as described in Section 7.

17 Using a suitable socket, undo the pump sprocket retaining nut. The sprocket can be held stationary by inserting a suitably-sized locking pin, drill or rod through the hole in the sprocket, and into the corresponding hole in the backplate **(see illustration)**, or by using a suitable forked tool engaged with the holes in the sprocket **(see Tool Tip with paragraph 2)**.

18 The pump sprocket is a taper fit on the pump shaft and it will be necessary to make up another tool to release it from the taper **(see Tool Tip)**.

19 Partially unscrew the sprocket retaining nut, fit the home-made tool, and secure it to the sprocket with two suitable bolts. Prevent the sprocket from rotating as before, and

8.17 Insert a suitable drill bit through the sprocket into the hole in the backplate

unscrew the sprocket retaining nut. The nut will bear against the tool as it is undone, forcing the sprocket off the shaft taper. Once the taper is released, remove the tool, unscrew the nut fully, and remove the sprocket from the pump shaft.

20 Clean the sprocket thoroughly, and renew it if there are any signs of wear, damage or cracks.

21 Refit the pump sprocket and retaining nut, and tighten the nut to the specified torque. Prevent the sprocket rotating as the nut is tightened using the sprocket holding tool.

22 Refit the timing belt as described in Section 7.

TOOL TiP

Make a sprocket releasing tool from a short strip of steel. Drill two holes in the strip to correspond with the two holes in the sprocket. Drill a third hole just large enough to accept the flats of the sprocket retaining nut.

8.31 timing belt idler pulley retaining nut (arrowed)

9.5 Vacuum pump bolts (arrowed)

9.7 Timing belt inner cover bolts (arrowed)

Coolant pump sprocket

23 The coolant pump sprocket is integral with the pump, and cannot be removed. Coolant pump removal is described in Chapter 3.

Tensioner pulley

24 Remove the timing belt as described in Section 7.

25 Remove the tensioner pulley retaining bolt, and slide the pulley off its mounting stud.

26 Clean the tensioner pulley, but do not use any strong solvent which may enter the pulley bearings. Check that the pulley rotates freely, with no sign of stiffness or free play. Renew the pulley if there is any doubt about

its condition, or if there are any obvious signs of wear or damage.

27 Examine the pulley mounting stud for signs of damage and if necessary, renew it.

28 Refit the tensioner pulley to its mounting stud, and fit the retaining bolt.

29 Refit the timing belt as described in Section 7.

Idler pulley

30 Remove the timing belt as described in Section 7.

31 Undo the retaining bolt/nut and withdraw the idler pulley from the engine **(see illustration)**.

32 Clean the idler pulley, but do not use any

strong solvent which may enter the bearings. Check that the pulley rotates freely, with no sign of stiffness or free play. Renew the idler pulley if there is any doubt about its condition, or if there are any obvious signs of wear or damage.

33 Locate the idler pulley on the engine, and fit the retaining bolt/nut. Tighten the bolt/nut to the specified torque.

34 Refit the timing belt as described in Section 7.

9 Camshafts, rocker arms and hydraulic tappets – removal, inspection and refitting

Removal

1 Remove the cylinder head cover/manifold as described in Section 4.

2 Remove the injectors as described in Chapter 4A.

3 Remove the camshaft sprocket as described in Section 8.

4 Refit the right-hand engine mounting, but only tighten the bolts moderately; this will keep the engine supported during the camshaft removal.

5 Undo the bolts and remove the vacuum pump (see Chapter 9). Recover the pump O-ring seals **(see illustration)**.

6 Remove the fuel filter (see Chapter 4A), then undo the bolts and remove the fuel filter mounting bracket.

7 Release the wiring harness clips, then undo the 3 bolts and remove the timing belt inner, upper cover **(see illustration)**.

8 Disconnect the wiring plug, unscrew the retaining bolt, and remove the camshaft position sensor from the camshaft cover/ bearing ladder.

9 Undo the bolts/nut and remove the upper rear sections of the turbocharger heat shield, then working gradually and evenly, slacken and remove the bolts securing the camshaft cover/bearing ladder to the cylinder head in sequence **(see illustrations)**. Lift the cover/ ladder from position complete with the camshafts.

10 Undo the retaining bolts and remove the bearing caps. Note their fitted positions,

9.9a Undo the nuts/bolts (arrowed) and remove the upper, outer section of the turbo heat shield . . .

9.9b . . . followed by the inner section bolts (arrowed)

9.9c Camshaft cover/bearing ladder bolt slackening sequence

9.10 The camshaft bearing caps are numbered 1 to 4 from the flywheel end. A for inlet, and E for exhaust (arrowed)

9.11a Undo the tensioner bolts (arrowed) . . .

9.11b . . . then lift the camshafts, chain and tensioner from place

as they must be refitted into their original positions **(see illustration)**. Note that the bearing caps are marked A for inlet, and E for exhaust, and 1 to 4 from the flywheel end of the cylinder head.

11 Undo the bolts securing the chain tensioner assembly to the camshaft cover/bearing ladder, then lift the camshafts, chain and tensioner from place **(see illustrations)**. Discard the camshaft oil seal.

12 Obtain 16 small, clean plastic containers, and number them 1 to 8 inlet and 1 to 8 exhaust; alternatively, divide a larger container into 16 compartments.

9.21 Refit the hydraulic tappets . . .

13 Lift out each rocker arm. Place the rocker arms in their respective positions in the box or containers.

14 A compartmentalised container filled with engine oil is now required to retain the hydraulic tappets while they are removed from the cylinder head. Withdraw each hydraulic follower and place it in the container, keeping them each identified for correct refitting. The tappets must be totally submerged in the oil to prevent air entering them.

Inspection

15 Inspect the cam lobes and the camshaft bearing journals for scoring or other visible evidence of wear. Once the surface hardening of the cam lobes has been eroded, wear will occur at an accelerated rate. **Note:** *If these symptoms are visible on the tips of the camshaft lobes, check the corresponding rocker arm, as it will probably be worn as well.*

16 Examine the condition of the bearing surfaces in the cylinder head and camshaft bearing housing. If wear is evident, the cylinder head and bearing housing will both have to be renewed, as they are a matched assembly.

17 Inspect the rocker arms and tappets for scuffing, cracking or other damage and renew any components as necessary. Also check the condition of the tappet bores in the cylinder

head. As with the camshafts, any wear in this area will necessitate cylinder head renewal.

Refitting

18 Thoroughly clean the sealant from the mating surfaces of the cylinder head and camshaft bearing housing. Use a suitable liquid gasket dissolving agent (available from Volvo dealers) together with a soft putty knife; do not use a metal scraper or the faces will be damaged. As there is no conventional gasket used, the cleanliness of the mating faces is of the utmost importance. Prise out the oil injector oil seals from the camshaft bearing housing.

19 Clean off any oil, dirt or grease from both components and dry with a clean lint-free cloth. Ensure that all the oilways are completely clean.

20 Liberally lubricate the hydraulic tappet bores in the cylinder head with clean engine oil.

21 Insert the hydraulic tappets into their original bores in the cylinder head unless they have been renewed **(see illustration)**.

22 Lubricate the rocker arms and place them over their respective tappets and valve stems **(see illustration)**.

23 Engage the timing chain around the camshaft sprockets, aligning the black links with the marked teeth on the camshaft sprockets **(see illustration)**. If the black

9.22 . . . and rocker arms to their original locations

9.23 Align the marks on the sprockets with the centre of the black chain links (arrowed). There must be 12 link pins between the sprocket marks

9.24a Assemble the chain tensioner between the upper and lower runs of the chain . . .

9.24b . . . and lower the camshaft, chain and tensioner into position

9.25 Apply sealant to the camshaft cover/bearing ladder as indicated by the heavy block lines. Ensure sealant doesn't enter the tensioner oil holes marked A

9.26 Camshaft cover/bearing ladder bolt tightening sequence

9.32a Fit the new seal around a 20mm outside diameter socket . . .

9.32b . . . and push it into place

colouring has been lost, there must be 12 chain link pins between the marks on the sprockets.

24 Fit the chain tensioner between the upper and lower runs of the chain, then lubricate the bearing surfaces with clean engine oil, and fit the camshafts into position on the underside of the camshaft cover/bearing ladder. Refit the bearing caps to their original positions and tighten the retaining bolts to the specified torque (see illustrations). Tighten the tensioner retaining bolts to the specified torque.

25 Apply a thin bead of silicone sealant to the mating surface of the camshaft cover/bearing ladder as shown (see illustration). Do not allow the sealant to obstruct the oil channels for the hydraulic chain tensioner.

26 Check that the black links on the chain are still aligned with the marks on the camshaft sprockets, then refit the camshaft cover/bearing ladder, and gradually and evenly tighten the retaining bolts until the cover/ladder is in contact with the cylinder head. Tighten the bolts to the specified torque in sequence (see illustration). Note: Ensure the cover/ladder is correctly located by checking the bores of the vacuum pump and camshaft oil seal at each end of the cover/ladder.

27 Fit a new camshaft oil seal as described in Section 14.

28 Refit the camshaft sprocket, and tighten the retaining bolt finger-tight.

29 Using a spanner on the camshaft sprocket bolt, rotate the camshafts approximately 40 complete revolutions clockwise. Check the black links on the chain still align with the marks on the camshaft sprockets.

30 If the marks still align, refit the camshaft sprocket as described in Section 8.

31 Refit and adjust the camshaft position sensor as described in Chapter 4A.

32 Press the new oil seals into the bearing housing, using a tube/socket of approximately 20 mm outside diameter, ensuring the inner lip of the seal fits around the injector guide tube (see illustrations). Refit the injectors as described in Chapter 4A.

33 Refit the cylinder head cover/manifold as described in Section 4.

10 Cylinder head – removal and refitting

Removal

1 Apply the handbrake, then jack up the front of the vehicle and support it on axle stands (see Jacking and vehicle support). Remove the front right-hand roadwheel, the engine undershield, and the front wheel arch liner.

2 Disconnect the battery negative lead as described in Chapter 5A.

3 Drain the cooling system as described in Chapter 3.

4 Remove the air cleaner housing as described in Chapter 4A.

5 Remove the camshafts, rocker arms and hydraulic tappets as described in Section 9.

10.11 Pump mounting bracket upper nut and lower mounting bolt (arrowed)

10.17a Pull the non-return valve from the cylinder head . . .

10.17b . . . and push a new one into place

6 Remove the turbocharger and exhaust manifold as described in Chapter 4A.

7 Remove the glow plugs as described in Chapter 5B.

8 Remove the thermostat (see Chapter 3) and the fuel pump (see Chapter 4A).

9 Undo the upper mounting bolts, and pivot the alternator away from the engine, undo the oil dipstick guide tube bolt, then undo the bolts securing the alternator mounting bracket to the cylinder head/block.

10 Undo the coolant outlet housing (left-hand end of the cylinder head) retaining bolts, slacken the two bolts securing the housing support bracket to the top of the transmission bellhousing, and move the outlet housing away from the cylinder head a little. There is no need to disconnect the hoses.

11 Disconnect the high-pressure fuel pipe from the common rail to the pump, and disconnect the fuel supply and return hoses. Remove the bracket at the rear of the pump, then undo the bolt/nut and remove the pump and mounting bracket as an assembly **(see illustration)**. Note that a new high-pressure pipe must be fitted – see Chapter 4A.

12 Working in the **reverse** of the sequence shown **(see illustration 10.31)** undo the cylinder head bolts. Discard the bolts – new ones must be fitted.

13 Release the cylinder head from the cylinder block and location dowels by rocking it. Do not prise between the mating faces of the cylinder head and block, as this may damage the gasket faces.

14 Lift the cylinder head from the block, and recover the gasket.

Preparation for refitting

15 The mating faces of the cylinder head and cylinder block must be perfectly clean before refitting the head. Use a hard plastic or wood scraper to remove all traces of gasket and carbon. The same method can be used to clean the piston crowns. Take particular care to avoid scoring or gouging the cylinder head/cylinder block mating surfaces during the cleaning operations, as aluminium alloy is easily damaged. Make sure that the carbon is not allowed to enter the oil and water passages – this is particularly important for the lubrication system, as carbon could block

the oil supply to the engine's components. Using adhesive tape and paper, seal the water, oil and bolt holes in the cylinder block. To prevent carbon entering the gap between the pistons and bores, smear a little grease in the gap. After cleaning each piston, use a small brush to remove all traces of grease and carbon from the gap, then wipe away the remainder with a clean rag.

16 Check the mating surfaces of the cylinder block and the cylinder head for nicks, deep scratches and other damage. If slight, they may be removed carefully with a file, but if excessive, machining may be the only alternative to renewal. If warpage of the cylinder head gasket surface is suspected, use a straight-edge to check it for distortion. Refer to Part D of this Chapter if necessary.

17 Thoroughly clean the threads of the cylinder head bolt holes in the cylinder block. Ensure that the bolts run freely in their threads, and that all traces of oil and water are removed from each bolt hole. If required, pull the oil feed non-return valve from the cylinder head, and check the ball moves freely. Push a new valve into place if necessary **(see illustrations)**.

Gasket selection

18 The gasket thickness is indicated by notches/holes on the front edge of the gasket. If the crankshaft or pistons/connecting rods have not been disturbed, fit a new gasket with the same number of notches/holes as the previous one. If the crankshaft/piston or connecting rods have been disturbed, it's necessary to work out the piston protrusion as follows:

10.22 Measure the piston protrusion using a DTi gauge

19 Remove the crankshaft timing pin, then turn the crankshaft until pistons 1 and 4 are at TDC (Top Dead Centre). Position a dial test indicator (dial gauge) on the cylinder block adjacent to the rear of No 1 piston, and zero it on the block face. Transfer the probe to the crown of No 1 piston (10.0 mm in from the rear edge), then slowly turn the crankshaft back-and-forth past TDC, noting the highest reading on the indicator. Record this reading as protrusion A.

20 Repeat the check described in paragraph 19, this time 10.0 mm in from the front edge of the No 1 piston crown. Record this reading as protrusion B.

21 Add protrusion A to protrusion B, then divide the result by 2 to obtain an average reading for piston No 1.

22 Repeat the procedure described in paragraphs 19 to 21 on piston 4, then turn the crankshaft through 180° and carry out the procedure on the piston Nos 2 and 3 **(see illustration)**. Check that there is a maximum difference of 0.07 mm protrusion between any two pistons.

23 If a dial test indicator is not available, piston protrusion may be measured using a straight-edge and feeler blades or Vernier calipers. However, this is much less accurate, and cannot therefore be recommended.

24 Note the greatest piston protrusion measurement, and use this to determine the correct cylinder head gasket from the table below. The series of notches/holes on the side of the gasket are used for thickness identification **(see illustration)**.

10.24 Cylinder head gasket thickness identification notches

10.27 Ensure the gasket locates over the dowels (arrowed)

10.31 Cylinder head bolt tightening sequence

Refitting

25 Turn the crankshaft and position Nos 1 and 4 pistons at TDC, then turn the crankshaft a quarter turn (90°) anti-clockwise.

26 Thoroughly clean the surfaces of the cylinder head and block.

27 Make sure that the locating dowels are in place, then fit the correct gasket the right way round on the cylinder block **(see illustration)**.

28 Carefully lower the cylinder head onto the gasket and block, making sure that it locates correctly onto the dowels.

29 Apply a smear of grease to the threads, and to the underside of the heads of the new cylinder head bolts.

30 Carefully insert the cylinder head bolts into their holes (*do not drop them in*) and initially finger-tighten them.

31 Working progressively and in sequence **(see illustration)**, tighten the cylinder head bolts to their Stage 1 torque setting, using a torque wrench and suitable socket.

32 Once all the bolts have been tightened to their Stage 1 torque setting, working again in the specified sequence, tighten each bolt to the specified Stage 2 setting. Finally, angle-tighten the bolts through the specified Stage 3 angle. It is recommended that an angle-measuring gauge is used during this stage of tightening, to ensure accuracy. **Note:** *Retightening of the cylinder head bolts after running the engine is not required.*

33 Refit the hydraulic tappets, rocker arms, and camshaft housing (complete with camshafts) as described in Section 9.

34 Refit the timing belt as described in Section 7.

35 The remainder of refitting is a reversal of removal, noting the following points.

a) *Use a new seal when refitting the coolant outlet housing.*

b) *When refitting a cylinder head, it is good practice to renew the thermostat.*

c) *Refit the camshaft position sensor and set the air gap with reference to Chapter 4A.*

d) *Tighten all fasteners to the specified torque where given.*

e) *Refill the cooling system as described in Chapter 1.*

f) *The engine may run erratically for the first few miles, until the engine management ECM relearns its stored values.*

11 Sump – removal and refitting

Removal

1 Drain the engine oil, then clean and refit the engine oil drain plug, tightening it securely. If the engine is nearing its service interval when the oil and filter are due for renewal, it is recommended that the filter is also removed, and a new one fitted. After reassembly, the engine can then be refilled with fresh oil. Refer to Chapter 1 for further information.

2 Apply the handbrake, then jack up the front of the vehicle and support it on axle stands (see *Jacking and vehicle support*). Undo the bolts and remove the engine undershield.

3 Where necessary, disconnect the wiring connector from the oil temperature sender unit, which is screwed into the sump.

4 Progressively slacken and remove all the sump retaining bolts/nuts. Since the sump bolts vary in length, remove each bolt in turn, and store it in its correct fitted order by pushing it through a clearly-marked cardboard template. This will avoid the possibility of installing the bolts in the wrong locations on refitting.

5 Try to break the joint by striking the sump with the palm of your hand, then lower and withdraw the sump from under the car. If the sump is stuck (which is quite likely) use a putty knife or similar carefully inserted between the sump and block. Ease the knife along the joint until the sump is released. While the sump is removed, take the opportunity to check the oil pump pick-up/strainer for signs of clogging or splitting. If necessary, remove the pump as described in this chapter, and clean or renew the strainer.

Refitting

6 Clean all traces of sealant from the mating surfaces of the cylinder block/crankcase and sump, then use a clean rag to wipe out the sump and the engine's interior.

7 On engines where the sump was fitted without a gasket, ensure that the sump mating surfaces are clean and dry, then apply a thin coating of silicone sealant (Volvo 116 1771) to the sump or crankcase mating surface **(see illustration)**. Note that the sump must be installed within 10 minutes of applying the sealant, and the bolts tightened within a further 5 minutes.

8 Offer up the sump to the cylinder block/crankcase. Refit its retaining bolts/nuts, ensuring that each bolt is screwed into its original location. Tighten the bolts evenly and progressively to the specified torque setting **(see illustration)**.

11.7 Apply a bead of sealant to the sump or crankcase mating surface. Ensure the sealant is applied to the inside of the retaining bolt holes

11.8 Refit the sump and tighten the bolts

12.4 Oil pick-up tube bolts (arrowed)

12.5 Oil pump retaining bolts (arrowed)

9 Reconnect the wiring connector to the oil temperature sensor (where fitted).
10 Lower the vehicle to the ground, then refill the engine with oil as described in Chapter 1.
11 After applying sealant, Volvo recommend waiting a minimum of 2 hours before starting the engine.

12 Oil pump – removal, inspection and refitting

Removal

1 Remove the sump as described in Section 11.
2 Remove the crankshaft sprocket as described in Section 8. Recover the locating key from the crankshaft.

3 Disconnect the wiring plug, undo the bolts and remove the crankshaft position sensor, located on the right-hand end of the cylinder block.
4 Undo the three bolts and remove the oil pump pick-up tube from the pump/block **(see illustration)**. Discard the oil seal, a new one must be fitted.
5 Undo the 8 bolts, and remove the oil pump **(see illustration)**.

Inspection

6 Undo and remove the Torx bolts securing the cover to the oil pump **(see illustration)**. Examine the pump rotors and body for signs of wear and damage. If worn, the complete pump must be renewed.
7 Remove the circlip, and extract the cap, valve piston and spring, noting which way

around they are fitted **(see illustrations)**. The condition of the relief valve spring can only be measured by comparing it with a new one; if there is any doubt about its condition, it should be renewed.
8 Refit the relief valve piston and spring, then secure them in place with the circlip.
9 Refit the cover to the oil pump, and tighten the Torx bolts securely.

Refitting

10 Remove all traces of sealant, and thoroughly clean the mating surfaces of the oil pump and cylinder block.
11 Apply a 4 mm wide bead of silicone sealant to the mating face of the cylinder block **(see illustration)**. Ensure that no sealant enters any of the holes in the block.
12 With a new oil seal fitted, refit the oil

12.6 Undo the Torx bolts and remove the pump cover

12.7a Remove the circlip . . .

12.7b . . . cap . . .

12.7c . . . spring . . .

12.7d . . . and piston

12.11 Apply a bead of sealant to the cylinder block mating surfaces

12.12a Fit a new seal . . .

12.12b . . . and align the pump gear flats (arrowed) . . .

12.12c . . . with those of the crankshaft

pump over the end of the crankshaft, aligning the flats in the pump drive gear with the flats machined in the crankshaft **(see illustrations)**. Note that new oil pumps are supplied with the oil seal already fitted, and a seal protector sleeve. The sleeve fits over the end of the crankshaft to protect the seal as the pump is fitted.

13 Install the oil pump bolts and tighten them to the specified torque.

14 Refit the oil pick-up tube to the pump/cylinder block using a new O-ring seal. Ensure the oil dipstick guide tube is correctly refitted.

15 Refit the woodruff key to the crankshaft, and slide the crankshaft sprocket into place.

16 The remainder of refitting is a reversal of removal.

13 Oil cooler –
removal and refitting

Removal

1 The oil cooler is fitted to the front of the oil filter housing. To access the oil cooler, the diesel particulate filter/catalytic converter must be removed as described in Chapter 4B.

2 Drain the coolant and the engine oil as described in Chapter 1, or be prepared for fluid spillage.

3 Undo the bolts/stud and remove the oil cooler. Recover the O-ring seals **(see illustrations)**.

13.3a Undo the oil cooler bolts/stud (arrowed)

Refitting

4 Fit new O-ring seals into the recesses in the oil filter housing, and refit the cooler. Tighten the bolts securely.

5 Refit the diesel particulate filter/catalytic converter.

6 Refill or top-up the cooling system and engine oil level as described in Chapter 1 or *Weekly Checks* (as applicable). Start the engine, and check the oil cooler for signs of leakage.

14 Oil seals – renewal

Crankshaft
Right-hand oil seal

1 Remove the crankshaft sprocket and Woodruff key as described in Section 8.

13.3b Renew the O-ring seals

2 Measure and note the fitted depth of the oil seal.

3 Pull the oil seal from the housing using a screwdriver. Alternatively, drill a small hole in the oil seal, and use a self-tapping screw and a pair of pliers to remove it **(see illustration)**.

4 Clean the oil seal housing and the crankshaft sealing surface.

5 The seal has a Teflon lip and must not be oiled or marked. The new seal should be supplied with a protective sleeve, which fits over the end of the crankshaft to prevent any damage to the seal lip. With the sleeve in place, press the seal (open end first) into the pump to the previously-noted depth, using a suitable tube or socket **(see illustrations)**.

6 Where applicable, remove the plastic sleeve from the end of the crankshaft.

7 Refit the crankshaft sprocket as described in Section 8.

14.3 Take great care not to mark the crankshaft while levering out the seal

14.5a Slide the seal and protective sleeve over the end of the crankshaft . . .

14.5b . . . and press the seal into place

14.12 Slide the seal and protective sleeve over the left-hand end of the crankshaft

14.16 Drill a hole, insert a self-tapping screw and pull the seal from place using pliers

14.18 Fit the protective sleeve and seal over the end of the camshaft

Left-hand oil seal

8 Remove the flywheel, as described in Section 16.

9 Measure and note the fitted depth of the oil seal.

10 Pull the oil seal from the housing using a screwdriver. Alternatively, drill a small hole in the oil seal, and use a self-tapping screw and a pair of pliers to remove it.

11 Clean the oil seal housing and the crankshaft sealing surface.

12 The seal has a Teflon lip and must not be oiled or marked. The new seal should be supplied with a protective sleeve, which fits over the end of the crankshaft to prevent any damage to the seal lip **(see illustration)**. With the sleeve in place, press the seal (open end first) into the housing to the previously-noted depth using a suitable tube or socket.

13 Where applicable, remove the plastic sleeve from the end of the crankshaft.

14 Refit the flywheel, as described in Section 16.

Camshaft

15 Remove the camshaft sprocket as described in Section 8. In principle there is no need to remove the timing belt completely, but remember that if the belt has been contaminated with oil, it must be renewed.

16 Pull the oil seal from the housing using a hooked instrument. Alternatively, drill a small hole in the oil seal and use a self-tapping screw and a pair of pliers to remove it **(see illustration)**.

17 Clean the oil seal housing and the camshaft sealing surface.

18 The seal has a Teflon lip and must not be oiled or marked. The new seal should be supplied with a protective sleeve which fits over the end of the camshaft to prevent any damage to the seal lip **(see illustration)**. With the sleeve in place, press the seal (open end first) into the housing to the previously-noted depth, using a suitable tube or socket which bears only of the outer edge of the seal.

19 Refit the camshaft sprocket as described in Section 8.

20 Where necessary, fit a new timing belt with reference to Section 7.

15 Oil pressure switch – removal and refitting

Removal

1 The oil pressure switch is located at the front of the cylinder block, adjacent to the oil dipstick guide tube. Note that on some models, access to the switch may be improved if the vehicle is jacked up and supported on axle stands, then undo the bolts and remove the engine undershield so that the switch can be reached from underneath (see *Jacking and vehicle support*).

2 Remove the protective sleeve from the wiring plug (where applicable), then disconnect the wiring from the switch.

3 Unscrew the switch from the cylinder block, and recover the sealing washer **(see illustration)**. Be prepared for oil spillage, and if the switch is to be left removed from the engine for any length of time, plug the hole in the cylinder block.

Refitting

4 Examine the sealing washer for any signs of damage or deterioration, and if necessary renew.

5 Refit the switch, complete with washer, and tighten it to the specified torque.

6 Refit the engine undershield, and lower the vehicle to the ground.

15.3 The oil pressure switch is located on the front face of the cylinder block (arrowed)

16 Flywheel – removal, inspection and refitting

Removal

1 Remove the transmission as described in Chapter 7A, then remove the clutch assembly as described in Chapter 6.

2 Prevent the flywheel from turning. *Do not* attempt to lock the flywheel in position using the crankshaft pulley locking tool described in Section 3. Insert a 12 mm diameter rod or drill bit through the hole in the flywheel cover casting, and into a slot in the flywheel **(see illustration 5.2)**.

3 Make alignment marks between the flywheel and crankshaft to aid refitment. Slacken and remove the flywheel retaining bolts, and remove the flywheel from the end of the crankshaft. Be careful not to drop it; it is heavy. If the flywheel locating dowel (where fitted) is a loose fit in the crankshaft end, remove it and store it with the flywheel for safe-keeping. Discard the flywheel bolts; new ones must be used on refitting.

Inspection

4 Examine the flywheel for scoring of the clutch face, and for wear or chipping of the ring gear teeth. If the clutch face is scored, the flywheel may be surface-ground, but renewal is preferable. Seek the advice of a Volvo dealer or engine reconditioning specialist to see if machining is possible. If the ring gear is worn or damaged, the flywheel must be renewed, as it is not possible to renew the ring gear separately.

5 Note that on engines fitted with a dual-mass flywheel, the maximum travel of the primary mass in relation to the secondary must not exceed 15 teeth.

Refitting

6 Clean the mating surfaces of the flywheel and crankshaft. Remove any remaining locking compound from the threads of the crankshaft holes, using the correct size of tap, if available.

7 If the new flywheel retaining bolts are not

16.9 Flywheel retaining Torx bolts

supplied with their threads already pre-coated, apply a suitable thread-locking compound to the threads of each bolt.

8 Ensure that the locating dowel is in position. Offer up the flywheel, locating it on the dowel (where fitted), and fit the new retaining bolts. Where no locating dowel is fitted, align the previously-made marks to ensure the flywheel is refitted in its original position. Ensure the flywheel is in full contact with the crankshaft flange before installing the bolts.

9 Lock the flywheel using the method employed on dismantling, and tighten the retaining bolts to the specified torque **(see illustration)**.

10 Refit the clutch as described in Chapter 6. Remove the flywheel locking tool, and refit the transmission as described in Chapter 7A.

17 Engine/transmission mountings – inspection and renewal

This process was undertaken on the 2.4 litre 5-cylinder engine, along with relevant photographs, but the process will be similar for all engines. Refer to Chapter 2C.

Chapter 2 Part B:
2.0 litre 4-cylinder engine in-car repair procedures

Contents

Degrees of difficulty

Easy, suitable for novice with little experience | **Fairly easy,** suitable for beginner with some experience | **Fairly difficult,** suitable for competent DIY mechanic | **Difficult,** suitable for experienced DIY mechanic | **Very difficult,** suitable for expert DIY or professional

Specifications

General

Engine type.	Four-cylinder, in-line, double overhead camshaft, aluminium cylinder head and cast iron engine block with turbocharger
Engine code	D4204T
Capacity	1998 cc
Power output	100 kW @ 4000 rpm
Torque output	320 Nm @ 1750 rpm
Bore	85.0 mm
Stroke	88.0 mm
Compression ratio	18.0:1
Firing order	1-3-4-2 (No 1 cylinder at transmission end)
Direction of crankshaft rotation	Clockwise (seen from right-hand side of vehicle)

Cylinder head gasket identification

	Piston protrusion	Gasket thickness
1 notch	0.55 to 0.60 mm	1.21 to 1.29 mm
2 notches	0.61 to 0.65 mm	1.26 to 1.34 mm
3 notches	0.66 to 0.70 mm	1.31 to 1.39 mm
4 notches	0.71 to 0.75 mm	1.36 to 1.40 mm

Camshaft

Drive . . . . Toothed belt to exhaust camshaft and then roller chain to inlet camshaft

Lubrication

Oil pressure – minimum (engine at operating temperature):
At 2000 rpm	2.0 bar
At 4000 rpm	4.0 bar

Valves

Valve clearances . . . . Hydraulic compensators – no adjustment necessary

Torque wrench settings

	Nm	lbf ft
Big-end bearing cap bolts:*		
Stage 1	20	15
Stage 2	Angle-tighten a further 70°	
Camshaft bearing housing:		
Stage 1	5	4
Stage 2	10	7
Camshaft sprocket bolt:		
Stage 1	20	15
Stage 2	Angle-tighten a further 60°	
Camshaft position sensor	2	1.5
Crankshaft oil seal carrier	17	13
Crankshaft pulley bolt:*		
Stage 1	70	52
Stage 2	Angle-tighten a further 60°	
Cylinder head cover/inlet manifold:		
Stage 1	5	4
Stage 2	10	7
Cylinder head lower section-to-block bolts:		
Stage 1	60	44
Stage 2	Angle-tighten a further 220°	
Cylinder head upper section-to-lower section bolts:		
Stage 1	5	4
Stage 2	10	7
Engine mountings:		
Right-hand mounting nuts (M12)	80	59
Right-hand mounting bolts to cylinder head	133	98
Left-hand mounting bolts:		
M8	24	18
M12	80	59
Centre mounting bolt	130	96
Lower torque rod bolts	110	81
Engine oil drain plug	38	28
Flywheel bolts*	48	35
Fuel high-pressure pump mounting bolts	20	15
Fuel high-pressure pipe unions:		
Stage 1	19	14
Stage 2	30	22
Fuel injector mounting studs	10	7
Main bearing bolts:		
Stage 1	25	18
Stage 2	Angle-tighten a further 60°	
Oil cooler retaining bolts	10	7
Oil pressure switch	15	11
Oil pump bolts	17	13
Piston cooling jet	10	7
Sump bolts	17	13
Thermostat housing to cylinder head	17	13
Timing belt cover bolts	10	7
Timing belt tensioner	24	18
Timing chain tensioner	6	4
Vacuum pump	10	7

* Do not re-use

1 General information

Introduction

The engine is a result of a joint venture between the parent company Ford and Peugeot. This DOHC (double overhead camshaft) 16-valve engine features common rail direct injection, and a VNT (variable nozzle turbine) turbocharger.

All major components are made from aluminium, apart from the cast-iron cylinder block – no liners are fitted, the cylinders are bored directly into the block. An aluminium main bearing ladder is fitted. This arrangement offers greater rigidity than the normal sump arrangement, and helps to reduce engine vibration.

The crankshaft runs in five main bearings, thrustwashers are fitting either side of the No 1 cylinder main bearings to control crankshaft endfloat. The connecting rods rotate on horizontally-split bearing shells at their big-ends. The pistons are attached to the connecting rods by gudgeon pins which are a floating fit in the connecting rod small-end eyes, secured by circlips. The aluminium alloy pistons are fitted with three piston rings: two compression rings and an oil control ring. After manufacture, the cylinder bores and piston skirts are measured and classified into four grades, which must be carefully matched together to ensure the correct piston/cylinder clearance; no oversizes are available to permit reboring.

The inlet and exhaust valves are each closed by coil springs; they operate in guides which are shrink-fitted into the cylinder head, as are the valve seat inserts.

A rubber toothed-belt driven by the crankshaft sprocket rotates the coolant pump, injection high-pressure pump, and the exhaust camshaft sprocket. The inlet camshaft is driven by a short timing chain from the exhaust sprocket.

The camshafts operate the 16 valves via roller-rocker arms with hydraulic clearance compensators. The camshafts rotate in five bearings that are line-bored directly into the two sections of the cylinder head.

The vacuum pump (used for the brake servo and other vacuum actuators) is driven from the end of the inlet camshaft, whilst the fuel pump is driven from the end of the exhaust camshaft.

The coolant pump is bolted to the right-hand end of the cylinder block, and driven by the timing belt.

When working on this engine, note that Torx-type (both male and female heads) and hexagon socket (Allen head) fasteners are widely used; a good selection of bits, with the necessary adapters, will be required so that these can be unscrewed without damage and, on reassembly, tightened to the torque wrench settings specified.

Lubrication system

The oil pump is mounted under the cylinder block, and is chain-driven from a crankshaft sprocket. The pump forces oil through an externally-mounted full-flow cartridge-type filter. From the filter, the oil is pumped into a main gallery in the cylinder block/crankcase, from where it is distributed to the crankshaft (main bearings) and cylinder head. An oil cooler is fitted next to the oil filter, at the rear of the block. The cooler is supplied with coolant from the engine cooling system.

While the crankshaft and camshaft bearings receive a pressurised supply, the camshaft lobes and valves are lubricated by splash, as are all other engine components. The undersides of the pistons are cooled by oil, sprayed from nozzles fitted above the upper main bearing shells. The turbocharger receives its own pressurised oil supply.

How to use this Chapter

This Chapter describes the repair procedures that can reasonably be carried out on the engine while it remains in the vehicle. If the engine has been removed from the vehicle and is being dismantled as described in Part D, any preliminary dismantling procedures can be ignored.

Note that, while it may be possible physically to overhaul items such as the piston/connecting rod assemblies while the engine is in the car, such tasks are not usually carried out as separate operations. Usually, several additional procedures are required (not to mention the cleaning of components and oilways); for this reason, all such tasks are classed as major overhaul procedures, and are described in Part D of this Chapter.

Part D describes the removal of the engine/transmission from the car, and the full overhaul procedures that can then be carried out.

Operations with engine in car

The following major repair operations can be accomplished without removing the engine from the vehicle. However, owners should note that any operation involving the removal of the sump requires careful forethought, depending on the level of skill and the tools and facilities available; refer to the relevant text for details.

a) Compression pressure – testing.
b) Cylinder head cover – removal and refitting.
c) Timing belt cover – removal and refitting.
d) Timing belt/chain – renewal.
e) Timing belt tensioner and sprockets – removal and refitting.
f) Camshaft oil seal – renewal.
g) Camshaft and cam followers – removal and refitting.
h) Cylinder head – removal, overhaul and refitting.
i) Cylinder head and pistons – decarbonising.
j) Sump – removal and refitting.
k) Crankshaft oil seals – renewal.
l) Oil pump – removal and refitting.
m) Piston/connecting rod assemblies – removal and refitting (but see note below).
n) Flywheel – removal and refitting.
o) Engine/transmission mountings – removal and refitting.

Note: It is possible to remove the pistons and connecting rods (after removing the cylinder head and sump) without removing the engine, however, this is not recommended. Work of this nature is more easily and thoroughly completed with the engine on the bench, as described in Chapter 2D.

Clean the engine compartment and the exterior of the engine with some type of degreaser before any work is done (and/or clean the engine using a steam cleaner). It will make the job easier and will help to keep dirt out of the internal areas of the engine.

Depending on the components involved, it may be helpful to remove the bonnet, to improve access to the engine as repairs are performed (refer to Chapter 11 if necessary). Cover the wings to prevent damage to the paint; special covers are available, but an old bedspread or blanket will also work.

2 Compression and leakdown tests – description and interpretation

Compression test

Note: A compression tester suitable for use with diesel engines will be required for this test.

1 When engine performance is down, or if misfiring occurs which cannot be attributed to the fuel or emissions systems, a compression test can provide diagnostic clues as to the engine's condition. If the test is performed regularly, it can give warning of trouble before any other symptoms become apparent.

2 The engine must be fully warmed-up to normal operating temperature, the battery must be fully-charged and the glow plugs must be removed. The aid of an assistant will be required.

3 Make sure that the ignition is switched off (take out the remote unit). Remove the fuel pump fuse from the engine compartment fusebox (see diagram on the fusebox lid), and disconnect the crankshaft speed/position sensor as described in Chapter 4A.

4 Remove the glow plugs as described in Chapter 5B.

5 Fit a compression tester to the No 1 cylinder glow plug hole. The type of tester which screws into the plug thread is preferred.

6 Crank the engine for several seconds on the starter motor. After one or two revolutions, the compression pressure should build-up to a maximum figure and then stabilise. Record the highest reading obtained.

7 Repeat the test on the remaining cylinders, recording the pressure in each.

8 The cause of poor compression is less easy to establish on a diesel engine than

on a petrol engine. The effect of introducing oil into the cylinders (wet testing) is not conclusive, because there is a risk that the oil will sit in the recess on the piston crown, instead of passing to the rings. However, the following can be used as a rough guide to diagnosis.

9 All cylinders should produce very similar pressures. Note that the compression should build-up quickly in a healthy engine. Low compression on the first stroke, followed by gradually increasing pressure on successive strokes, indicates worn piston rings. A low compression reading on the first stroke, which does not build-up during successive strokes, indicates leaking valves or a blown head gasket (a cracked head could also be the cause).

10 A low reading from two adjacent cylinders is almost certainly due to the head gasket having blown between them and the presence of coolant in the engine oil will confirm this.

11 On completion, remove the compression tester, and refit the glow plugs.

12 Take out the remote unit, then refit the fuel pump fuse and reconnect the crankshaft speed/position sensor. Note that carrying out this test as described may result in one or more fault codes being stored by the engine management ECM. Have these codes erased by a Volvo dealer or suitably-equipped specialist.

Leakdown test

13 A leakdown test measures the rate at which compressed air fed into the cylinder is lost. It is an alternative to a compression test, and in many ways it is better, since the escaping air provides easy identification of where pressure loss is occurring (piston rings, valves or head gasket).

14 The equipment required for leakdown testing is unlikely to be available to the home mechanic. If poor compression is suspected, have the test performed by a suitably-equipped garage.

3 Cylinder head cover/manifold – removal and refitting

Removal

1 The cylinder head cover is integral with the inlet manifold. Begin by removing the plastic cover from the top of the engine.

2 Release the clips and detach the wiring harness and fuel pipes from the timing belt upper cover.

3 Undo the bolt and remove the wiring bracket from the right-hand rear corner of the cylinder head.

4 Disconnect the wiring plug, undo the

retaining bolt and remove the camshaft position sensor **(see illustration)**.

5 Undo the bolts, slacken the nut, then remove the timing belt upper cover.

6 Disconnect the injectors' wiring plugs, then detach the harness duct from the cover/inlet manifold and position it to one side **(see illustration)**.

7 Disconnect the crankcase ventilation hoses from the cover/inlet manifold, then release the clamp and disconnect the EGR pipe from the inlet manifold **(see illustrations)**.

8 Release the glow plugs' wiring harness from the 2 clips on the manifold.

9 Slacken the clamp and disconnect the inlet hose from the inlet manifold.

10 Unclip the fuel temperature sensor (located on underside the inlet manifold).

11 Undo the manifold/cover retaining bolts in the **reverse** of the sequence shown **(see illustration 3.13)**. Discards the gaskets, new ones must be fitted.

Refitting

12 Clean the sealing surfaces of the manifold/cover and the head.

13 Fit the new seals to the cover/inlet manifold, then fit it to the cylinder head. Use a little petroleum jelly on the manifold O-rings to ease assembly. Tighten the bolts to the specified torque in sequence **(see illustration)**.

3.4 Undo the bolt and remove the camshaft position sensor from the right-hand end of the cylinder head cover

3.6 Release the clips (arrowed) and detach the injector wiring harness duct

3.7a Release the clamps and disconnect the breather hose (arrowed) from the cylinder head cover . . .

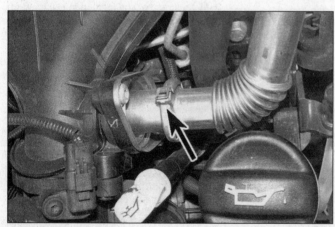

3.7b . . . and the EGR pipe from the inlet manifold

3.13 Cylinder head cover/inlet manifold bolt tightening sequence

4.6a Undo the bolt and remove the crankshaft pulley . . .

4.6b . . . followed by the TDC sensor ring/spacer

14 The remainder of refitting is a reversal of removal, noting the following points:
 a) *Tighten all fasteners to their specified torque where given.*
 b) *The camshaft position sensor must be refitted in accordance with the instructions given in Chapter 4A, otherwise it will not function correctly.*

4 Crankshaft pulley – removal and refitting

Removal

1 Loosen the right-hand front roadwheel nuts, then raise the front of the vehicle, and support securely on axle stands (see *Jacking and vehicle support*). Remove the roadwheel. Access is greatly improved once the wheel arch liner has been removed.
2 Release the 7 Torx screws and withdraw the engine undershield from under the car.
3 Remove the auxiliary drivebelt as described in Chapter 1.
4 The centre bolt which secures the crankshaft pulley must now be slackened. This bolt is tightened to a high torque, and it is first of all essential to ensure that the car is adequately supported, as considerable effort will be needed.
5 Volvo technicians use a special holding tool (999 7119/999 7120) which bolts to the transmission housing and engages with the starter ring gear teeth once the starter motor has been removed. If this is not available, select a gear, and have an assistant apply the handbrake and footbrake as the bolt is loosened.
6 Unscrew the bolt securing the pulley to the crankshaft, and remove the pulley. It is essential to obtain a new bolt for reassembly **(see illustrations)**. If required, remove the sensor ring/spacer.
7 With the pulley removed, it is advisable

to check the crankshaft oil seal for signs of oil leakage. If necessary, fit a new seal as described in Section 15.

Refitting

8 Refit the pulley to the crankshaft sprocket, then fit the new pulley securing bolt and tighten it as far as possible before the crankshaft starts to rotate.
9 Holding the pulley against rotation as for removal, first tighten the bolt to the specified Stage 1 torque.
10 Stage 2 involves tightening the bolt though an angle, rather than to a torque. The bolt must be rotated through the specified angle – special angle gauges are available from tool outlets.
11 The remainder of refitting is a reversal of removal.

5 Timing belt covers – removal and refitting

Removal

1 Jack up the front of the vehicle and support it on axle stands (see *Jacking and vehicle support*).
2 Remove the right-hand side front wheel, and the wheel arch liner.
3 Remove the crankshaft pulley as described in Section 4.
4 Undo the 3 bolts and remove the lower cover. Undo the 3 bolts and remove the upper cover.

Refitting

5 Refitting of all the covers is a reversal of the relevant removal procedure, ensuring that each cover section is correctly located, and that the cover retaining bolts are securely tightened. Ensure that all disturbed hoses are reconnected and retained by their relevant clips.

6 Timing belt and tensioner – removal and refitting

Removal

1 Disconnect the battery negative lead as described in Chapter 5A and remove the plastic cover on top of the engine.
2 Lift the coolant expansion tank up from its position, and move the tank to one side without disconnecting the hoses.
3 Release the clamp and detach the charge air pipe from the inlet manifold.
4 Slacken the front right-hand roadwheel bolts, then jack up the front of the vehicle and support it securely on axle stands (see *Jacking and vehicle support*). Remove the roadwheel.
5 Release the 7 Torx screws and remove the engine undershield.
6 Remove the auxiliary drivebelt as described in Chapter 1.
7 The engine must now be supported before the right-hand mounting is removed. Volvo technicians use an engine support bar, which locates in the channels at the top of each inner wing, and a further beam attached to this, which rests on the front crossmember. If such an arrangement is not available, use an engine crane; either way, use a suitable length of chain and hooks to attach the lifting gear to the engine lifting eye. If the engine must be supported from below (and this is not recommended), use a large piece of wood on a trolley jack to spread the load and reduce the chance of damage to the sump.
8 With the weight of the engine supported remove the right-hand engine mounting as described in Chapter 2C.
9 Release the cable clip from the timing belt cover.
10 Undo the 2 bolts, slacken the nut, and remove the upper timing belt cover.
11 Slacken the crankshaft pulley bolt as

6.15a The tool fits through the hole in the cylinder block flange . . .

6.15b . . . and into a hole in the rear of the flywheel

6.16 The tool fits through a hole in the exhaust camshaft sprocket, into the timing hole in the cylinder head

described in Section 4. Do not discard the old bolt yet – it is used during reassembly.

12 Two special tools are now required to set the engine at TDC (Top Dead Centre) for No 1 cylinder (at the transmission end). Volvo tool No 999 7121 locates through a hole in the rear flange of the cylinder block into a corresponding hole in the rear of the flywheel, whilst tool No 999 7122 locates through a hole in the exhaust camshaft sprocket into a hole in the cylinder head casting. In the absence of these tools, use an 8 mm drill bit to lock the camshaft sprocket, and an 8 mm rod to lock the flywheel. **Note:** *The flywheel locking bolt must be flat (not tapered at all) at the end.*

13 Undo the starter motor bolts and position the motor to one side, to expose the crankshaft setting tool hole in the cylinder block flange. Refer to Chapter 5A if necessary.

14 Using a spanner or socket on the crankshaft pulley bolt, rotate the engine in a clockwise direction (viewed from the timing belt end of the engine) until the hole in the camshaft sprocket begins to align with the corresponding hole in the cylinder head.

15 Insert the crankshaft setting tool though the hole in the cylinder block flange and press it against the back of the flywheel. Have an assistant very slowly rotate the crankshaft clockwise, and the tool should slide into the back of the flywheel as the holes align **(see illustrations).**

16 It should now be possible to insert the camshaft locking tool (999 7122) or equivalent through the hole in the camshaft sprocket into the hole in the cylinder head **(see illustration).** Note that it may be necessary to rotate the camshaft sprocket backwards or forwards very slightly to be able to insert the tool.

17 At this point, Volvo technicians use the

tool described in paragraph 5 of Section 4 to lock the crankshaft in this position. The use of this tool, or an equivalent, is strongly recommended.

18 Disconnect the crankshaft position sensor wiring plug, then undo the bolt and remove the sensor **(see illustration).**

19 Remove the crankshaft pulley, followed by the sensor ring/spacer.

20 Undo the screws/nut and remove the lower timing belt cover **(see illustration).**

21 Raise the engine slightly, then relieve the timing belt tension by slackening the bolt in the centre of the tensioning pulley **(see illustration).**

22 Remove the timing belt from the sprockets. Note that the belt must not be re-used.

23 Slacken the 4 bolts a few turns, remove the engine mounting bracket and the idler pulley, then undo the tensioner bolt **(see illustration).** Discard both the tensioner and idler pulleys – new ones must be fitted.

24 If a new timing belt is not being fitted straight away (or if the belt is being removed as part of another procedure, such as cylinder head removal), temporarily refit the engine right-hand mounting and tighten the bolts securely.

Refitting

25 Ensure that the crankshaft and camshaft are still set to TDC on No 1 cylinder.

26 Position the new idler pulley and insert the retaining bolt **(see illustration).**

27 Refit the engine mounting bracket, then tighten the retaining bolts (including the idler

6.18 Crankshaft position sensor bolt (arrowed)

6.20 Timing belt lower cover bolts (arrowed)

6.21 Slacken the tensioner pulley bolt (arrowed)

6.23 Slacken the engine mounting bracket bolts and remove the idler pulley

6.26 Fit the new idler pulley

6.29a Timing belt routing

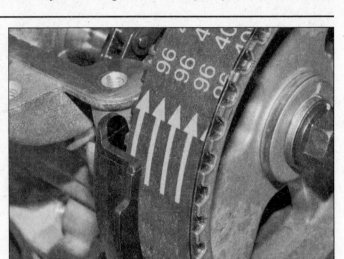

6.29b The arrows on the belt must point in the direction of rotation

pulley bolt) to the specified torque, where given.

28 Fit the new timing belt tensioner into position, but tighten the retaining finger-tight only at this stage.

29 Fit the new timing belt over the various sprockets in the following order: crankshaft, idler pulley, camshaft, tensioner and coolant pump **(see illustrations)**. Pay attention to any arrows on the belt indicating direction of rotation.

30 Using an Allen key in the tensioner arm, rotate the arm anti-clockwise until the pointer is positioned between the sides of the adjustment 'window' **(see illustrations)**. Fully-tighten the tensioner retaining bolt.

31 Refit the timing belt lower cover and tighten the bolts securely.

32 Refit the sensor ring/spacer and the crankshaft pulley, then tighten the old pulley bolt to 50 Nm (37 lbf ft).

33 Remove the crankshaft and camshaft setting/locking tools, then rotate the crankshaft 2 complete revolutions clockwise, until the crankshaft setting tool can be re-inserted. Check that the camshaft locking tool can be inserted.

34 Check position of the tensioner pointer, and if necessary slacken the retaining bolt and

6.30a Use an Allen key in the tensioner arm hole (arrowed)

use the Allen key to align the pointer in the centre of the adjustment 'window'. Tighten the retaining bolt securely.

35 Remove the old crankshaft pulley bolt, and fit the new one. Tighten the bolt to the specified torque, using the method employed during removal to prevent the crankshaft from rotating.

36 Remove the crankshaft and camshaft locking tools.

37 The remainder of refitting is a reversal of removal, remembering to tighten all fasteners to their specified torque where given.

6.30b Rotate the arm anti-clockwise until the pointer is between the sides of the adjustment 'window' (arrowed)

7 Timing chain and tensioner – removal and refitting

Timing chain

1 Removal of the timing chain is included in the camshaft removal and refitting procedure, as described in Section 8.

Tensioner

2 Remove the cylinder head cover as described in Section 3.

3 Press the tensioner upper guide rail upwards into the housing, then insert a 2.0 mm locking pin/drill bit to secure the rail in position **(see illustration)**.

4 Undo the 2 retaining bolts and withdrawn the tensioner **(see illustration)**.

5 Begin refitting by ensuring the tensioner and cylinder head mating faces are clean and free of debris.

6 Install the tensioner and tighten the retaining bolts to the specified torque.

7 Press the tensioner upper guide rail into the housing, pull out the locking pin/drill bit, then slowly release the guide rail.

8 Refit the cylinder head cover as described in Section 3.

7.3 Lift up the chain upper guide rail and insert a 2 mm drill bit/rod into the hole in the tensioner housing

7.4 Undo the tensioner retaining bolts (arrowed)

8.4a Depress the release tab (arrowed) and disconnect the servo hose from the pump

8.4b Undo the nut securing the EGR pipe and fuel hose

8.4c Vacuum pump securing bolts (arrowed)

8 Camshafts, rocker arms and hydraulic adjusters – removal, inspection and refitting

Note: *A new camshaft oil seal will be required on refitting.*

Removal

1 Remove the timing belt as described in Section 6.
2 Remove the timing chain tensioner as described in Section 7.
3 Remove the air cleaner assembly as described in Chapter 4A.
4 Working at the left-hand end of the cylinder head, depress the release tab and disconnect the hose from the vacuum pump, undo the nut securing the EGR pipe and fuel supply hose, then undo the 3 Allen bolts and remove the pump from the cylinder head **(see illustrations)**. Check the condition of the pump O-ring seals and renew if necessary.
5 Undo the unions and remove the high-pressure fuel pipe between the fuel rail and the high-pressure pump located at the left-hand end of the cylinder head **(see illustration)**. Discard the pipe, a new one must be fitted. Plug or seal the openings to prevent contamination.
6 Slide off the retaining clip/depress the release tab and disconnect the fuel supply and return hoses from the high-pressure pump **(see illustrations)**. Plug or seal the openings to prevent contamination.
7 Note their fitted positions, and disconnect the wiring plug(s) from the high-pressure fuel pump.
8 Undo the 3 retaining bolts and pull the high-pressure fuel pump out from the cylinder head **(see illustration)**. Be prepared for fuel spillage.
9 Remove the injectors as described in Chapter 4A.
10 Undo the retaining bolt and pull the sprocket from the exhaust camshaft. Use a tool to prevent the camshaft and sprocket from rotating whilst the bolt is released **(see Tool Tip)**.
11 Undo the bolts and remove the engine mounting bracket from the right-hand end of the cylinder head/block.

8.5 Undo the unions and remove the high-pressure fuel pipe between the fuel rail and pump

8.6a Disconnect the fuel return hose . . .

8.6b . . . then slide out the clip and disconnect the fuel supply hose

8.8 High-pressure fuel pump retaining bolts (arrowed)

HAYNES HINT

To make a camshaft sprocket holding tool, obtain two lengths of steel strip about 6 mm thick by 30 mm wide or similar, one 600 mm long, the other 200 mm long (all dimensions are approximate). Bolt the two strips together to form a forked end, leaving the bolt slack so that the shorter strip can pivot freely. At the end of each 'prong' of the fork, use nuts and bolts or bend the strips through 90° about 50 mm from their ends to act as fulcrums; these will engage with the holes in the sprockets. It may be necessary to grind or cut off the side slightly to allow them to fit in the sprocket holes.

8.12 Remove the bolts (arrowed) securing the inner belt cover

8.14 Injector mounting stud removal sequence

12 Undo the bolts securing the timing belt inner cover to the cylinder head **(see illustration)**.

13 Undo the 2 bolts and remove the EGR pipe from over the left-hand end of the cylinder head.

14 Unscrew the injector mounting studs using a Torx socket, in sequence **(see illustration)**.

15 Working in the **reverse** of the sequence given in paragraph 28 **(see illustration 8.28)**, gradually and evenly remove the bolts securing the upper section of the cylinder head.

16 Carefully tap around the edge of the cylinder head upper section and lift it from position. Note that the cover will probably be reluctant to lift due to the sealant used, and possible corrosion around the two locating dowels at the front edge.

17 Lift the camshafts from position, disengage the timing chain from the sprockets, and remove the exhaust camshaft seal.

18 Have ready a box divided into 16 segments, or some containers or other means of storing and identifying the rockers arms and hydraulic adjusters after removal. It's essential that if they are to be refitted, they return to their original positions. Mark the segments in the box or the containers with the cylinder number for each rocker arm/adjuster, and left or right, for the particular cylinder.

19 Lift out the rockers arms and hydraulic adjusters, Keep them identified for position, and place them in their respective positions in the box or container **(see illustration)**.

Inspection

20 With the camshaft removed, examine the bearing surfaces in the upper and lower sections of the cylinder head for signs of obvious wear or pitting. If evident, a new cylinder head will probably be required. Also check that the oil supply holes in the cylinder head are free from obstructions.

21 Visually inspect the camshaft for evidence of wear on the surfaces of the lobes and journals. Normally their surfaces should be smooth and have a dull shine; look for scoring, erosion or pitting and areas that appear highly polished, indicating excessive wear. Accelerated wear

will occur once the hardened exterior of the camshaft has been damaged, so always renew worn items. **Note:** *If these symptoms are visible on the tips of the camshaft lobes, check the rocker arm, as it will probably be worn as well.*

22 If any doubt exists as to the condition of the camshafts or cylinder head, have them examined at a Volvo dealer workshop or suitably-equipped automotive repair facility.

23 Inspect the rocker arms and hydraulic adjusters for obvious signs of wear or damage, and renew if necessary.

Refitting

24 Make sure that the top surfaces of

the cylinder head, and in particular the camshaft bearings and the mating surfaces are completely clean. Ensure the secondary timing chain lower guide rail is in place **(see illustration)**.

25 Smear some clean engine oil onto the sides of the hydraulic adjusters, and offer each one into position in their original bores in the cylinder head, together with its rocker arm **(see illustrations)**.

26 Locate the timing chain on the camshaft sprockets, aligning the two coloured chain links with the marks on the camshaft sprockets, then lubricate the camshaft and cylinder head bearing journals with clean engine oil,

8.19 Lift out the rocker arms and hydraulic adjusters

8.24 Fit the secondary timing chain lower guide rail

8.25a Apply clean oil to the hydraulic adjusters . . .

8.25b . . . and refit them to their original positions

8.26a Align the coloured links on the chain with the marks on the camshaft sprockets . . .

8.26b . . . the mark on the sprockets is a dot and a line . . .

8.26c . . . then fit the camshafts with the mark on the inlet camshaft (arrowed) in the 12 o'clock position

H46404

8.27a Apply a thin bead of sealant as indicated by the heavy black line

and lower the camshafts into position (see illustrations). The mark on the inlet camshaft must be in the 12 o'clock position.

27 Apply a thin bead of Volvo sealant (No 116 1771) to the mating surface of the cylinder head (see illustration). Take great care to ensure the chain tensioner oil supply hole is free from sealant (see illustration).

28 Lower the upper section of the cylinder head into place, and tighten the retaining bolts to the specified torque in sequence (see illustration).

29 Refit the injector mounting studs and tighten them to the specified torque.

30 Refit the camshaft timing chain tensioner assembly, and tighten the retaining bolts to the specified torque. Press the tensioner guide rail up into the housing and pull out the locking pin/drill bit. Slowly release the guide rail to tension the chain.

31 Fit a new exhaust camshaft oil seal as described in Section 9.

32 Refit the 2 bolts securing the timing belt inner cover to the cylinder head, and the single bolt to the cylinder block, then tighten the bolts securely.

33 Slide the exhaust camshaft sprocket into place, aligning the integral key with the camshaft and fit the camshaft sprocket locking tool.

34 Fit the sprocket retaining bolt and tighten it to the specified torque, preventing the sprocket from turning using the tool used during removal.

35 Refit the engine mounting bracket to the right-hand end of the cylinder head/block, and tighten the bolts to the specified torque.

36 The remainder of refitting is a reversal of removal, noting the following points:
a) Refit the injectors as described in Chapter 4A.
b) Fit the new timing belt, tensioner and idler pulley as described in Section 6.
c) Tighten all fasteners to their specified torque, where given.
d) Check the engine oil and coolant levels as described in Chapter 1.

8.27b We inserted a tapered rod into the tensioner oil supply hole to prevent any sealant from entering

8.28 Cylinder head upper section bolt tightening sequence

9.4a Apply a little clean oil to the oil seal inner lip . . .

9.4b . . . then using a socket (or similar) to drive the seal into place . . .

9.4c . . . until the seal is flush with the casing surface

9 Camshaft oil seal – renewal

1 Remove the timing belt as described in Section 6, and the camshaft sprocket as described in paragraph 10 of the previous Section. Recover the sprocket locating key from the end of the camshaft.
2 Carefully prise or pull the seal from position.
3 Clean out the seal housing and the sealing surface of the camshaft by wiping it with a lint-free cloth. Remove any swarf or burrs that may cause the seal to leak.
4 Apply a little oil to the new camshaft oil seal, and fit it over the end of the camshaft, lips facing inwards. To avoid damaging the seal lips, wrap a little tape over the end of the camshaft. Volvo dealers have a special tool (No 999 7123) for fitting the seal, but if this is not available, a deep socket of suitable size can be used. **Note:** *Select a socket that bears only on the hard outer surface of the seal, not the inner lip which can easily be damaged.* It is important that the seal is fitted square to the shaft, and is fully-seated **(see illustrations)**.
5 Refit the camshaft sprocket (and key – Section 8) and timing belt as described in Section 6.

10 Cylinder head – removal, inurmation inspection and refitting

Removal

1 Remove the battery as described in Chapter 5A, then unscrew the 4 bolts securing the battery tray, and remove the tray from the engine compartment.
2 Drain the coolant as described in Chapter 1.
3 Remove the camshafts, rocker arms and hydraulic adjusters as described in Section 8.
4 Undo the 4 bolts, and remove the bracket over the fuel filter.
5 Undo the Torx screw, lift out the filter housing, then undo the bolts and remove

the fuel filter bracket. Refit the bolt securing the lifting bracket to the cylinder head **(see illustration)**.
6 Remove the turbocharger/exhaust manifold as described in Chapter 4A.
7 Disconnect the wiring plugs, then undo the 4 nuts, unscrew the 4 mounting studs and detach the thermostat housing from the left-hand of the cylinder head. Be prepared for coolant spillage **(see illustration)**.
8 Disconnect the wiring plug from the pressure sensor on the underside of the common fuel rail at the front of the cylinder head.
9 Undo the retaining bolt, and remove the oil filler pipe support bracket.
10 Working in the **reverse** of the sequence shown **(see illustration 10.34)**, gradually and evenly slacken and remove the cylinder head bolts. Discard the bolts, new ones must be fitted.
11 Lift the cylinder head away; use assistance if possible, as it is a very heavy assembly. Do not place the cylinder head flat on its sealing surface, as the ends of the glow plugs may be damaged – support the ends of the cylinder head on wooden blocks.
12 If the head is stuck (as is possible), be careful how you choose to free it. Striking the head with tools carries the risk of damage, and the head is located on two dowels, so its movement will be limited. Do not, under any circumstances, lever the head between the mating surfaces, as this will certainly damage the sealing surfaces for the gasket, leading to leaks.

13 Once the head has been removed, recover the gasket from the two dowels.
14 Do not discard the gasket at this stage – it will be needed for correct identification of the new gasket.

Inspection

15 If required, dismantling and inspection of the cylinder head is covered in Part D of this Chapter.

Cylinder head gasket selection

16 Examine the old cylinder head gasket for manufacturer's identification markings. These will be in the form of holes on the front edge of the gasket, which indicate the gasket's thickness.
17 Unless new components have been fitted, or the cylinder head has been machined (skimmed), the new cylinder head gasket must be of the same type as the old one. Purchase the required gasket, and proceed to paragraph 24.
18 If the head has been machined, or if new pistons have been fitted, it is likely that a head gasket of different thickness to the original will be needed.
19 Gasket selection is made on the basis of the measured piston protrusion above the cylinder head gasket surface (the protrusion must fall within the range specified at the start of this Chapter).
20 To measure the piston protrusion, anchor a dial test indicator (DTI) to the top face (cylinder head gasket mating face) of the cylinder block,

10.5 Undo the bolts (arrowed) and remove the filter bracket

10.7 Thermostat housing studs (arrowed)

10.20 Zero the DTi gauge on the gasket face

10.31 Fit the new gasket over the dowels with the thickness identification holes at the front (arrowed)

and zero the gauge on the gasket mating face **(see illustration)**.

21 Rest the gauge probe above No 1 piston crown, and turn the crankshaft slowly by hand until the piston reaches TDC (its maximum height). Measure and record the maximum piston projection at TDC.

22 Repeat the measurement for the remaining pistons, and record the results.

23 If the measurements differ from piston to piston, take the highest figure, and use this to determine the thickness of the head gasket required.

Preparation for refitting

24 The mating faces of the cylinder head and cylinder block must be perfectly clean before refitting the head. Use a hard plastic or wooden scraper to remove all traces of gasket and carbon; also clean the piston crowns. **Note:** *The new head gasket has rubber-coated surfaces, which could be damaged from sharp edges or debris left by a metal scraper. Take particular care when cleaning the piston crowns, as the soft aluminium alloy is easily damaged.*

25 Make sure that the carbon is not allowed to enter the oil and water passages – this is particularly important for the lubrication system, as carbon could block the oil supply to the engine's components. Using adhesive tape and paper, seal the water, oil and bolt holes in the cylinder block.

26 To prevent carbon entering the gap between the pistons and bores, smear a little grease in the gap.

27 After cleaning each piston, use a small brush to remove all traces of grease and carbon from the gap, then wipe away the remainder with a clean rag. Clean all the pistons in the same way.

28 Check the mating surfaces of the cylinder block and the cylinder head for nicks, deep scratches and other damage (refer to the Note in paragraph 24). If slight, they may be removed carefully with a file, but if excessive, machining may be the only alternative to renewal.

29 If warpage of the cylinder head gasket surface is suspected, use a straight-edge to check it for distortion. Refer to Part D of this Chapter if necessary.

30 Ensure that the cylinder head bolt holes in the crankcase are clean and free of oil. Syringe or soak up any oil left in the bolt holes. This is most important in order that the correct bolt tightening torque can be applied, and to prevent the possibility of the block being cracked by hydraulic pressure when the bolts are tightened.

Refitting

31 Ensure that the cylinder head locating dowels are in place at the corners of the cylinder block, then fit the new cylinder head gasket over the dowels, ensuring that the identification holes are at the front **(see illustration)**. Take care to avoid damaging the gasket's rubber coating.

32 Lower the cylinder head into position on the gasket, ensuring that it engages correctly over the dowels.

33 Fit the new cylinder head bolts and screw them in as far as possible by hand.

34 Working in the sequence shown **(see illustration)**, tighten all the cylinder head bolts to the specified Stage 1 torque using an E14 Torx socket.

35 Stage 2 involves tightening the bolts though an angle, rather than to a torque **(see illustration)**. Each bolt in sequence must be rotated through the specified angle – special angle gauges are available from tool outlets. As a guide, a 180° angle is equivalent to a half-turn, and this is easily judged by assessing the start and end positions of the socket handle or torque wrench.

36 The remainder of the refitting procedure is a reversal of the removal procedure, bearing in mind the following points:

a) *Refit the camshafts, rocker arms and hydraulic adjusters as described in Section 8.*

b) *Reconnect the exhaust front section to the exhaust manifold with reference to Chapter 4B.*

c) *Fit new high-pressure fuel delivery pipes as described in Chapter 4A.*

d) *Refit the cylinder head cover/inlet manifold with reference to Section 3.*

e) *Refit the air cleaner as described in Chapter 4A.*

f) *Refill the cooling system as described in Chapter 3.*

g) *Check and if necessary top-up the engine oil level as described in 'Weekly checks'.*

h) *Before starting the engine, read through the section on engine restarting after overhaul, at the end of Chapter 2D.*

10.34 Cylinder head lower section bolt tightening sequence

H46406

10.35 Use an angle gauge for the Stage 2 torque setting

11 Sump – removal and refitting

Note: *The full procedure outlined below must be followed so that the mating surfaces can be cleaned and prepared to achieve an oil-tight joint on reassembly.*

Removal

1 Apply the handbrake, then jack up the front of the vehicle and support it on axle stands (see *Jacking and vehicle support*). Undo the fasteners and remove the engine undershield.
2 Referring to Chapter 1 if necessary, drain the engine oil, then clean and refit the engine oil drain plug, tightening it to the specified torque wrench setting. We strongly advise renewing the oil filter element, also described in Chapter 1.
3 Pull the plastic cover on the top of the engine upwards from its mountings.
4 Slacken the hose clamps, undo the bracket bolt and remove the charge air pipe from the underside of the engine **(see illustration)**.
5 Remove the air conditioning compressor drivebelt as described in Chapter 1, then undo the mounting bolts and move the compressor to one side without disconnecting the refrigerant pipes. Suspend the compressor from the radiator crossmember using wires or straps.
6 Progressively unscrew the sump retaining Allen bolts, including the 2 bolts securing the sump to the transmission housing **(see illustrations)**. Don't forget the 4 bolts at the left-hand end accessed through the holes. Break the joint by carefully inserting a putty knife (or similar) between the sump and cylinder block. Take care not to damage the sealing surfaces.

Refitting

7 On reassembly, thoroughly clean and degrease the mating surfaces of the cylinder block/crankcase and sump, removing all traces of sealant, then use a clean rag to wipe out the sump and the engine's interior.

11.4 Undo the charge air pipe bracket bolt (arrowed)

11.6b . . . access to the sump end bolts is through the holes (arrowed)

8 Apply a 3 mm thick bead of sealant (Volvo part No 116 1771) to the sump flange, making sure the bead is around the inside edge of the bolt holes. Do not allow the sealant to enter the bolt holes **(see illustration)**. **Note:** *The sump must be refitted within 5 minutes of applying the sealant.*
9 Refit the sump and fit the retaining bolts, tightening them by hand only at this stage.
10 Tighten the 2 bolts securing the sump to the transmission casing to the specified torque, then tighten the remaining bolts, gradually and evenly to the specified torque.
11 Lower the car to the ground. Refill the engine with oil, and if removed fit a new oil filter with reference to Chapter 1.
12 Volvo recommend waiting a minimum of 2 hours before starting the car to allow the sealant to cure fully.

11.6a Undo the 2 bolts securing the sump to the transmission (arrowed) . . .

11.8 Apply sealant around the inside of the bolt holes

12 Oil pump – removal, inspection and refitting

Removal

1 Remove the timing belt as described in Section 6, then slide off the crankshaft sprocket **(see illustrations)**.
2 Remove the sump as described in Section 11.
3 Undo the retaining bolts and remove the front cover and crankshaft seal. Note the original locations of the cover screws – they are of different lengths.
4 Undo the bolt securing the oil level pipe **(see illustration)**.
5 Pull out the key from the crankshaft

12.1a Slide off the crankshaft sprocket . . .

12.1b . . . and recover the crankshaft key

12.4 Oil level pipe bracket bolt (arrowed)

12.5a Remove the sprocket key . . .

12.5b . . . undo the oil pump mounting bolts (arrowed) and slide the assembly from the crankshaft

12.5c . . . and recover the O-ring between the sprocket and the crankshaft

12.6 Oil pump cover bolts

12.7 Oil pressure relief valve plug

12.13 Fit the O-ring to the end of the crankshaft

sprocket, then undo the pump mounting bolts, slide the pump, chain, and crankshaft sprocket from the end of the engine **(see illustrations)**. Recover the O-ring between the sprocket and crankshaft.

Inspection

6 Undo the retaining screws and remove the cover from the oil pump **(see illustration)**. Note the location of any identification marks on the inner and outer rotors for refitting.

7 Unscrew the plug and remove the pressure relief valve, spring and plunger, clean out and check the condition of the components **(see illustration)**.

8 No specifications for the pump internal components are given by Volvo.

9 Check the general condition of the oil pump, and in particular, its mating face to the cylinder block. If the mating face is damaged significantly, this may lead to oil loss (and a resulting drop in available oil pressure).

10 Inspect the rotors for obvious signs of wear or damage; at the time of writing, no parts are available. If the pump is faulty, it must be renewed as a complete unit. Lubricate the rotors with fresh engine oil and refit them into the body, making sure that the identification marks are positioned as noted on removal.

11 If the oil pump has been removed as part of a major engine overhaul, it is assumed that the engine will have completed a substantial mileage. In this case, it is often considered

good practice to fit a new (or reconditioned) pump as a matter of course. In other words, if the rest of the engine is being rebuilt, the engine has completed a large mileage, or there is any question as to the old pump's condition, it is preferable to fit a new oil pump.

Refitting

12 Before fitting the oil pump, ensure that the mating faces on the pump and the engine block are completely clean.

13 Fit the O-ring to the end of the crankshaft **(see illustration)**.

14 Engage the drive chain with the oil pump and crankshaft sprockets, then slide the crankshaft sprocket into place (aligning the slot in the sprocket with the keyway in the crankshaft) as the pump is refitted. Refit the crankshaft key.

15 Refit the mounting bolts and tighten them to the specified torque. Note that the front, left-hand bolt is slightly longer than the others.

16 Apply a 3 mm wide bead of sealant (part No 116 1771) to the oil seal carrier flange. Refit the cover and tighten the bolts to the specified torque. Note that the bolts must be tightened within 4 minutes of the sealant being applied.

17 Fit a new oil seal to the cover as described in Section 15.

18 Refit the bolt securing the oil level pipe.

19 The remainder of refitting is a reversal of removal, remembering to fit a new oil filter element, and replenish the engine oil.

13 Oil pressure warning light switch – removal and refitting

Removal

1 The switch is screwed into the oil filter housing **(see illustration)**. Access is from under the vehicle. Undo the fasteners and remove the engine undershield. To further improve access, undo the mounting bolts and move the air conditioning compressor to one side. Suspend the compressor from the radiator crossmember using wire or straps. There is no need to disconnect the refrigerant pipes.

2 Disconnect the switch wiring plug.

3 Unscrew the switch from the housing; be prepared for some oil loss.

13.1 Oil pressure warning light switch

14.2 Oil cooler retaining bolts (arrowed)

15.4a Drill a small hole in the seal . . .

15.4b . . . insert a self-tapping screw and pull out the seal

Refitting

4 Refitting is the reverse of the removal procedure; fit a new pressure switch sealing washer, and tighten the switch to the specified torque wrench setting.

5 Reconnect the switch wiring plug.

6 Refit all components removed for access to the switch.

7 Check the engine oil level and top-up as necessary (see *Weekly checks*).

8 Check for correct warning light operation, and for signs of oil leaks, once the engine has been restarted and warmed-up to normal operating temperature.

14 Oil cooler – removal and refitting

Note: *New sealing rings will be required on refitting – check for availability prior to commencing work.*

Removal

1 The cooler is fitted to the oil filter housing on the front of the cylinder block. Access is from under the vehicle. Undo the fasteners and remove the engine undershield. To further improve access, remove the auxiliary drivebelt (Chapter 1), undo the mounting bolts and move the air conditioning compressor to one side. Suspend the compressor from the radiator crossmember using wire or straps. There is no need to disconnect the refrigerant pipes.

2 Undo the 4 retaining bolts and detach the cooler from the housing **(see illustration)**. Recover the sealing rings and be prepared for oil/coolant spillage.

Refitting

3 Refitting is a reversal of removal, bearing in mind the following points:
a) *Use new sealing rings.*
b) *Tighten the cooler mounting bolts securely.*
c) *On completion, lower the car to the ground. Check and if necessary top-up the oil and coolant levels, then start the engine and check for signs of oil or coolant leakage.*

15 Crankshaft oil seals – renewal

Timing belt end seal

1 Remove the timing belt as described in Section 6.

2 Slide the belt sprocket from the crankshaft, and recover the locating key from the groove on the crankshaft.

3 Note the fitted depth of the oil seal as a guide for fitting the new one.

4 Using a screwdriver or similar tool, carefully prise the oil seal from its location. Take care not to damage the oil seal contact surfaces or crankshaft. Alternatively, drill a small hole in the seal (taking care not to drill any deeper than necessary), then insert a self-tapping screw and use pliers to pull out the seal **(see illustrations)**.

5 Wipe clean the oil seal contact surfaces and seating, and clean up any sharp edges or burrs which might damage the new seal as it is fitted, or which might cause the seal to leak once in place.

6 No oil should be applied to the oil seal, which is made of PTFE. Volvo technicians use a special seal-fitting tool (No 999-7124), but an adequate substitute can be achieved using a large socket or piece of tubing of sufficient size to bear on the outer edge of the new seal. Note that the new seal is supplied with a guide which fits over the end of the crankshaft.

7 Locate the new seal (with guide still fitted) over the end of the crankshaft, using the tool **(see illustrations)**, socket, or tubing to press the seal squarely and fully into position, to the previously-noted depth. Remove the guide from the end of the crankshaft.

8 The remainder of reassembly is the reverse of the removal procedure, referring to the relevant text for details where required. Check for signs of oil leakage when the engine is restarted.

Flywheel end seal

9 Remove the transmission as described in Chapter 7A, and the clutch assembly as described in Chapter 6.

10 Unbolt the flywheel (see Section 16).

11 Using a screwdriver or similar, carefully prise the oil seal from place. Take great care not to damage the seal seating area or the crankshaft sealing surface. Alternatively, punch or drill two small holes opposite each other in the oil seal, then screw a self-tapping screw into each hole, and pull the screws with pliers to extract the seal **(see illustrations)**.

15.7a Locate the new seal and guide over the end of the crankshaft . . .

15.7b . . . then drive the seal home until it's flush with the cover

15.11a Drill a hole in the seal . . .

15.11b . . . then insert a self-tapping screw and pull out the seal

15.14 Locate the seal and locating sleeve over the end of the crankshaft

15.15 Press the seal in until it's flush with the surface

12 Clean the end of the crankshaft, polishing off any burrs or raised edges, which may have caused the seal to fail in the first place. Clean also the seal mating face on the engine block, using a suitable solvent for degreasing if necessary.

13 The new oil seal is supplied fitted with a locating sleeve, which must **not** be removed prior to fitting (it will drop out on its own when the seal is fitted). Do not lubricate the seal.

14 Offer the new seal into position, feeding the locating sleeve over the end of the crankshaft **(see illustration)**.

15 Volvo technicians use a special tool (No 999 7126) to pull the seal into position. In the absence of the tool, use a large socket/piece of tubing which bears only on the hard outer edge of the seal, and carefully tap the seal into position **(see illustration)**.

16 If the seal locating sleeve is still in position, remove it now.

17 The remainder of the reassembly procedure is the reverse of dismantling, referring to the relevant text for details where required. Check for signs of oil leakage when the engine is restarted.

16 Flywheel – removal, inspection and refitting

Removal

1 Remove the transmission as described

in Chapter 7A. Now is a good time to check components such as the oil seals and renew them if necessary.

2 Remove the clutch as described in Chapter 6. Now is a good time to check or renew the clutch components and release bearing.

3 Use a centre-punch or paint to make alignment marks on the flywheel and crankshaft, to ensure correct alignment during refitting.

4 Prevent the flywheel from turning by locking the ring gear teeth, or by bolting a strap between the flywheel and the cylinder block/crankcase. Slacken the Torx bolts evenly until all are free.

5 Remove each bolt in turn and ensure that new ones are obtained for reassembly; these bolts are subjected to severe stresses and so must be renewed, regardless of their apparent condition, whenever they are disturbed **(see illustration)**.

6 Withdraw the flywheel, remembering that it is very heavy – do not drop it.

Inspection

7 Clean the flywheel to remove grease and oil. Inspect the surface for cracks, rivet grooves, burned areas and score marks. Light scoring can be removed with emery cloth. Check for cracked and broken ring gear teeth. Lay the flywheel on a flat surface and use a straight-edge to check for warpage.

8 Clean and inspect the mating surfaces

of the flywheel and the crankshaft. If the crankshaft seal is leaking, renew it before refitting the flywheel. If the engine has covered a high mileage, it may be worth fitting a new seal as a matter if course, given the amount of work needed to access it.

9 Thoroughly clean the threaded bolt holes in the crankshaft, removing all traces of locking compound.

Refitting

10 Fit the flywheel to the crankshaft ensuring the dowel aligns with the hole in the crankshaft – it will fit only one way **(see illustration)**. Insert the new bolts.

11 Lock the flywheel by the method used on dismantling **(see illustration)**. Working in a diagonal sequence, tighten the bolts to the specified torque wrench setting.

12 Refit the clutch (Chapter 6) and the transmission (Chapter 7A).

17 Engine/transmission mountings – inspection and renewal

This process was undertaken on the 2.4 litre 5-cylinder engine, along with relevant photographs, but the process will be similar for all engines. Refer to Chapter 2C.

16.5 Flywheel retaining bolts

16.10 Note the locating dowel and corresponding hole (arrowed)

16.11 A simple home-made tool to lock the flywheel

Chapter 2 Part C
5-cylinder engine in-car repair procedures

Contents

Degrees of difficulty

Easy, suitable for novice with little experience 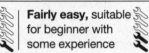	Fairly easy, suitable for beginner with some experience	Fairly difficult, suitable for competent DIY mechanic	Difficult, suitable for experienced DIY mechanic	Very difficult, suitable for expert DIY or professional

Specifications

General

Engine type.	Water-cooled, double overhead camshaft, 20 valve, in-line five cylinders, with both the cylinder block and cylinder head made from aluminium-alloy, with cast-iron cylinder sleeves
Engine codes	D5204 T2, D5244 T4, D5244 T5, D5244 T10, D5244 T14, D5244 T16 and D5244 T19

Capacity:
D5204	1984 cc
D5244	2400 cc

Bore:
D5204	81.0 mm
D5244	81.0 mm

Stroke:
D5204	77.0 mm
D5244	93.15 mm

Engine code:	Power output	Torque
D5204 T2	120 kW	400 Nm at 1400 to 2750 rpm
D5244 T4	136 kW	350 Nm at 1750 to 3250 rpm
D5244 T5	120 kW	340 Nm at 1750 to 3000 rpm
D5244 T10	151 kW	420 Nm at 1500 to 3000 rpm
D5244 T14	129 kW	420 Nm at 1500 to 2750 rpm
D5244 T16	120 kW	420 Nm at 1500 to 2500 rpm
D5244 T19	129 kW	420 Nm at 1500 to 2750 rpm

Compression ratio	17.3:1 to 18.0:1 depending on engine. Refer to a Volvo dealer for exact specification
Firing order	1-2-4-5-3
Cylinder No 1 location	Timing belt end

Cylinder head gasket selection

Piston protrusion over gasket face (see text):	Min	Max
1 hole	0.26 mm	0.47 mm
2 holes	0.47 mm	0.52 mm
3 holes	0.52 mm	0.57 mm
4 holes	0.57 mm	0.62 mm
5 holes	0.62 mm	0.74 mm

Camshaft

Drive . . . . Toothed belt

Lubrication system

Oil pump type . . . . Mounted on front of cylinder block and driven directly from crankshaft
Oil pressure – minimum (engine at operating temperature):
  At idle (at 800 rpm on 2 litre engine) . . . . 1.0 bar
  At 4000 rpm . . . . 3.5 bar

Valves

Valve clearances . . . . Hydraulic compensators – no adjustment necessary

Torque wrench settings

	Nm	lbf ft
Auxiliary drivebelt tensioner	24	18
Camshaft bearing cap	10	7
Camshaft cover	10	7
Camshaft end sealing/bearing caps (M7)	17	13
Camshaft position sensor	10	7
Camshaft sprocket bolt	30	22
Catalytic converter crossmember	24	18
Catalytic converter mounting screws	10	7
Connecting rod cap:*		
Stage 1	30	22
Stage 2	Angle-tighten a further 90°	
Coolant temperature sensor	22	16
Crankcase intermediate section:		
Tighten in the following sequence:		
M10*	20	15
M10	40	30
M8	24	18
M7	17	13
M10	Angle-tighten a further 110°	
Crankshaft pulley screws:		
Stage 1	35	26
Stage 2	Angle-tighten a further 50°	
Crankshaft sprocket nut	300	221
Cylinder head bolts:*		
Stage 1	20	15
Stage 2	Slacken	
Stage 3	20	15
Stage 4	50	37
Stage 5	Angle-tighten a further 90°	
Stage 6	Angle-tighten a further 90°	
Driveplate:*		
Stage 1	45	33
Stage 2	Angle-tighten a further 50°	
Engine mountings:		
Right-hand side:*		
Mounting bracket (M12)	80	59
Mounting to cylinder head	48	35
Left-hand side:*		
Mounting bracket:		
M8	24	18
M12	80	59
Mounting to gearbox	175	129
Torque rod bolts*	110	81
Exhaust pipe to turbocharger	24	18

Torque wrench settings (continued)

	Nm	lbf ft
Flywheel:*		
Stage 1	45	33
Stage 2	Angle-tighten a further 65°	
Fuel injection pump	18	13
Fuel rail/injector pipe unions:		
Stage 1	10	7
Stage 2	Angle-tighten a further 60°	
Fuel rail mounting bolts	24	18
Glow plugs	8	6
Injector screws*	13	10
Oil cooler retaining bolts	17	13
Oil filter	25	18
Oil pick-up pipe	17	13
Oil pressure switch	27	20
Oil pump bolts	10	7
Piston cooling jets	17	13
Piston cooling valve	51	38
Sump:		
Sump to transmission	50	37
Sump to engine	17	13
Sump drain plug (engine oil)	38	28
Timing belt idler pulley	24	18
Timing belt tensioner	24	18
Torque converter bolts*	60	44
Turbocharger oil drain pipe union	12	9
Turbocharger to manifold	35	26
Vacuum pump	17	13

Do not re-use

1   General information

Introduction

The engines are water-cooled, double overhead camshaft, 20 valve, in-line five cylinder units of 2.0 and 2.4 litre capacities, with both the cylinder block and cylinder head made from aluminium-alloy, with cast-iron cylinder sleeves. The engine is mounted transversely at the front of the vehicle, with the transmission bolted to the left-hand end of the engine.

The cylinder head carries the camshafts, which are driven by a toothed timing belt from the crankshaft to the inlet camshaft. A toothed gear on the inlet shaft drives a corresponding gear on the exhaust camshaft. An Oldham coupling on the left-hand end of the inlet camshaft drives the low/high-pressure fuel pump, whilst the vacuum pump is driven from the left-hand end of the exhaust camshaft. The cylinder head also incorporates the 20 inlet and exhaust valves (4 per cylinder), which are closed by single coil springs, and which run in guides pressed into the cylinder head. The camshafts actuate the valves via roller type rocker arms acting upon hydraulic tappets, mounted in the cylinder head. The cylinder head contains internal oilways which supply and lubricate the hydraulic tappets.

All engines are of direct injection design where the swirl chambers are incorporated in the tops of the pistons. The cylinder head incorporates two separate inlet ports per cylinder. These ports are of different length and geometry to ensure more efficient combustion and reduced emissions.

The forged steel crankshaft is of six-bearing type, and the No 5 (from timing belt end) main bearing shells incorporate separate thrustwashers to control crankshaft endfloat. The inlet camshaft is driven by a toothed belt from the crankshaft sprocket, and the belt also drives the water pump mounted on the rear of the block.

The pistons are manufactured from aluminium-silicon alloy, with graphite coated skirts to reduce friction. The pistons incorporate cooling channels, through which oil flows, supplied by fixed jets mounted at the base of the cylinders. As each piston reaches the lower end of its stroke, the oil jet aligns with a hole in the base of the piston, and oil is forced through the cooling channel.

The engine has a full-flow lubrication system. A duocentric internal gear type oil pump is mounted on the front of the crankshaft. The oil filter is of the paper element type, mounted on the front side of the cylinder block.

Using this Chapter

This Chapter describes the repair procedures that can reasonably be carried out on the engine while it remains in the vehicle. If the engine has been removed from the vehicle and is being dismantled as described in Part D, any preliminary dismantling procedures can be ignored.

Note that, while it may be possible physically to overhaul items such as the piston/connecting rod assemblies while the engine is in the car, such tasks are not usually carried out as separate operations. Usually, several additional procedures are required (not to mention the cleaning of components and oilways); for this reason, all such tasks are classed as major overhaul procedures, and are described in Part D of this Chapter.

Part D describes the removal of the engine/transmission from the car, and the full overhaul procedures that can then be carried out.

Operations with engine in car

The following operations can be performed without removing the engine:

a) Auxiliary drivebelt – removal and refitting.
b) Camshafts – removal and refitting.
c) Camshaft oil seals – renewal.
d) Camshaft sprocket – removal and refitting.
e) Coolant pump – removal and refitting (refer to Chapter 3)
f) Crankshaft oil seals – renewal.
g) Crankshaft sprocket – removal and refitting.
h) Cylinder head – removal and refitting.
i) Engine mountings – inspection and renewal.
j) Oil pump and pickup assembly – removal and refitting.
k) Sump – removal and refitting.
l) Timing belt, sprockets and cover – removal, inspection and refitting.

Note: *It is possible to remove the pistons and connecting rods (after removing the cylinder head and sump) without removing the engine from the vehicle. However, this procedure is not recommended. Work of this nature is more easily and thoroughly completed with the engine on the bench – refer to Chapter 2D.*

2 Compression and leakdown tests – description and interpretation

Compression test

Note: *A compression tester specifically designed for diesel engines must be used for this test.*

1 When engine performance is down, or if misfiring occurs, a compression test can provide diagnostic clues as to the engine's condition. If the test is performed regularly, it can give warning of trouble before any other symptoms become apparent.

2 A compression tester specifically intended for diesel engines must be used, because of the higher pressures involved. The tester is connected to an adapter which screws into the glow plug hole. It is unlikely to be worthwhile buying such a tester for occasional use, but it may be possible to borrow or hire one – if not, have the test performed by a garage.

3 Unless specific instructions to the contrary are supplied with the tester, observe the following points:

a) *The battery must be in a good state of charge, the air filter clean, and the engine should be at normal operating temperature.*

b) *All the glow plugs should be removed before starting the test.*

c) *The engine management ECM relay must be removed from the fuse/relay box.*

4 There is no need to hold the accelerator pedal down during the test, because the diesel engine air inlet is not throttled.

5 The manufacturers do not specify a wear limit for compression pressure. Seek the advice of a Volvo dealer or other diesel specialist if in doubt as to whether a particular pressure reading is acceptable.

6 The cause of poor compression is less easy to establish on a diesel engine than on a petrol one. The effect of introducing oil into the cylinders (wet testing) is not conclusive, because there is a risk that the oil will sit in the recess on the piston crown, instead of passing to the rings. However, the following can be used as a rough guide to diagnosis.

7 All cylinders should produce very similar pressures; a difference of more than 5.0 bars between any two cylinders indicates the existence of a fault. Note that the compression should build-up quickly in a healthy engine; low compression on the first stroke, followed by gradually-increasing pressure on successive strokes, indicates worn piston rings. A low compression reading on the first stroke, which does not build-up during successive strokes, indicates leaking valves or a blown head gasket (a cracked head could also be the cause).

8 A low reading from two adjacent cylinders is almost certainly due to the head gasket having blown between them.

3.1 Unbolt the bracket (arrowed) on the front of the timing belt cover

Leakdown test

9 A leakdown test measures the rate at which compressed air fed into the cylinder is lost. It is an alternative to a compression test, and in many ways it is better, since the escaping air provides easy identification of where pressure loss is occurring (piston rings, valves or head gasket).

10 The equipment needed for leakdown testing is unlikely to be available to the home mechanic. If poor compression is suspected, have the test performed by a suitably-equipped garage.

3 Timing belt covers – removal and refitting

Removal

1 Undo the bolt and remove the pipe bracket on the front face of the timing belt cover **(see illustration)**.

2 Release the 5 securing clips and remove the cover **(see illustration)**.

Refitting

3 Refitting of the cover is a reversal of the relevant removal procedure. Ensure that all disturbed hoses are reconnected and retained by their relevant clips.

4 Timing belt – removal, inspection and refitting

Note: *Whenever the timing belt is renewed, the tensioner and idler pulley should also be renewed as described in Section 5.*

Removal

1 The camshaft and coolant pump sprockets are driven by the timing belt from the crankshaft sprocket. The crankshaft and camshaft sprockets move in phase with each other to ensure correct valve timing. Should the timing belt slip or break in service, the valve timing will be disturbed and piston-to-valve contact will occur, resulting in serious engine damage.

3.2 Release the clips (arrowed) securing the timing belt cover

2 The design of the engines covered in this Chapter is such that piston-to-valve contact will occur if the crankshaft is turned with the timing belt removed. For this reason, it is important that the correct phasing between the camshaft and crankshaft is preserved whilst the timing belt is off the engine. This is achieved by setting the engine in a reference condition (known as Top Dead Centre or TDC) before the timing belt is removed, and then not rotating the shafts until the belt is refitted. Similarly, if the engine has been dismantled for overhaul, the engine must be set to TDC during reassembly to ensure that the correct shaft phasing is restored.

3 TDC is the highest position a piston reaches within its respective cylinder – in a four-stroke engine, each piston reaches TDC twice per cycle, once on the compression stroke and once on the exhaust stroke. In general, TDC normally refers to No 1 cylinder on the compression stroke. The cylinders are numbered one to five, starting from the timing belt end of the engine. Note that on this particular engine, when the timing marks are aligned, the No 1 piston is positioned very slightly before TDC.

4 Before starting work, disconnect the battery (see Chapter 5A).

5 Slacken the right-hand front roadwheel bolts, then jack up the front of the vehicle and support it securely on axle stands (see *Jacking and vehicle support*). Remove the roadwheel.

6 Remove the right-hand wheel arch liner for access to the crankshaft pulley **(see illustration)**.

4.6 Remove the wheel arch liner for access to the crankshaft pulley (arrowed)

4.11 Align the mark on the camshaft sprocket with the mark on the timing belt cover (arrowed)

4.13 The mark on the crankshaft pulley flange should align with the mark on the oil pump housing (arrowed)

4.14 Use a 6 mm Allen key to position the tensioner arm (arrowed) at approximately the 10 o'clock position

7 Remove the timing belt outer cover as described in Section 3.

8 Release the return hose cable-tie from the engine cross-stay mounting bracket, then release the top clip and lift the power steering fluid reservoir from place, and move it to one side over the top of the engine. Do not disconnect the hoses.

9 Remove the auxiliary drivebelt as described in Chapter 1.

10 Undo the bolts and remove the timing belt lower cover.

11 Using a socket on the crankshaft pulley nut, rotate the crankshaft clockwise until the markings on the camshaft sprocket and timing belt rear cover align **(see illustration)**.

12 Undo the four bolts and one nut securing the crankshaft pulley to the crankshaft sprocket and remove the crankshaft pulley, leaving the sprocket in place. Note that the centre nut is very tight. In order to prevent the crankshaft from rotating on manual models, engage top gear and have an assistant fully depress the brake pedal. On automatic models, remove the starter motor as described in Chapter 5A, and use a large flat-bladed screwdriver wedged between the driveplate ring gear teeth and the transmission housing.

13 Check that the marks on the camshaft sprocket and timing belt rear cover are still aligned, and the lug on the oil pump housing aligns with the mark cast into crankshaft pulley mounting boss. If the marks do not align,

temporarily refit two of the crankshaft pulley retaining bolts and the centre nut loosely and, using a large screwdriver/lever, rotate the crankshaft clockwise until the marks are in alignment **(see illustration)**.

14 Slacken the timing belt tensioner centre bolt slightly, and use a 6 mm Allen key to rotate the tensioner arm clockwise to the 10 o'clock position, then lightly tighten the centre bolt **(see illustration)**.

15 Remove the timing belt from the sprockets, without turning the crankshaft or camshaft.

Inspection

16 Examine the belt for evidence of contamination by coolant or lubricant. If this is the case, find the source of the contamination before progressing any further. Check the belt for signs of wear or damage, particularly around the leading edges of the belt teeth. Renew the belt if its condition is in doubt; the cost of belt renewal is negligible compared with potential cost of the engine repairs, should the belt fail in service. The belt must be renewed if it has covered the mileage stated by the manufacturer (see Chapter 1), however if it has covered less it is prudent to renew it regardless of condition, as a precautionary measure. **Note:** *If the timing belt is not going to be refitted for some time, it is a wise precaution to hang a warning label on the steering wheel, to remind yourself (and others) not to attempt to start the engine.*

17 Spin the belt tensioner and idler pulleys

and listen for noise which may indicate wear in the pulley bearings. If in any doubt, renew the pulleys as described in Section 5.

Refitting

18 Ensure that the crankshaft and camshaft are still aligned as described in paragraphs 11 and 13.

19 Fit the new belt around the crankshaft sprocket, idler pulley, camshaft sprocket, coolant pump sprocket, and finally, the tensioner pulley. Ensure the belt teeth seat correctly on the sprockets.

20 Ensure that the front run of the belt is taut – ie, all the slack should be in the section of the belt that passes over the tensioner roller.

21 Slacken the tensioner roller centre bolt slightly, then using a 6 mm Allen key, rotate the tensioner arm anti-clockwise until it passes the position shown, then rotate it clockwise until the indicator reaches the correct position **(see illustration)**. Tighten the centre bolt to the specified torque.

22 Gently press the belt between the camshaft sprocket and coolant pump sprocket, and check the tensioner arm moves freely as the belt is pressed.

23 Turn the crankshaft through two complete turns, then check that the timing marks on the crankshaft pulley boss and camshaft sprocket align correctly as described in paragraphs 11 and 13.

24 Check that the timing belt tensioner indicator is still position as described in paragraph 21. If not, repeat the operation described in paragraph 21.

25 The remainder of refitting is a reversal of removal, remembering to tighten all fasteners to their specified torque where given.

5 Timing belt tensioner and sprockets – removal and refitting

Note: *Whenever the timing belt is renewed, the tensioner and idler pulley should also be renewed at the same time.*

Timing belt tensioner

1 Remove the timing belt as described in Section 4.

-20°C	20°C	50°C
-5°F	68°F	120°F

J45770

4.21 Timing belt tensioner settings at various temperatures

5.4 Ensure the tensioner locates correctly over the rib (arrowed) on the cylinder block

5.7 Use a simple tool to counterhold the camshaft sprocket whilst slackening the bolts

5.10a Insert the camshaft aligning tool through the hole in the cylinder head and into the exhaust camshaft sprocket

10.5mm

12mm

10mm

At Least 50mm

J45754

Not To Scale

5.10b Camshaft aligning tool

2 Undo the centre bolt and remove the tensioner.
3 Spin the tensioner roller, feeling and listening for any roughness or noise, which would indicated wear in the tensioner roller bearing. If in any doubt as the condition of the tensioner, renew it.
4 Refit the tensioner and insert the bolt – do not fully tighten the bolt at this stage. Ensure the tensioner 'fork' locates correctly over the rib on the cylinder block **(see illustration)**.
5 Refit and tension the timing belt as described in Section 4.

Camshaft sprocket

6 Remove the timing belt as described in Section 4.
7 Unscrew the camshaft sprocket bolts, while holding the sprocket stationary using a tool which engages the holes in the sprocket **(see illustration)**. Do not allow the camshaft to rotate.
8 Remove the sprocket from the camshaft.
9 Remove the vacuum pump from the left-hand end of the exhaust camshaft as described in Chapter 9.
10 Insert a camshaft locking pin (Volvo No 999 7007) into the hole in the cylinder head

and into the hole in the camshaft sprocket. If necessary, rotate the camshaft slightly to enable the pin to be inserted. If the Volvo pin is not available, a home-made equivalent can be fabricated **(see illustrations)**.
11 Check the mark on the crankshaft sprocket still aligns with the mark on the oil pump housing as described in Section 4, then rotate the crankshaft clockwise (viewed from the timing belt end) approximately 15 degrees.
12 Refit the sprocket to the camshaft, but only tighten the retaining bolts sufficiently to allow the sprocket to just move independently of the camshaft. Position the sprocket so the retaining bolts are not at the ends of the slots, and the mark on the sprocket edge aligns with the mark on the timing belt inner cover **(see illustration)**.
13 Unscrew the blanking plug from the front left-hand face of the cylinder block, and insert Volvo Tool No 999 7005, then rotate the crankshaft anti-clockwise (viewed from timing belt of the engine) until the crankshaft web of No 5 cylinder comes to a stop against the tool. Check the marks on the crankshaft pulley flange and oil pump housing align. If the tool is not available, a home-made equivalent may be fabricated using the dimensions shown **(see illustrations)**.
14 Refit the timing belt as described in paragraphs 18 to 23 of Section 4.
15 Ensure the marks of the crankshaft sprocket aligns with the mark on the oil pump housing, and the marks on the camshaft

5.12 Align the mark on the camshaft with the mark on the timing belt inner cover (arrowed)

5.13a Unscrew the blanking plug . . .

5.13b . . . and insert the crankshaft stop tool

5.13c Crankshaft stop tool

5.19 If necessary, use a puller to remove the crankshaft sprocket

5.27 Timing belt idler pulley

sprocket and timing belt inner cover align, then tighten the camshaft sprocket bolts to the specified torque, using the tool to counterhold the sprocket (see paragraph 7).

16 Remove the camshaft locking tool, crankshaft stop tool, and refit the vacuum pump as described in Chapter 9. Refit the blanking plug to the front face of the cylinder block.

17 Proceed as described from paragraph 24 of Section 4.

Crankshaft sprocket

18 Remove the timing belt as described in Section 4.

19 The crankshaft sprocket locates on a master spline on the crankshaft, and a puller may be required to work the sprocket off **(see illustration)**. Levering the sprocket off is not advisable – the rim of the sprocket itself is easily broken if care is not taken.

20 Wipe the sprocket and crankshaft mating surfaces clean.

21 Refit the sprocket to the crankshaft, and check the timing marks still align. Note the sprocket is located by means of a master spline on the crankshaft.

22 Install the timing belt around the crankshaft sprocket, idler pulley, camshaft sprocket, coolant pump, and finally the tensioner pulley.

23 Refit the pulley to the sprocket and refit the crankshaft nut, finger-tight only at this stage, then rotate the crankshaft anti-clockwise approximately 45°.

24 Stop the crankshaft from rotating and tighten the sprocket nut to the specified torque, then tighten the pulley bolts to their specified torque.

25 Tension the timing belt and complete the refitting procedure as described in Section 4.

Idler pulley

26 Remove the timing belt as described in Section 4.

27 Undo the bolt and remove the idler pulley **(see illustration)**.

28 Refitting is a reversal of removal, remembering to tighten all fasteners to their specified torque where given.

---

6 Cylinder head cover/inlet manifold – removal and refitting

Removal

1 The cylinder head cover is integral with the inlet manifold. Remove the plastic cover on top of the engine **(see illustration)**.

2 Remove the high-pressure fuel pipes and the fuel injectors as described in Chapter 4A. Discard the fuel pipes as new ones must be fitted on refitting.

3 Undo the clamps and remove the air pipe at the front of the engine, including the pipe securing bolt **(see illustrations)**.

4 Remove the crankcase ventilation hose from the cover.

6.1 Pull the engine cover straight up from its mountings

6.3a Remove the air pipe over the front of the engine, undoing the clamp at the air cleaner housing . . .

6.3b . . . unclipping the support bracket . . .

6.3c . . . and undoing the clamp at the rear of the engine compartment

6.7 An intricate rubber gasket is fitted to the camshaft cover

7.3a Fit the new seal using a tubular spacer which bears only on the hard, outer surface of the seal

7.3b The outside edge of the seal should be flush with the outer edge of the sealing cap/cylinder head casting

5 Undo the 3 bolts and remove the oil filler neck from the cover.
6 Undo the remaining bolts and carefully lift the cover from place.

Refitting

7 Refit the camshaft cover by following the removal procedure in reverse, noting the following points:
  a) *A rubber sealing gasket is fitted to the underside of the camshaft cover (see illustration). Ensure the gasket remains in place whilst the cover is refitted.*
  b) *Tighten the camshaft cover retaining nuts to the specified torque, starting from the centre and working outwards.*

7 Camshaft oil seal – renewal

1 Remove the camshaft sprocket as described in Section 5.
2 Using a screwdriver or lever, carefully prise out the oil seal taking care not to damage the camshaft surface.
3 Clean the seating in the bearing cap, then smear a little oil on the lips of the new oil seal. Fit the new oil seal and tap it into position carefully using a tubular spacer, socket or block of wood that bears only on the hard outer surface of the seal **(see illustrations)**.

The outside edge of the seal should be flush with the outer edge of the sealing cap/cylinder head casting.
4 Refit the camshaft sprocket as described in Section 5.

8 Crankshaft oil seals – renewal

Right-hand oil seal

1 Remove the crankshaft sprocket, with reference to Section 5.
2 The seal may be renewed without removing the oil pump by drilling a small hole, inserting a self-tapping screw, and pulling on the head of the screw with pliers **(see illustrations)**.

Take great care not to mark the crankshaft surface with the drill bit.
3 Wrap some adhesive tape around the end of the crankshaft to prevent damage to the new oil seal. Dip the new seal in engine oil and drive it into the oil pump housing with a block of wood or a socket until flush. Make sure that the closed end of the seal is facing outwards **(see illustrations)**.
4 Remove the adhesive tape.
5 Refit the timing belt and crankshaft sprocket, with reference to Section 5.

Left-hand oil seal

6 Remove the flywheel/driveplate with reference to Section 11.
7 Clean the surfaces of the block and crankshaft.
8 Remove the old oil seal and fit the new one

8.2a Drill a small hole into the hard, outer edge of the seal . . .

8.2b . . . then insert a self-tapping screw and pull the seal from place

8.3a Wrap tape around the shoulder on the crankshaft to protect the seal lips . . .

8.3b . . . then use a tubular spacer or socket . . .

8.3c . . . to drive the seal home

8.8 Drill a hole, insert a self-tapping screw and pull the crankshaft left-hand oil seal from place

as described in paragraphs 2 to 4 above **(see illustration)**.

9 Refit the flywheel/driveplate (Section 11).

---

9 Cylinder head – removal, inspection and refitting

Removal

1 Disconnect the battery negative lead (see Chapter 5A).

2 Jack up the front of the vehicle and support it securely on axle stands (see *Jacking and vehicle support*).

3 Drain the engine oil with reference to Chapter 1.

4 Drain the cooling system with reference to Chapter 1.

5 Loosen the clips and disconnect all air, coolant and vacuum hoses from the cylinder head noting their locations.

6 Remove the air cleaner assembly as described in Chapter 4A.

7 Remove the timing belt as described in Section 4.

8 Remove the camshafts, rocker arm and hydraulic tappets as described in Section 10.

9 Remove the power steering pump support bracket from the cylinder head along with the vacuum pump and fuel pump.

10 Undo the bolts securing the fuel rail and fuel pipes to the cylinder head.

11 Undo the retaining bolts and remove the heat shield above the exhaust manifold.

12 Slacken the EGR pipe clamp at the exhaust manifold, then undo the bolts securing the EGR valve/cooler/pipe assembly to the cylinder head and move it to one side.

13 Remove the front section of the exhaust pipe, and undo the bolts securing the exhaust manifold to the cylinder head as described in Chapter 4A. Disconnect and remove the oil return and supply pipes from the turbocharger and engine block, then slacken the clamp and disconnect the turbocharger outlet pipe. Disconnect the vacuum hose from the turbocharger control valve, and the rubber intake hose from the turbocharger, then carefully lower the turbocharger and manifold assembly onto the driveshaft and steering rack. Discard the turbocharger oil supply and return pipe sealing washers – new ones must be fitted.

14 Undo the bolts securing the coolant pipe to the cylinder head **(see illustration)**.

15 Make a final check to ensure all wiring plugs have been disconnected from the cylinder head.

16 Following the **reverse** of the tightening sequence **(see illustration 9.30)**, progressively slacken the cylinder head bolts, by half a turn at a time, until all bolts can be unscrewed by hand and removed. Discard the bolts – new ones must be fitted on reassembly.

17 Check that nothing remains connected to the cylinder head, then lift the head away from the cylinder block; seek assistance if possible, as it is heavy. Do not lay the cylinder head on the worktop face down – this may damage the sealing face.

18 Remove the gasket from the top of the block, noting the identification holes on its front edge. If the dowels are a loose fit, remove them and store them with the head for safe-keeping. Do not discard the gasket yet – it will be needed for identification purposes.

19 If the cylinder head is to be dismantled for overhaul, refer to Chapter 2D.

Inspection

20 The mating faces of the cylinder head and cylinder block/crankcase must be perfectly clean before refitting the head. Use a hard plastic or wood scraper to remove all traces of gasket and carbon; also clean the piston crowns. Take particular care during the cleaning operations, as aluminium alloy is easily damaged. Also, make sure that the carbon is not allowed to enter the oil and water passages – this is particularly important for the lubrication system, as carbon could block the oil supply to the engine's components. Using adhesive tape and paper, seal the water, oil and bolt holes in the cylinder block/crankcase.

21 Check the mating surfaces of the cylinder block/crankcase and the cylinder head for nicks, deep scratches and other damage. If slight, they may be removed carefully with abrasive paper, but note that head machining will not be possible – refer to Chapter 2D.

22 If warpage of the cylinder head gasket surface is suspected, use a straight-edge to check it for distortion.

23 Clean out the cylinder head bolt drillings using a suitable tap. If a tap is not available, use an old head bolt with two slots cut along the length of the threads. It is most important that no oil or coolant is present in the bolts holes, otherwise the block may be cracked by the hydraulic action as the head bolts are inserted and tightened.

Refitting

24 Examine the old cylinder head gasket for manufacturer's identification markings. These are in the form of holes along the front edge of the gasket **(see illustration)**. Unless new pistons have been fitted, the new cylinder head gasket must be the same type as the old one.

25 If new piston assemblies have been fitted as part of an engine overhaul, before purchasing the new cylinder head gasket, refer to Chapter 2D and measure the piston projection. Purchase a new gasket according to the results of the measurement.

26 Lay the new head gasket on the cylinder block, engaging it with the locating dowels **(see illustration)**. Ensure that the manufacturer's part number markings are facing upwards.

27 With the help of an assistant, place the cylinder head centrally on the cylinder block,

9.14 Undo the bolt (arrowed) securing the coolant pipe to the right-hand rear corner of the cylinder head

9.24 The holes (arrowed) along the edge of the cylinder head gasket indicate the thickness

9.26 Ensure the cylinder head gasket locates over the dowels in the block surface

9.30 Cylinder head bolt tightening sequence

H48475

9.31 Use an angle-measuring gauge to accurately tighten the bolts

ensuring that the locating dowels engage with the recesses in the cylinder head. Check that the head gasket is correctly seated before allowing the full weight of the cylinder head to rest on it.

28 Apply a smear of grease to the threads, and to the underside of the heads, of the new cylinder head bolts.

29 Carefully enter each bolt into its relevant hole (*do not drop them in*) and screw in, by hand only, until finger-tight.

30 Working progressively and in the sequence shown, tighten the cylinder head bolts to their Stage 1 torque setting, using a torque wrench and socket. them slacken the bolts in sequence (Stage 2) and tighten them to the Stage 3 setting. Then working in the

sequence shown tighten them to the Stage 4 setting **(see illustration)**.

31 Once all the bolts have been tightened to their Stage 4 settings, working again in the given sequence, angle-tighten the bolts through the specified Stage 5 angle, using a socket and extension bar **(see illustration)**. It is recommended that an angle-measuring gauge is used during this stage of the tightening, to ensure accuracy. If a gauge is not available, use paint to make alignment marks between the bolt head and cylinder head prior to tightening; the marks can then be used to check the bolt has been rotated through the correct angle during tightening. Repeat the procedure, tightening the bolts to the Stage 6 angle.

32 The remainder of refitting is a reversal of removal, noting the following points:
a) *No retightening of the cylinder head bolts is required.*
b) *Tighten all fasteners to their specified torque where given.*
c) *Refill the cooling system and replenish the engine oil as described in Chapter 1.*

10 Camshafts, rocker arms and hydraulic tappets – removal, inspection and refitting

Removal

1 Remove the inlet camshaft sprocket as described in Section 5.

2 Remove the camshaft cover as described in Section 6.

3 Undo the screw securing the timing inner cover to the right-hand camshaft bearing cap **(see illustration)**.

4 Remove the vacuum pump (Chapter 9), and the fuel pump (Chapter 4A).

5 Undo the screws securing the left- and right-hand camshaft bearing/sealing caps **(see illustrations)**.

6 The camshaft bearing caps should be marked to indicate their position. If they are not, number them starting from the timing belt end **(see illustration)**. It is essential they are refitted to their original positions.

7 Starting on the inlet camshaft, slacken each of the bearing cap screws one turn at a time until the camshaft is no longer under tension, then remove the screws and caps. The screws must be released gradually and evenly to prevent excess stress and possible damage to the exhaust camshaft. Repeat this procedure on the exhaust camshaft.

8 Lift out the camshafts, and discard the oil seal on the inlet camshaft.

9 Carefully lift the rocker arms and hydraulic tappets from the cylinder head. Lay them out on a clean, dry surface and, using paint, mark their positions in the cylinder head, eg, E1, E2 (exhaust 1, exhaust 2, etc).

Inspection

10 Unclip the hydraulic tappets from the rocker arms, and check for any signs

10.3 Inner timing cover screw

10.5a Undo the screws and remove the left-hand . . .

10.5b . . . and right-hand bearing caps

10.6 The bearing caps should be numbered, starting from the timing belt end

10.10 Unclip the tappets from the rocker arms

10.11 Spin the roller and listen for any noise

10.15 Ensure the end of the rocker arms are correctly located over the end of the valve stems

of damage **(see illustration)**. Renew as necessary.
11 Spin the roller on each of the rocker arms and listen for any noise from the bearing **(see illustration)**. Renew as necessary.
12 Inspect the cam lobes and the camshaft bearing journals for scoring or other visible evidence of wear. Once the surface hardening of the lobes has been penetrated, wear will progress rapidly.
13 No specific bearing journal diameters or running clearances are given by Volvo for the camshafts. However, if there is a visual deterioration, then component renewal will be necessary.

Refitting

14 Clip each tappet onto the underside of their respective rocker arms.
15 Ensure the bores for the tappets in the cylinder head are clean and free of debris, then lubricate the tappets with clean engine oil, and lower them into their original positions. Check the ends of the rocker arms are correctly located over the valve stems **(see illustration)**.
16 Check to make sure the camshaft bearing positions in the cylinder head are clean, then lubricate them, and the rocker arm rollers, with clean engine oil.
17 Position the camshafts together, so the marks on the drive gears align, then lower the camshafts into position on the cylinder head

(see illustration). Lubricate the camshaft journals with clean engine oil.
18 Refit the camshaft bearing caps and screws into their original positions, and hand-tighten the screws evenly until the caps lie flat against the camshaft journals. Do not install the right- and left-hand bearing/sealing caps yet.
19 Tighten the bearing cap screws one turn at a time on both camshafts, until the bearing caps contact the cylinder head. It's essential the bearing caps are tightened down gradually and evenly, or damage to the camshaft may result. Finally, tighten the bearing cap screws to the specified torque.
20 Insert a camshaft locking pin (Volvo No 999 7007) though the hole in the cylinder head and into the hole in the camshaft sprocket. If necessary, rotate the camshaft slightly to enable the pin to be inserted using a large screwdriver in the camshaft end slots – do not turn the camshafts more than is absolutely necessary. If the Volvo pin is not available, a home-made equivalent can be fabricated.
21 Ensure the mating surfaces of the right- and left-hand camshaft bearing/sealing caps are clean and dry, then apply a light, even film of Volvo liquid sealant (Volvo No 11 61 059) to the mating surfaces **(see illustration)**. Ideally, use a short-haired roller.
22 Refit the right- and left-hand bearing/sealing caps, and tighten the retaining screws to their specified torque.
23 Clean the oil seal seating in the bearing

cap, then smear a little oil on the lips of the new camshaft oil seal. Wrap adhesive tape around the end of the camshaft, then fit the new oil seal and tap it into position carefully using a tubular bar or socket on the hard outer surface of the seal. Remove the tape on completion.
24 The remainder of refitting is a reversal of removal, noting the following points:
a) *Tighten all fasteners to the specified torque where given.*
b) *Wait a minimum of 30 minutes (or preferably, leave overnight) after fitting the hydraulic tappets before turning the engine over, to allow the tappets time to settle, otherwise the valve heads will strike the pistons.*

11 Flywheel/driveplate – removal, inspection and refitting

Removal

1 On manual transmission models, remove the gearbox (see Chapter 7A) and clutch (see Chapter 6).
2 On automatic transmission models, remove the automatic transmission as described in Chapter 7B.
3 Undo the bolts and move the engine speed sensor, complete with bracket, to one side **(see illustration)**.

10.17 Position the camshafts together so the marks (arrowed) on the drive gears align

10.21 Apply sealant to the cylinder head/ bearing cap sealing surfaces

11.3 Undo the bolts and remove the engine speed sensor, complete with bracket

11.4 Ideally, make up a tool to lock the flywheel in place

11.8 Align the locating dowel in the crankshaft with the hole in the flywheel marled by the dimple (arrowed)

12.5 Pull the plastic engine cover straight up from its mountings

4 Temporarily insert a bolt in the cylinder block, and use a wide-bladed screwdriver to hold the flywheel/driveplate, or make up a holding tool **(see illustration)**.

5 Slacken and remove the multi-spline bolts securing the flywheel/driveplate to the crankshaft, and lift the flywheel/driveplate from place – the flywheel's heavy! Discard the bolts, new ones must be fitted.

Inspection

6 Check the flywheel/driveplate for wear and damage. Examine the starter ring gear for excessive wear to the teeth. If the driveplate or ring gear are damaged, the complete driveplate must be renewed. The flywheel ring gear, however, may be renewed separately from the flywheel, but the work should be entrusted to a Volvo dealer. If the clutch friction face is discoloured or scored excessively, it may be possible to regrind it, but this work should also be entrusted to a Volvo dealer.

7 On models with a dual mass flywheel, check the radial play by turning the flywheel secondary mass one way until the spring begins to tension, then allow the flywheel to spring back – make an alignment mark between the primary and secondary masses. Now turn the flywheel in the opposite direction until the spring begins to tension – make another alignment mark between the two masses. The distance between the 2 marks must be less than 35 mm.

Refitting

8 Position the flywheel/driveplate against the crankshaft, aligning the locating dowel

with the corresponding hole in the flywheel/driveplate **(see illustration)**.

9 Insert the new bolts, and tighten them gradually and evenly, in a diagonal pattern to the Stage 1 torque setting, followed by the Stage 2 angle setting. Prevent the flywheel/driveplate from rotating using the same method as during removal.

10 The remainder of refitting is a reversal of removal.

---

12 Engine mountings –
inspection and renewal

Inspection

1 If improved access is required, raise the front of the car and support it securely on axle stands then remove the undershield.

2 Check the mounting rubbers to see if they are cracked, hardened or separated from the metal at any point; renew the mounting if any such damage or deterioration is evident.

3 Check that all the mounting's fasteners are securely tightened; use a torque wrench to check if possible.

4 Using a large screwdriver or a crowbar, check for wear in the mounting by carefully levering against it to check for free play. Where this is not possible, enlist the aid of an assistant to move the engine/transmission back-and-forth, or from side-to-side, while you watch the mounting. While some free play is to be expected even from new components,

excessive wear should be obvious. If excessive free play is found, check first that the fasteners are correctly secured, then renew any worn components as described below.

Renewal

Right-hand mounting

5 Pull the plastic cover on the engine straight upwards and remove it from the engine compartment **(see illustration)**.

6 Remove the upper torque rod as described below.

7 Place a trolley jack under the right-hand end of the engine sump and take the weight. Position a block of wood between the jack head and sump to prevent damage to the casing.

8 Undo the 4 upper mounting bolts and the 3 lower mounting bolts **(see illustrations)**. The mounting can now be removed.

9 Refitting is a reversal of removal, tightening the mounting bolts to the correct torque.

Left-hand mounting

10 Pull the plastic cover on the engine straight upwards and remove it from the engine compartment.

11 Remove the air cleaner housing as described in Chapter 4A.

12 Remove the battery and battery tray as described in Chapter 5A.

13 Move the fusebox to one side by undoing the retaining bolt, releasing the clip at the base, and sliding out towards the engine **(see illustration)**.

12.8a Undo the upper mounting bolts (arrowed) . . .

12.8b . . . and the lower mounting bolts

12.13 Move the fusebox to one side

14 Place a trolley jack under the right-hand end of the engine sump and take the weight. Position a block of wood between the jack head and sump to prevent damage to the casing.

15 Undo the 4 large nuts and the 2 small bolts on top of the mounting, then undo the 2 lower bolts **(see illustrations)**. The mounting can now be removed.

16 Refitting is a reversal of removal, tightening the mounting bolts to the correct torque.

Upper torque rod

17 Undo the bolt securing the coolant expansion tank and move the tank to one side **(see illustrations)**.

18 Undo the torque rod mounting bolt at the suspension strut turret, and at the engine mounting bracket, and manoeuvre the torque rod from place **(see illustrations)**.

19 Position the torque rod and tighten the new fasteners to the correct torque.

20 Refit the coolant expansion tank.

Lower torque rod

21 Jack up the front of the vehicle and support it securely on axle stands (see *Jacking and vehicle support*).

22 Undo the screws and remove the engine undershield.

23 Undo the bolts and manoeuvre the torque rod from place **(see illustration)**.

24 Position the torque rod and tighten the new fasteners to the correct torque.

25 Refit the undershield and lower the vehicle to the ground.

---

13 Sump – removal, inspection and refitting

Removal

1 Jack up the front of the vehicle and support it securely on axle stands (see *Jacking and vehicle support*).

2 Undo the screws and remove the engine undershield.

12.15a Undo the upper mounting bolts . . .

12.15b . . . and the lower mounting bolts

12.17a Undo the screw securing the coolant expansion tank . . .

12.17b . . . and move it to one side

3 Drain the engine oil as described in Chapter 1.

4 Remove the auxiliary drivebelt as described in Chapter 1.

5 Undo the 3 bolts and move the air conditioning compressor to one side. Use wire to secure the compressor to a suitable part of the bodywork or chassis.

6 Undo the bolt/nut and pull the oil level dipstick guide tube from the sump.

7 Disconnect the wiring plug, undo the 3 bolts, and remove the oil level sensor from the sump.

8 The oil cooler (where fitted) is secured to the sump by four bolts. Undo the bolts and pull the cooler to the rear. Be prepared for oil spillage.

9 Remove the charge air pipe below the sump. Undo the clips at each end and

undo the bolt securing the mounting bracket.

10 Slacken the bolts securing the sump, and remove them all, apart from one bolt in each corner.

11 Gently tap the sides and ends of the sump until the joint between the engine and sump releases. Undo the remaining bolts and remove the sump. Discard the O-rings at the right-hand end/front edge of the sump, new ones must be fitted.

Refitting

12 Clean the contact faces of the sump and block.

13 Apply a thin and even layer of Volvo sealant (No 116 1771) to the sump mating face, and position the new O-ring seals on

12.18a Undo the mounting bolt at the suspension strut turret . . .

12.18b . . . and at the engine mounting bracket

12.23 Undo the lower torque rod securing bolts (arrowed)

13.13a Apply a thin and even layer of Volvo sealant . . .

13.13b . . . and renew the O-rings (arrowed)

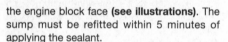

13.14 The four slightly shorter bolts are
fitted at the transmission end

14.2 Undo the four oil pump bolts
(arrowed)

14.5 Undo the two oil pump cover screws
(arrowed)

the engine block face (see illustrations). The sump must be refitted within 5 minutes of applying the sealant.

14 Refit the sump casing and refit the retaining bolts, finger-finger tight only at this stage. Note that the three longest bolts are fitted to the oil pump end, and the four slightly shorter bolts are fitted at the transmission end (see illustration).

15 Refit the sump-to-transmission bolts and tighten them to the specified torque.

16 Starting from the transmission end, tighten the sump-to-engine bolts in pairs to the specified torque.

17 The remainder of refitting is a reversal of refitting, noting the following points:

a) Renew the oil cooler-to-sump O-ring seals.

b) Tighten all fasteners to their specified torque where given.

c) Fit a new engine oil filter, and refill the engine with oil as described in Chapter 1.

d) Volvo recommend waiting a minimum of 2 hours before starting the engine to allow the sealant to cure fully.

14 Oil pump – removal, inspection and refitting

Removal

1 Remove the crankshaft right-hand oil seal as described in Section 8.

2 Undo the four bolts securing the oil pump to the front of the cylinder block (see illustration).

3 Carefully withdraw the pump assembly by levering behind the upper and lower parting lugs using a screwdriver. Remove the pump and recover the gasket.

4 Thoroughly clean the pump and cylinder block mating faces and remove all traces of old gasket. Discard the O-ring seal, a new one must be fitted.

Inspection

5 Undo the two pump cover retaining Allen screws whilst holding the two halves of the pump together, then remove the cover. Be prepared for the ejection of the pressure relief valve spring (see illustration).

6 Note their fitted positions, then remove the pressure relief valve spring, plunger and pump rotors (see illustrations).

14.6a Remove the plunger . . .

14.6b . . . spring . . .

14.6c . . . and rotors

7 If not already done, lever out the crankshaft oil seal.

8 Clean all the components thoroughly, then inspect the rotors, body and cover for damage or signs of wear.

9 At the time of writing, no specifications concerning the overhaul or inspection of the pump were available, and it would appear that no pump internal parts are available separately.

10 Refit the inner rotor with the marks facing the pump body **(see illustration)**.

11 Refit the outer rotor to the body, ensuring the mark on the rotor faces the cylinder block **(see illustration)**.

12 Refit the pressure relief valve spring and plunger, and fit the cover, tightening the retaining screws securely.

Refitting

13 Using a new gasket and O-ring, fit the pump to the block. Use the pump retaining bolts as guides, and draw the pump into place with the crankshaft pulley nut and spacers. With the pump seated, tighten the retaining bolts diagonally to the specified torque.

14 Fit a new crankshaft right-hand oil seal as described in Section 8.

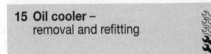

15 Oil cooler –
removal and refitting

Removal

1 Drain the engine oil and coolant as described in Chapter 1.

2 Release the hose clamp and disconnect the coolant hoses from the cooler, located on the rear face of the sump.

14.10 Fit the inner rotor with the marks (arrowed) facing the pump body . . .

3 Undo the bolts securing the cooler to the sump, and recover the O-ring seals as the cooler is withdrawn. Be prepared for fluid spillage **(see illustration)**.

Refitting

4 Check the mating faces of the sump and

15.3 Undo the oil cooler bolts (arrowed)

14.11 . . . and the outer rotor with the mark (arrowed) facing the cylinder block

oil cooler are clean, then refit the cooler using new O-ring seals. Tighten the retaining bolts securely **(see illustration)**.

5 Reconnect the coolant hoses and secure them with new clips where necessary.

6 Refill the engine oil and cooling systems as described in Chapter 1.

15.4 Oil cooler O-rings

Notes

Chapter 2 Part D:
Engine removal and overhaul procedures

Contents

Degrees of difficulty

Easy, suitable for novice with little experience	**Fairly easy,** suitable for beginner with some experience	**Fairly difficult,** suitable for competent DIY mechanic	**Difficult,** suitable for experienced DIY mechanic	**Very difficult,** suitable for expert DIY or professional

Specifications

Cylinder head

1.6 litre engine

Warp limit – maximum acceptable for use:
Lengthways . . . . 0.025 mm
Across . . . . Not available
Height . . . . Not available

2.0 litre 4-cylinder engine

Warp limit – maximum acceptable for use:
Lengthways . . . . 0.030 mm
Across . . . . Not available
Height . . . . Not available

5-cylinder engine

Warp limit – maximum acceptable for use:
Lengthways . . . . 0.05 mm
Across . . . . 0.02 mm
Height . . . . 149.4 ± 0.15 mm

Inlet valves

1.6 litre engine

Head diameter . . . . Not available
Stem diameter . . . . Not available
Length . . . . Not available
Valve seat angle . . . . Not available

2.0 litre 4-cylinder engine

Head diameter . . . . Not available
Stem diameter . . . . 5.969 to 5.987 mm
Length . . . . Not available
Valve seat angle . . . . Not available

5-cylinder engine

Head diameter . . . . 28.0 ± 0.01 mm
Stem diameter . . . . 5.975 ± 0.015 mm
Length . . . . 98.1 ± 0.07 mm
Valve seat angle . . . . 45° ± 0.5°

Exhaust valves

1.6 litre engine
Head diameter .... Not available
Stem diameter .... Not available
Length .... Not available
Valve seat angle .... Not available

2.0 litre 4-cylinder engine
Head diameter .... Not available
Stem diameter .... 5.969 to 5.987 mm
Length .... Not available
Valve seat angle .... Not available

5-cylinder engine
Head diameter .... 26.2 ± 0.1 mm
Stem diameter .... 5.975 ± 0.015 mm
Length .... 97.7 ± 0.07 mm
Valve seat angle .... 45.0° ± 0.5°

Valve guides
Valve stem-to-guide clearance:
   1.6 litre engine .... Not available
   2.0 litre 4-cylinder engine:
      Inlet valve .... 0.013 to 0.049 mm
      Exhaust valve .... 0.023 to 0.059 mm
   5-cylinder engine .... Not available

Pistons
Piston-to-bore clearance:
   1.6 litre engine .... 0.164 to 0.196 mm
   2.0 litre 4-cylinder engine................................... 0.056 to 0.103 mm
   5-cylinder engine .... 0.010 to 0.030 mm

Piston rings

1.6 litre engine
Clearance in groove:
   Top compression .... 0.200 to 0.350 mm
   Second compression .... 0.200 to 0.400 mm
   Oil control.. 0.800 to 1.000 mm
End gap (measured in cylinder):
   Compression rings .... Not available
   Oil control.. Not available

2.0 litre 4-cylinder engine
Clearance in groove:
   Top compression .... 0.200 to 0.350 mm
   Second compression .... 0.800 to 1.000 mm
   Oil control.. 0.250 to 0.500 mm
End gap (measured in cylinder):
   Compression rings .... Not available
   Oil control.. Not available

5-cylinder engine
Clearance in groove:
   Top compression .... 0.120 to 0.160 mm
   Second compression .... 0.070 to 0.110 mm
   Oil control.. 0.030 to 0.070 mm
End gap (measured in cylinder):
   Compression rings .... 0.20 to 0.40 mm
   Oil control.. 0.25 to 0.50 mm

Crankshaft
Endfloat:
   1.6 litre engine .... 0.10 to 0.30 mm
   2.0 litre 4-cylinder engine................................... 0.07 to 0.32 mm
   5-cylinder engine .... 0.08 to 0.19 mm

Torque wrench settings
Refer to Chapter 2A, 2B and 2C Specifications for torque wrench settings.

1 General information

Included in this Chapter are details of removing the engine/transmission from the car and general overhaul procedures for the cylinder head, cylinder block and all other engine internal components.

The information ranges from advice concerning preparation for an overhaul and the purchase of parts, to detailed step-by-step procedures covering removal, inspection, renovation and refitting of engine internal components.

After Section 5, all instructions are based on the assumption that the engine has been removed from the car. For information concerning engine in-car repair, as well as removal and installation of those external components necessary for full overhaul, refer to Chapter 2A, 2B or 2C as applicable, and to Section 4. Ignore any preliminary dismantling operations described in Part A, B or C that are no longer relevant once the engine has been removed from the car.

2 Engine/transmission removal – preparation and precautions

If you have decided that an engine must be removed for overhaul or major repair work, several preliminary steps should be taken.

Locating a suitable place to work is extremely important. Adequate work space, along with storage space for the car, will be needed. If a workshop or garage is not available, at the very least, a flat, level, clean work surface is required.

If possible, clear some shelving close to the work area, and use it to store the engine components and ancillaries as they are removed and dismantled. In this manner, the components stand a better chance of staying clean and undamaged during the overhaul. Laying out components in groups together with their fixing bolts, screws, etc, will save time and avoid confusion when the engine is refitted.

Clean the engine compartment and engine/transmission before beginning the removal procedure; this will help visibility and help to keep tools clean.

The help of an assistant should be available; there are certain instances when one person cannot safely perform all of the operations required to remove the engine from the vehicle. Safety is of primary importance, considering the potential hazards involved in this kind of operation. A second person should always be in attendance to offer help in an emergency. If this is the first time you have removed an engine, advice and aid from someone more experienced would also be beneficial.

Plan the operation ahead of time. Before starting work, obtain (or arrange for the hire of) all of the tools and equipment you will need. Access to the following items will allow the task of removing and refitting the engine/transmission to be completed safely and with relative ease: an engine hoist – rated in excess of the combined weight of the engine/transmission, a heavy-duty trolley jack, complete sets of spanners and sockets as described at the rear this manual, wooden blocks, and plenty of rags and cleaning solvent for mopping-up spilled oil, coolant and fuel. A selection of different-sized plastic storage bins will also prove useful for keeping dismantled components grouped together. If any of the equipment must be hired, make sure that you arrange for it in advance, and perform all of the operations possible without it beforehand; this may save you time and money.

Plan on the vehicle being out of use for quite a while, especially if you intend to carry out an engine overhaul. Read through the whole of this Section and work out a strategy based on your own experience and the tools, time and workspace available to you. Some of the overhaul processes may have to be carried out by a Volvo dealer or an engineering works – these establishments often have busy schedules, so it would be prudent to consult them before removing or dismantling the engine, to get an idea of the amount of time required to carry out the work.

When removing the engine from the vehicle, be methodical about the disconnection of external components. Labelling cables and hoses as they removed will greatly assist the refitting process.

Always be extremely careful when lifting the engine/transmission assembly from the engine bay. Serious injury can result from careless actions. If help is required, it is better to wait until it is available rather than risk personal injury and/or damage to components by continuing alone. By planning ahead and taking your time, a job of this nature, although major, can be accomplished successfully and without incident.

On all models covered by this manual, the engine and transmission are removed as a complete assembly, upwards and out of the engine bay. The engine and transmission are then separated with the assembly on the bench.

3 Engine and transmission – removal, separation and refitting

Note: *There may be detail differences depending on the engine fitted. However, the process is essentially the same for all engines.*

Removal

1 Open the bonnet. If there is any possibility of the engine hoist being obstructed, remove the bonnet as described in Chapter 11.

2 Remove the battery and battery tray as described in Chapter 5A.

3 Remove the plastic cover on top of the engine.

4 Remove the air cleaner assembly, and all air ducting, including turbocharger inlet (where applicable) with reference to the relevant part of Chapter 4A.

5 Refer to the relevant chapters:
  a) *Drain the cooling system (Chapter 1).*
  b) *If the engine is going to be dismantled, drain the engine oil (Chapter 1).*
  c) *Remove the auxiliary drivebelt (Chapter 1).*
  d) *Remove the catalytic converter (Chapter 4B).*
  e) *On 5-cylinder engines, remove the cooling fan (Chapter 3).*
  f) *Remove the driveshafts (Chapter 8).*
  g) *Remove the upper and lower torque rods (Chapter 2C).*
  h) *Remove the alternator (Chapter 5A).*

6 Disconnect the transmission selector cables as described in Chapter 7A and 7B.

7 Move the engine bay fusebox (central electrical unit) to one side and undo the earth cables beneath the air cleaner housing **(see illustration)**.

8 Disconnect all relevant wiring plugs, air pipes, and coolant hoses **(see illustrations)**.

3.7 Disconnect the earth cables beneath the air cleaner housing

3.8a Disconnect all relevant hoses . . .

3.8b . . . and brackets

3.9 Automatic transmission oil cooler pipes

9 On automatic transmission models, disconnect the transmission oil cooler fluid pipes at the gearbox **(see illustration)**.

10 Remove the right-hand side wheel arch liner and disconnect the wiring plug **(see illustration)**.

11 Undo the bolts securing the power steering pump to the mounting bracket and secure it the front of the subframe using cable-ties.

12 Disconnect the air conditioning compressor wiring plug, undo the retaining bolts, and secure the compressor to a suitable point on the front panel or subframe using cable-ties. Take care not to damage the air conditioning pipes. There is no need to discharge the air conditioning refrigerant.

13 Attach a lifting chain/strap to the transport brackets on the top of the engine, then manoeuvre an engine hoist/crane into position and take the weight of the engine.

14 Make a final check to ensure all hoses, pipes and electrical wiring between the engine/transmission and vehicle have been disconnected.

15 Undo the bolts securing the engine mountings as described in Chapter 2C, then lift and manoeuvre the engine/transmission assembly from the engine compartment **(see illustration)**. The aid of an assistant will be essential to support and manoeuvre

the assembly without damaging the vehicle bodywork, etc.

Separation

16 Remove the starter motor.

Manual transmission models

17 Remove the bolts securing the transmission to the engine.

18 With the aid of an assistant, draw the transmission off the engine. Once it is clear of the dowels, do not allow it to hang on the input shaft.

Automatic transmission models

19 Rotate the crankshaft, using a socket on the sprocket nut, until one of the torque converter-to-driveplate retaining bolts becomes accessible through the opening on the rear facing side of the engine. Working through the opening, undo the bolt using a TX50 socket. Rotate the crankshaft as necessary and remove the remaining bolts in the same way. Note that new bolts will be required for refitting.

20 Remove the bolts securing the transmission to the engine.

21 With the aid of an assistant, draw the transmission squarely off the engine dowels making sure that the torque converter remains in position on the transmission. Use the access hole in the transmission housing to hold the converter in place.

Refitting

Manual transmission models

22 Make sure that the clutch is correctly centred and that the clutch release components are fitted to the bellhousing. Do not apply any grease to the transmission input shaft, the guide sleeve, or the release bearing itself, as these components have a friction-reducing coating which does not require lubrication.

23 Manoeuvre the transmission squarely into position, and engage it with the engine dowels.

Refit the bolts securing the transmission to the engine, and tighten them to the specified torque. Refit the starter motor.

Automatic transmission models

24 Before refitting the transmission, flush out the fluid cooler with fresh transmission fluid. To do this, attach a hose to the upper union, pour the specified ATF through the hose and collect it in a container positioned beneath the return hose (see *Lubricants and fluids*).

25 Clean the contact surfaces on the torque converter and driveplate, and the transmission and engine mating faces. Lightly lubricate the torque converter guide projection and the engine/transmission locating dowels with grease.

26 Manoeuvre the transmission squarely into position, and engage it with the engine dowels. Refit the bolts securing the transmission to the engine and tighten lightly first in a diagonal sequence, then again to the specified torque.

27 Attach the torque converter to the driveplate using new bolts. Rotate the crankshaft for access to the bolts as was done for removal, then rotate the torque converter by means of the access hole in the transmission housing. Fit and tighten all the bolts hand-tight first, then tighten again to the specified torque.

All models

28 The remainder of refitting is essentially a reversal of removal, noting the following points:

 a) *Tighten all fastenings to the specified torque and, where applicable, torque angle. Refer to the relevant Chapters of this manual for torque wrench settings not directly related to the engine.*

 b) *Refill the engine with lubricant and coolant as necessary as described in Chapter 1.*

 c) *Refer to Section 16 before starting the engine.*

3.10 Disconnect the wiring plug (arrowed) behind the right-hand front wheel arch liner

3.15 Attach a lifting chain/strap to the transport brackets (arrowed)

4 Engine overhaul – preliminary information

It is much easier to dismantle and work on the engine if it is mounted on a portable engine stand. These stands can often be hired from a tool hire shop. Before the engine is mounted on a stand, the flywheel/driveplate should be removed so that the stand bolts can be tightened into the end of the cylinder block/crankcase.

If a stand is not available, it is possible to dismantle the engine with it suitably supported on a sturdy, workbench or on the floor. Be careful not to tip or drop the engine when working without a stand.

If you intend to obtain a reconditioned engine, all ancillaries must be removed first, to be transferred to the new engine (just as they will if you are doing a complete engine overhaul yourself). These components include the following:

a) Engine mountings and brackets (Chapter 2C).
b) Alternator including accessories mounting bracket (Chapter 5A).
c) Starter motor (Chapter 5A).
d) The fuel pump and common rail (Chapter 4A).
e) Exhaust manifold, with turbocharger if fitted (Chapter 4A).
f) Inlet manifold with fuel injection components (Chapter 4A).
g) All electrical switches, actuators and sensors, and the engine wiring harness (Chapter 12).
h) Coolant pump, thermostat, hoses, and distribution pipe (Chapter 3).
i) Clutch components – manual transmission models (Chapter 6).
j) Flywheel/driveplate (Chapter 2A, 2B or 2C).
k) Oil filter (Chapter 1).
l) Dipstick, tube and bracket.

Note: When removing the external components from the engine, pay close attention to details that may be helpful or important during refitting. Note the fitting positions of gaskets, seals, washers, bolts and other small items.

5.4a Compress the valve spring with a suitable valve spring compressor

If you are obtaining a 'short' engine (cylinder block/crankcase, crankshaft, pistons and connecting rods all assembled), then the cylinder head, timing belt (together with tensioner, tensioner and idler pulleys and covers) and auxiliary drivebelt tensioner will have to be removed also.

If a complete overhaul is planned, the engine can be dismantled in the order given below:

a) Inlet and exhaust manifolds and turbocharger (where applicable).
b) Timing belt, sprockets, tensioner, pulleys and covers.
c) Cylinder head.
d) Oil pump.
e) Flywheel/driveplate.
f) Sump.
g) Oil pick-up pipe.
h) Intermediate section.
i) Pistons/connecting rods.
j) Crankshaft.

5 Cylinder head – dismantling, cleaning, inspection and reassembly

Note: New and reconditioned cylinder heads are available from the manufacturer and from engine overhaul specialists. Specialist tools are required for the dismantling and inspection procedures, and new components may not be readily available. It may, therefore, be more practical and economical for the home

5.4b Extract the collets and release the spring compressor

mechanic to purchase a reconditioned head rather than dismantle, inspect and recondition the original head.

Dismantling

2.0 and 2.4 litre engines

1 Remove the cylinder head as described in Part B or C of this Chapter.

2 According to components still fitted, remove the thermostat housing (Chapter 3) and any other unions, pipes, sensors or brackets as necessary. On 5-cylinder engines, lift the swirl valve assembly from the top of the cylinder head.

3 Tap each valve stem smartly, using a light hammer and drift, to free the spring and associated items.

4 Fit a deep-reach type valve spring compressor to each valve in turn, and compress each spring until the collets are exposed (see illustration). Lift out the collets; a small screwdriver, a magnet or a pair of tweezers may be useful (see illustration). Carefully release the spring compressor and remove it.

5 Remove the valve spring upper seat and the valve spring (see illustrations). Pull the valve out of its guide.

6 Pull off the valve stem oil seal with a pair of long-nosed pliers. It may be necessary to use a tool such as a pair of electrician's wire strippers, the 'legs' of which will engage under the seal, if the seal is tight (see illustration).

7 Recover the valve spring lower seat (see

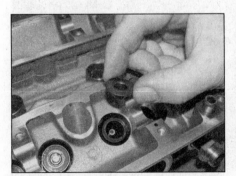
5.5a Remove the spring retainer . . .

5.5b . . . followed by the valve spring

5.6 Pull put the valve stem oil seal with a pair of long-nosed pliers

5.7 Remove the spring seat

5.12 Metal tube adapter for access to the valve collets

5.15 Secure a self-locking nut of suitable diameter to a long bolt, then use the tool to remove the valve stem oil seal

illustration). If there is much carbon build-up round the outside of the valve guide, this will have to be scraped off before the seat can be removed.

1.6 litre engine

8 Remove the cylinder head as described in Part A of this Chapter.

9 If not already done, remove the inlet and the exhaust manifolds with reference to Chapter 4A. Remove any remaining brackets or housings as required.

10 Remove the camshafts, hydraulic followers and rockers as described in Part A of this Chapter.

11 If not already done, remove the glow plugs as described in Chapter 5B.

12 Using a valve spring compressor, compress each valve spring in turn until the split collets can be removed. Release the compressor, and lift off the spring retainer and spring. Access to the valves is limited, and it may be necessary to make up an adapter out of metal tube – cut out a 'window' so that the valve collets can be removed **(see illustration).**

13 If, when the valve spring compressor is screwed down, the spring retainer refuses to free and expose the split collets, gently tap the top of the tool, directly over the retainer, with a light hammer. This will free the retainer.

14 Withdraw the valve from the combustion chamber.

15 Using a pair of pliers, carefully extract

the valve stem oil seal from the top of the guide, noting that the valve stem oil seal also forms the spring seat and is deeply recessed in the cylinder head. It is also a tight fit on the valve guide making it difficult to remove with pliers or a conventional valve stem oil seal removal tool. It can be easily removed, however, using a self-locking nut of suitable diameter screwed onto the end of a bolt and locked with a second nut. Push the nut down onto the top of the seal; the locking portion of the nut will grip the seal allowing it to be withdrawn from the top of the valve guide **(see illustration).**

All engines

16 It is essential that each valve is stored together with its collets, spring and seats. The valves should also be kept in their correct sequence, unless they are so badly worn or burnt that they are to be renewed. If they are going to be kept and used again, place each valve assembly in a labelled polythene bag or similar container **(see illustration).**

17 Continue removing all the remaining valves in the same way.

Cleaning

18 Thoroughly clean all traces of old gasket material and sealing compound from the cylinder head upper and lower mating surfaces. Use a suitable liquid gasket

dissolving agent together with a soft putty knife; do not use a metal scraper, or the faces will be damaged. Note that the gasket surface cannot be refaced.

19 Remove the carbon from the combustion chambers and ports, then clean all traces of oil and other deposits from the cylinder head, paying particular attention to the bearing journals, tappet bores, valve guides and oilways.

20 Wash the head thoroughly with paraffin or a suitable solvent. Take plenty of time and do a thorough job. Be sure to clean all oil holes and galleries very thoroughly, dry the head completely and coat all machined surfaces with light oil.

21 Scrape off any heavy carbon deposits that may have formed on the valves, then use a power-operated wire brush to remove deposits from the valve heads and stems.

Inspection

Note: *Be sure to perform all the following inspection procedures before concluding that the services of an engineering works are required. Make a list of all items that require attention.*

Cylinder head

22 Inspect the head very carefully for cracks, evidence of coolant leakage, and other damage. If cracks are found, a new cylinder head should be obtained.

23 Use a straight-edge and feeler blade to check that the cylinder head gasket surface is not distorted **(see illustration).**

24 Examine the valve seats in each of the combustion chambers. If they are severely pitted, cracked or burned, then they will need to be renewed or recut by an engine overhaul specialist. If they are only slightly pitted, this can be removed by grinding-in the valve heads and seats with fine valve-grinding compound, as described below.

25 If the valve guides appear worn, indicated by a side-to-side motion of the valve, new guides must be fitted. Verify this by mounting a dial gauge on the cylinder head, and check the side-to-side rock with the valve lifted 2.0

5.16 Keep groups of components together in labelled bags or boxes

5.23 Check the cylinder head gasket surface for distortion

5.25 Measure the maximum deflection of the valve in its guide using a dial gauge

5.30 Measure the valve stem diameter with a micrometer

5.33 Grinding-in a valve

to 3.0 mm clear of its seat **(see illustration)**. Measure the diameter of the existing valve stems (see below) and the bore of the guides, renew the valves or guides as necessary. The renewal of valve guides should be carried out by an engine overhaul specialist.

26 If the valve seats are to be recut, this must be done *only after* the guides have been renewed.

27 The threaded holes in the cylinder head must be clean to ensure accurate torque readings when tightening fixings during reassembly. Carefully run the correct size tap (which can be determined from the size of the relevant bolt which fits in the hole) into each of the holes to remove rust, corrosion, thread sealant or other contamination, and to restore damaged threads. If possible, use compressed air to clear the holes of debris produced by this operation. Do not forget to clean the threads of all bolts and nuts as well.

28 Any threads which cannot be restored in this way can often be reclaimed by the use of thread inserts. If any threaded holes are damaged, consult your dealer or engine overhaul specialist and have them install any thread inserts where necessary.

Valves

29 Examine the head of each valve for pitting, burning, cracks and general wear, and check the valve stem for scoring and wear ridges. Rotate the valve, and check for any obvious indication that it is bent. Look for pits and excessive wear on the tip of each valve stem. Renew any valve that shows any such signs of wear or damage.

5.39 Lubricate the stem of the valve and insert it into the guide

30 If the valve appears satisfactory at this stage, measure the valve stem diameter at several points, using a micrometer **(see illustration)**. Any significant difference in the readings obtained indicates wear of the valve stem. Should any of these conditions be apparent, the valve(s) must be renewed.

31 If the valves are in satisfactory condition, they should be ground (lapped) into their respective seats, to ensure a smooth gas-tight seal. If the seat is only lightly pitted, or if it has been recut, fine grinding compound *only* should be used to produce the required finish. Coarse valve-grinding compound should *not* be used unless a seat is badly burned or deeply pitted; if this is the case, the cylinder head and valves should be inspected by an expert, to decide whether seat recutting, or even the renewal of the valve or seat insert, is required.

32 Valve grinding is carried out as follows. Place the cylinder head upside-down on a bench, with a block of wood at each end to give clearance for the valve stems.

33 Smear a trace of (the appropriate grade) valve-grinding compound on the seat face, and press a suction grinding tool onto the valve head. With a semi-rotary action, grind the valve head to its seat, lifting the valve occasionally to redistribute the grinding compound. A light spring placed under the valve head will greatly ease this operation **(see illustration)**.

34 If coarse grinding compound is being used, work only until a dull, matt even surface is produced on both the valve seat and the valve, then wipe off the used compound, and repeat the process with fine compound. When a smooth unbroken ring of light grey matt finish is produced on both the valve and seat, the grinding operation is complete. *Do not* grind in the valves any further than absolutely necessary, or the seat will be prematurely sunk into the cylinder head.

35 When all the valves have been ground-in, carefully wash off *all* traces of grinding compound, using paraffin or a suitable solvent, before reassembly of the cylinder head.

Valve components

36 Examine the valve springs for signs of damage and discoloration, and also measure their free length by comparing each of the

existing springs with a new component.

37 Stand each spring on a flat surface, and check it for squareness. If any of the springs are damaged, distorted, or have lost their tension, obtain a complete set of new springs. It is normal to fit new springs as a matter of course if a major overhaul is being carried out.

38 Renew the valve stem oil seals regardless of their apparent condition.

Reassembly

39 Oil the stem of one valve and insert it into its guide then fit the spring lower seat **(see illustration)**.

40 The new valve stem oil seals should be supplied with a plastic fitting sleeve to protect the seal when it is fitted over the valve. If not, wrap a thin piece of polythene around the valve stem allowing it to extend about 10 mm above the end of the valve stem.

41 With the fitting sleeve, or polythene in place around the valve, fit the valve stem oil seal, pushing it onto the valve guide as far as it will go with a suitable socket or piece of tube. Once the seal is seated, remove the protective sleeve or polythene.

42 Fit the valve spring and upper seat. Compress the spring and fit the two collets in the recesses in the valve stem. Carefully release the compressor.

43 Cover the valve stem with a cloth and tap it smartly with a light hammer to verify that the collets are properly seated.

44 Repeat these procedures on all the other valves.

45 Refit the remainder of the disturbed components then refit the cylinder head as described in Part A, B or C of this Chapter.

---

6 Intermediate section/main bearing caps – removal

Note: *This section does not apply to the 1.6 litre engine.*

1 If not already done, drain the engine oil then remove the oil filter, referring to Chapter 1 if necessary.

2 Remove the oil pump as described in Part A or C of this Chapter.

6.3 Oil cooler mounting bolts (arrowed)

6.6 Undo the oil pick-up bracket bolt (arrowed)

6.12 Screw two sump bolts into the main bearing cap, then lever it upwards

5-cylinder engines

3 On models with an oil cooler mounted on the rear face of the sump, remove the four retaining bolts and take off the cooler, if possible without disconnecting the coolant pipes **(see illustration)**.

4 Undo the bolts securing the sump to the intermediate section, noting the different bolt lengths and their locations.

5 Carefully tap the sump free using a rubber or hide mallet. Recover the O-ring seals.

6 Undo the mounting bracket bolt and remove the oil pick-up pipe **(see illustration)**. Recover the O-ring seal on the end of the pipe.

7 Remove the pistons and connecting rods as described in Section 7.

8 Undo all the M7 bolts securing the intermediate section to the cylinder block, working from the outside in. With all the M7 bolts removed, undo the M8, then the M10 bolts in the same order.

9 Carefully tap the intermediate section free using a rubber or hide mallet. Lift off the intermediate section complete with crankshaft lower main bearing shells. If any of the shells have stayed on the crankshaft, transfer them to their correct locations in the intermediate section. Do not rotate the crankshaft with the intermediate section removed.

10 Remove the crankshaft left-hand oil seal.

2.0 litre 4-cylinder engine

11 Remove the pistons and connecting rods as described in Section 7.

12 Undo the rear main bearing cap bolts, then remove the cap. Screw 2 sump bolts into

the cap, and pull on them to remove the cap **(see illustration)**.

13 Make identification/alignment marks on the remaining bearing caps, then unscrew the retaining bolts and remove the caps. Note the fitted locations of the thrustwashers at the bearing position for No 1 cylinder.

14 Prise out the oil seal.

7 Pistons and connecting rods – removal and inspection

Removal

1 Remove the cylinder head, sump oil pump and flywheel/driveplate as described in Part A, B or C of this Chapter. On 5-cylinder models, remove the intermediate section, as described in Section 6.

2 Feel inside the tops of the bores for a pronounced wear ridge. Some experts recommend that such a ridge be removed (with a scraper or ridge reamer) before attempting to remove the pistons. However, a ridge big enough to damage the pistons and/ or piston rings will almost certainly mean that a rebore and new pistons/rings are needed anyway.

3 Check that there are identification numbers or marks on each connecting rod and cap; paint or punch suitable marks if necessary, so that each rod can be refitted in the same position and the same way round **(see illustration)**. Note their positions, eg, markings on the exhaust side, etc.

2.0 and 2.4 litre engines

4 Remove the two connecting rod bolts. Tap the cap with a soft-faced hammer to free it. Remove the cap and lower bearing shell. Note that new bolts will be needed for reassembly. New shells should always be fitted.

5 Push the connecting rod and piston up and out of the bore. Recover the other half bearing shell if it is loose.

6 Refit the cap to the connecting rod, the correct way round, so that they do not get mixed up. Note that on some engines, the surface between the cap and rod is not machined, but fractured. Take great care not to damage or mark the fractured surfaces otherwise the cap will not fit properly with the shell, and new connecting rods will be required.

7 Check to see if there is an arrow on the top of the piston which should be pointing toward the timing belt end of the engine. If no arrow can be seen, make a suitable direction mark yourself.

8 Repeat the operations on the remaining connecting rods and pistons.

1.6 litre engine

9 Turn the crankshaft to bring pistons 1 and 4 to BDC (bottom dead centre).

10 Unscrew the nuts or bolts, as applicable from No 1 piston big-end bearing cap. Take off the cap, and recover the bottom half bearing shell **(see illustration)**. If the bearing shells are to be re-used, tape the cap and the shell together.

11 Where applicable, to prevent the possibility of damage to the crankshaft bearing journals, tape over the connecting rod stud threads **(see illustration)**.

7.3 Connecting rod and big-end bearing cap identification marks

7.10 Remove the big-end bearing cap and shell

7.11 To protect the crankshaft journals, tape over the connecting rod stud threads

7.17 Remove the piston rings with the aid of feeler gauges

7.30a Prise out the circlip . . .

7.30b . . . and withdraw the gudgeon pin

12 Using a hammer handle, push the piston up through the bore, and remove it from the top of the cylinder block. Recover the bearing shell, and tape it to the connecting rod for safe-keeping.

13 Loosely refit the big-end cap to the connecting rod, and secure with the nuts/bolts – this will help to keep the components in their correct order.

14 Remove No 4 piston assembly in the same way.

15 Turn the crankshaft through 180° to bring pistons 2 and 3 to BDC (bottom dead centre), and remove them in the same way.

Inspection

16 Before the inspection process can be carried out, the piston/connecting rod assemblies must be cleaned, and the original piston rings removed from the pistons.

17 Carefully expand the old rings and remove them from the top of the pistons. The use of two or three old feeler blades will be helpful in preventing the rings dropping into empty grooves **(see illustration)**. Be careful not to scratch the pistons with the ends of the ring. The rings are brittle and will snap if they are spread too far. They are also very sharp – protect your hands and fingers.

18 Scrape all traces of carbon from the top of the piston. A hand-held wire brush (or a piece of fine emery cloth) can be used, once the majority of the deposits have been scraped away.

19 Remove the carbon from the ring grooves in the piston, using an old ring. Break the ring in half to do this (be careful not to cut your fingers – piston rings are sharp). Be careful to remove only the carbon deposits – do not remove any metal, and do not nick or scratch the sides of the ring grooves.

20 Once the deposits have been removed, clean the piston/rod assemblies with paraffin or a suitable solvent, and dry thoroughly. Make sure the oil return holes in the ring grooves, are clear.

21 If the pistons and cylinder bores are not damaged or worn excessively, and if the cylinder block does not need to be rebored (where applicable), the original pistons can be refitted. Normal piston wear appears as even vertical wear on the piston thrust surfaces, and

slight looseness of the top ring in its groove. New piston rings should always be used when the engine is reassembled.

22 Carefully inspect each piston for cracks around the skirt, around the gudgeon pin holes, and at the ring 'lands' (between the ring grooves).

23 Look for scoring and scuffing on the piston skirt, holes in the piston crown, and burned areas at the edge of the crown.

24 If the skirt is scored or scuffed, the engine may have been suffering from overheating and/or abnormal combustion, which caused excessively-high operating temperatures. The cooling and lubrication systems should be checked thoroughly. Scorch marks on the sides of the piston show that blow-by has occurred.

25 A hole in the piston crown or burned areas at the edge of the piston crown, indicates that abnormal combustion (pre-ignition, knocking, or detonation) has been occurring.

26 If any of the above piston problems exist, the causes must be investigated and corrected, or the damage will occur again. The causes may include inlet air leaks, incorrect fuel/air mixture or an emission control system fault.

27 Corrosion of the piston, in the form of pitting, indicates that coolant has been leaking into the combustion chamber and/or the crankcase. Again, the cause must be corrected, or the problem may persist in the rebuilt engine.

28 Examine each connecting rod carefully for signs of damage, such as cracks around the big-end and small-end bearings. Check

7.33 Measure the ring-to-groove clearance using feeler gauges

that the rod is not bent or distorted. Damage is highly unlikely, unless the engine has been seized or badly overheated. Detailed checking of the connecting rod assembly can only be carried out by an engine overhaul specialist with the necessary equipment.

29 The gudgeon pins are of the floating type, secured in position by two circlips. Where necessary, the pistons and connecting rods can be separated as follows.

30 Remove one of the circlips which secure the gudgeon pin. Push the gudgeon pin out of the piston and connecting rod **(see illustrations)**.

31 If any doubt exists concerning the condition of the pistons, have them measured by an automotive engine reconditioning specialist. If new pistons are required, the specialist will be able to supply new pistons and rebore the cylinder block to the appropriate size (where applicable).

32 If any one of the pistons is worn, then all the pistons must be renewed. Note that if the cylinder block was rebored during a previous overhaul, oversize pistons may have been fitted.

33 Hold a new piston ring in the appropriate groove, and measure the ring-to-groove clearance using a feeler blade **(see illustration)**. Note that the rings are of different sizes, so use the correct ring for the groove. Compare the measurements with those listed in the Specifications; if the clearances are outside the tolerance range, then the pistons must be renewed.

34 Check the fit of the gudgeon pin in the connecting rod bush and in the piston. If there is perceptible play, a new bush or an oversize gudgeon pin must be fitted. Consult a Volvo dealer or engine reconditioning specialist.

35 Examine all components and obtain any new parts required. If new pistons are purchased, they will be supplied complete with gudgeon pins and circlips. Circlips can also be purchased separately.

36 Oil the gudgeon pin. Reassemble the connecting rod and piston, making sure the rod is the right way round as noted during removal, and secure the gudgeon pin with the circlip. Position the circlip so that its opening is facing downward.

37 Repeat these operations for the remaining pistons.

8.2 Check the crankshaft end float using a dial gauge

8.7 Prise up the two caps to expose the main bearing bolts at the flywheel end

8.8 Remove the crankshaft bearing cap housing

8 Crankshaft – removal and inspection

Note: *If no work is to be done on the pistons and connecting rods, then removal of the cylinder head and pistons will not be necessary. Instead, the pistons need only be pushed far enough up the bores so that they are positioned clear of the crankpins.*

Removal

1 With reference to Part A, B or C of this Chapter, and earlier Sections of this part as applicable, carry out the following:
a) Remove the oil pump.
b) Remove the sump.
c) Remove the clutch components and flywheel/driveplate.
d) Remove the pistons and connecting rods (refer to the Note above).

2 Before the crankshaft is removed, it is advisable to check the endfloat. To do this, mount a dial gauge with the stem in line with the crankshaft and just touching the crankshaft **(see illustration)**.

3 Push the crankshaft fully away from the gauge, and zero it. Next, lever the crankshaft towards the gauge as far as possible, and check the reading obtained. The distance that the crankshaft moved is its endfloat; if it is greater than specified, check the crankshaft thrust surfaces for wear. If no wear is evident, new thrustwashers (which are integral with the main bearing shells on 2.4 litre models) should correct the endfloat.

2.0 and 2.4 litre engines

4 Remove the intermediate section/main bearing caps, then lift out the crankshaft. Do not drop it, it is heavy.

5 Remove the upper half main bearing shells from their seats in the crankcase by pressing the end of the shell furthest from the locating tab. Keep all the shells in order.

1.6 litre engine

6 Working around the inner periphery of the crankcase, unscrew the small bolts securing the crankshaft bearing cap housing to the base of the cylinder block. Note the correct

fitted depth of the left-hand crankshaft oil seal in the cylinder block/bearing cap housing.

7 Working in the **reverse** of the tightening sequence **(see illustration 12.8)**, evenly and progressively slacken the ten large bearing cap housing retaining bolts by a turn at a time. Once all the bolts are loose, remove them from the housing. **Note:** *Prise up the two caps at the flywheel end of the housing to expose the two end main bearing bolts (see illustration).*

8 With all the retaining bolts removed, tap around the outer periphery of the bearing cap housing using a soft-faced mallet to break the seal between the housing and cylinder block. Once the seal is released and the housing is clear of the locating dowels, lift it up and off the crankshaft and cylinder block **(see illustration)**. Recover the lower main bearing shells, and tape them to their respective locations in the housing. If the two locating dowels are a loose fit, remove them and store them with the housing for safe-keeping.

9 Lift out the crankshaft, and collect the left-hand oil seal.

10 Recover the upper main bearing shells, and store them along with the relevant lower bearing shell. Also recover the two thrustwashers (one fitted either side of No 2 main bearing) from the cylinder block.

Inspection

11 Clean the crankshaft using paraffin or a suitable solvent, and dry it, preferably with compressed air if available. Be sure to clean the oil holes with a pipe cleaner or similar probe to ensure that they are not obstructed.

⚠️ *Warning: Wear eye protection when using compressed air.*

12 Check the main and big-end bearing journals for uneven wear, scoring, pitting and cracking.

13 Big-end bearing wear is accompanied by distinct metallic knocking when the engine is running (particularly noticeable when the engine is pulling from low speed) and some loss of oil pressure.

14 Main bearing wear is accompanied by severe engine vibration and rumble – getting progressively worse as engine speed increases – and again by loss of oil pressure.

15 Check the bearing journal for roughness

by running a finger lightly over the bearing surface. Any roughness (which will be accompanied by obvious bearing wear) indicates that the crankshaft requires regrinding (where possible) or renewal.

16 Have the crankshaft measured and inspected by an engine reconditioning specialist. They will be able to advise concerning the availability of undersize bearings, and crankshaft reconditioning.

9 Cylinder block/crankcase – cleaning and inspection

Cleaning

1 Prior to cleaning, remove all external components and senders, and any gallery plugs or caps that may be fitted. Remove the piston cooling valve, and the cooling jets (where applicable) **(see illustration)**.

2 If any of the castings are extremely dirty, all should be steam-cleaned.

3 After the castings are returned from steam-cleaning, clean all oil holes and oil galleries one more time. Flush all internal passages with warm water until the water runs clear. If you have access to compressed air, use it to speed the drying process, and to blow out all the oil holes and galleries.

⚠️ *Warning: Wear eye protection when using compressed air.*

9.1 Piston cooling jets may be fitted to the base of each cylinder bore

4 If the castings are not very dirty, you can do an adequate cleaning job with hot soapy water (as hot as you can stand!) and a stiff brush. Take plenty of time, and do a thorough job. Regardless of the cleaning method used, be sure to clean all oil holes and galleries very thoroughly, and to dry all components completely. Apply clean engine oil to the cylinder bores to prevent rusting.

5 The threaded holes in the cylinder block must be clean to ensure accurate torque readings when tightening fixings during reassembly. Carefully run the correct size tap (which can be determined from the size of the relevant bolt which fits in the hole) into each of the holes to remove rust, corrosion, thread sealant or other contamination, and to restore damaged threads. If possible, use compressed air to clear the holes of debris produced by this operation. Do not forget to clean the threads of all bolts and nuts as well.

6 Any threads which cannot be restored in this way can often be reclaimed by the use of thread inserts. If any threaded holes are damaged, consult your dealer or engine overhaul specialist and have them install any thread inserts where necessary.

7 If the engine is not going to be reassembled right away, cover it with a large plastic bag to keep it clean; protect the machined surfaces as described above, to prevent rusting.

Inspection

8 Visually check the castings for cracks and corrosion. Look for stripped threads in the threaded holes. If there has been any history of internal coolant leakage, it may be worthwhile having an engine overhaul specialist check the cylinder block/crankcase for cracks with special equipment. If defects are found, have them repaired, if possible, or renew the assembly.

9 Check the condition of the cylinder head mating face and the intermediate section mating surfaces. Check the surfaces for any possible distortion using the straight-edge and feeler blade method described earlier for cylinder head inspection. If distortion is slight, consult an engine overhaul specialist as to the best course of action.

10 Check each cylinder bore for scuffing and scoring. Check for signs of a wear ridge at the top of the cylinder, indicating that the bore is excessively worn.

11 Have the bores inspected and measured by an automotive engine reconditioning specialist. They will be able to advise on possible cylinder reboring and supply appropriate pistons to match.

12 If the bores are in reasonably good condition and not excessively-worn, then it may only be necessary to renew the piston rings.

13 If this is the case, the bores should be honed, to allow the new rings to bed in correctly and provide the best possible seal. Honing is an operation that will be carried out for you by an engine reconditioning specialist.

14 After all machining operations are completed, the entire block/crankcase must be washed very thoroughly with warm soapy water to remove all traces of abrasive grit produced during the machining operations. When the cylinder block/crankcase is completely clean, rinse it thoroughly and dry it, then lightly oil all exposed machined surfaces, to prevent rusting.

15 Refit the piston cooling jets to the base of the cylinder bores, and tighten the retaining bolts to the specified torque.

16 Fit a new sealing washer to the piston cooling oil valve, or apply thread sealing compound to valve threads (as applicable), then refit the valve and tighten it to the specified torque.

10 Main and big-end bearings – inspection and selection

Inspection

1 Even though the main and big-end bearing shells should be renewed during the engine overhaul, the old shells should be retained for close examination, as they may reveal valuable information about the condition of the engine.

2 Bearing failure occurs because of lack of lubrication, the presence of dirt or other foreign particles, overloading the engine, and corrosion **(see illustration)**. Regardless of the cause of bearing failure, the cause must be corrected (where applicable) before the engine is reassembled, to prevent it from happening again.

3 When examining the bearing shells, remove them from the cylinder block/crankcase and main bearing caps, and from the connecting rods and the big-end bearing caps, then lay them out on a clean surface in the same

10.2 Typical bearing failures

general position as their location in the engine. This will enable you to match any bearing problems with the corresponding crankshaft journal. *Do not* touch any of the shell's bearing surface with your fingers while checking it, or the delicate surface may be scratched.

4 Dirt or other foreign matter gets into the engine in a variety of ways. It may be left in the engine during assembly, or it may pass through filters or the crankcase ventilation system. It may get into the oil, and from there into the bearings. Metal chips from machining operations and normal engine wear are often present. Abrasives are sometimes left in engine components after reconditioning, especially when parts are not thoroughly cleaned using the proper cleaning methods.

5 Whatever the source, any foreign objects often end up embedded in the soft bearing material, and are easily recognised. Large particles will not embed in the material, and will score or gouge the shell and journal. The best prevention for this cause of bearing failure is to clean all parts thoroughly, and to keep everything spotlessly-clean during engine assembly. Frequent and regular engine oil and filter changes are also recommended.

6 Lack of lubrication (or lubrication breakdown) has a number of inter-related causes. Excessive heat (which thins the oil), overloading (which squeezes the oil from the bearing face) and oil leakage (from excessive bearing clearances, worn oil pump or high engine speeds) all contribute to lubrication breakdown. Blocked oil passages, which usually are the result of misaligned oil holes in a bearing shell, will also starve a bearing of oil, and destroy it.

7 When lack of lubrication is the cause of bearing failure, the bearing material is wiped or extruded from the shell's steel backing. Temperatures may increase to the point where the steel backing turns blue from overheating.

8 Driving habits can have a definite effect on bearing life. Full-throttle, low-speed operation (labouring the engine) puts very high loads on bearings, which tends to squeeze out the oil film. These loads cause the shells to flex, which produces fine cracks in the bearing face (fatigue failure). Eventually, the bearing material will loosen in pieces, and tear away from the steel backing.

9 Short-distance driving leads to corrosion of bearings, because insufficient engine heat is produced to drive off condensed water and corrosive gases. These products collect in the engine oil, forming acid and sludge. As the oil is carried to the engine bearings, the acid attacks and corrodes the bearing material.

10 Incorrect shell refitting during engine assembly will lead to bearing failure as well. Tight-fitting shells leave insufficient bearing running clearance, and will result in oil starvation. Dirt or foreign particles trapped behind a bearing shell result in high spots on the bearing, which lead to failure.

11 *Do not* touch any shell's bearing surface with your fingers during reassembly; there is a risk of scratching the delicate surface, or of depositing particles of dirt on it.

Bearing selection

12 Have the crankshaft measured and examined by an automotive engine reconditioning specialist, who will be able to supply the appropriate bearing shells.

11 Engine overhaul – reassembly sequence

1 Before reassembly begins, ensure that all new parts have been obtained and that all necessary tools are available. Read through the entire procedure to familiarise yourself with the work involved, and to ensure that all items necessary for reassembly of the engine are at hand. In addition to all normal tools and materials, thread-locking compound will be needed in most areas during engine reassembly. A tube of Volvo liquid gasket solution together with a short-haired application roller will also be needed to assemble the main engine sections.

2 In order to save time and avoid problems, engine reassembly can be carried out in the following order:

  a) *Crankshaft.*
  b) *Intermediate section.*
  c) *Pistons/connecting rods.*
  d) *Sump.*
  e) *Oil pump.*
  f) *Flywheel/driveplate.*
  g) *Cylinder head.*
  h) *Camshaft and tappets.*
  i) *Timing belt, tensioner, sprockets and idler pulleys.*
  j) *Engine external components.*

3 At this stage, all engine components should be absolutely clean and dry, with all faults repaired. The components should be laid out (or in individual containers) on a completely clean work surface.

12 Crankshaft – refitting

1 Crankshaft refitting is the first stage of engine reassembly following overhaul. It is assumed at this point that the cylinder block/crankcase and crankshaft have been cleaned, inspected and repaired or reconditioned as necessary, and the piston cooling jets and valve have been refitted. Position the cylinder block on a clean level work surface, with the crankcase facing upwards.

1.6 litre engine

2 Place the bearing shells in their locations. If new shells are being fitted, ensure that all traces of protective grease are cleaned off using paraffin. Wipe dry the shells with a lint-free cloth. The upper bearing shells all have a grooved surface, whereas the lower shells

have a plain surface. It's essential that the lower bearing shells are centrally located in the bearing cap housing/ladder **(see illustration)**. It appears that a Volvo tool is required for this operation but we were unable to verify this at the time of writing. Refer to a Volvo dealer or engine reconditioning specialist.

3 Liberally lubricate each bearing shell in the cylinder block with clean engine oil then lower the crankshaft into position.

4 Insert the thrustwashers to either side of No 2 main bearing upper location and push them around the bearing journal until their edges are horizontal **(see illustration)**. Ensure that the oilway grooves on each thrustwasher face outwards (away from the bearing journal).

5 Thoroughly degrease the mating surfaces of the cylinder block and the crankshaft bearing cap housing. Apply a thin bead of silicone sealant to the bearing cap housing mating surface **(see illustration)**.

6 Lubricate the lower bearing shells with clean engine oil, then refit the bearing cap housing, ensuring that the shells are not displaced, and that the locating dowels engage correctly.

7 Install the ten large diameter, and sixteen smaller diameter crankshaft bearing cap housing retaining bolts, and screw them in until they are just making contact with the housing.

8 Working in sequence, tighten the bolts to

12.2 Main bearing shell fitment

1 Bearing shell		*3 Volvo tool*
2 Main bearing ladder		*4 Aligning pins*

the torque settings given in the Specifications **(see illustration)**.

9 With the bearing cap housing in place, check that the crankshaft rotates freely.

10 Refit the piston/connecting rod assemblies to the crankshaft as described in Section 14.

11 Refit the oil pump and sump.

12 Fit a new crankshaft left-hand oil seal, then refit the flywheel.

13 Where removed, refit the cylinder head, crankshaft sprocket and timing belt.

12.4 Place the thrustwashers each side of the No 2 bearing upper location

12.5 Apply a thin bead of sealant to the bearing cap housing mating surface

12.8 Main bearing cap housing/ladder retaining bolt tightening sequence

12.15a Ensure the thrustwashers are fitted with the oil grooves facing outwards

12.15b Fit new rubber seals to the main bearing cap at the transmission end

12.15c Apply a bead of sealant to the corners of the recess (arrowed) . . .

2.0 litre 4-cylinder engine

14 Wipe clean the bearing shell seats in the main bearing caps, and clean the back of the shells. Insert the previously-selected lower shells into their correct locations in the bearing caps. Press the shells home so that the tangs engage in the recesses provided.

15 Lightly lubricate the bearing shells in the main bearing caps, then refit the caps to their original positions, aligning the previously-made marks. Ensure the thrustwashers are fitted with the oil grooves against the bearing surfaces. Note that new rubber seals must be fitted to each side of the main bearing cap fitted at the transmission end **(see illustrations)**. The cap is then fitted using a Volvo special tool No 999 7223 (or strips of shim steel) to ease the cap and seals into position **(see illustrations)**. Apply a bead of silicone sealant to the corners of the main bearing cap recess in the block. Note that even with the Volvo tool it is impossible to fit the seals completely flush with the sump mating surface – a protrusion of approximately 1.0 mm is acceptable.

16 Tighten the main bearing cap bolts to the specified Stage 1 torque setting, working gradually from the centre outwards. Repeat the sequence tightening the bolts to the Stage 2 angle-tightening setting.

5-cylinder engines

17 If they're still in place, remove the old bearing shells from the block and the intermediate section.

18 Wipe clean the main bearing shell seats in the crankcase and clean the backs of the new bearing shells. Insert the previously selected upper shells into their correct position in the crankcase. Note the shells incorporating the thrustwashers must be fitted to the No 5 bearing position. Press the shells home so that the tangs engage in the recesses provided. Note the thicker of the two shells must be fitted to the intermediate section.

19 Liberally lubricate the bearing shells in the crankcase with clean engine oil.

20 Wipe clean the crankshaft journals, then lower the crankshaft into position. Make sure that the shells are not displaced.

21 Inject oil into the crankshaft oilways, then wipe any traces of excess oil from the crankshaft and intermediate section mating faces.

22 Using the short-haired application roller, apply an even coating of Volvo liquid gasket solution (No 116 1771) to the cylinder block mating face of the intermediate section. Ensure that the whole surface is covered, but note that a thin coating is sufficient for a good seal.

23 Wipe clean the main bearing shell seats in the intermediate section and clean the backs of the bearing shells. Insert the previously selected lower shells into their correct position in the intermediate section. Press the shells home so that the tangs engage in the recesses provided.

24 Lightly lubricate the bearing shells in the intermediate section, but take care to keep the oil away from the liquid gasket solution.

25 Lay the intermediate section on the crankshaft and cylinder block, and insert the retaining bolts. Tighten the bolts in the five stages listed in the Specifications to the specified torque and torque angle, starting from the outside in **(see illustration)**.

26 Rotate the crankshaft. Slight resistance is to be expected with new components, but there must be no tight spots or binding.

27 It is a good idea at this stage to once again check the crankshaft endfloat as described in Section 8. If the thrust surfaces of the crankshaft have been checked and new bearing shells have been fitted, then the endfloat should be within specification.

28 Lubricate the left-hand oil seal location, the crankshaft, and a new oil seal. Fit the seal, lips inwards, and use a piece of tube (or the old seal, inverted) to tap it into place until flush.

12.15d . . . then fit the cap using strips of shim steel to ease the seals into position

12.25 Intermediate section bolts
1 M7   2 M8   3 M10

13 Pistons and piston rings – assembly

1 At this stage, it is assumed that the pistons have been correctly assembled to their respective connecting rods, and that the piston ring-to-groove clearances have been checked. If not, refer to the end of Section 7.
2 Before the rings can be fitted to the pistons, the end gaps must be checked with the rings inserted into the cylinder bores.
3 Lay out the piston assemblies and the new ring sets so the components are kept together in their groups, during and after end gap checking. Position the cylinder block on the work surface, on its side, allowing access to the top and bottom of the bores.
4 Take the No 1 piston top ring and insert it into the top of the first cylinder. Push it down the bore using the top of the piston; this will ensure that the ring remains square with the cylinder walls. Position the ring near the bottom of the cylinder bore, at the lower limit of ring travel. Note that the top and second compression rings are different. The second ring is easily identified by the step on its lower surface.
5 Measure the ring gap using feeler blades **(see illustration)**.
6 Repeat the procedure with the ring at the top of the cylinder bore, at the upper limit of its travel, and compare the measurements with the figures given in the Specifications.
7 If new rings are being fitted, it is unlikely that the end gaps will be too small. If a measurement is found to be undersize, it must be corrected, or there is the risk that the ring ends may contact each other during engine operation, possibly resulting in engine damage. Ideally, new piston rings providing the correct end gap should be fitted; however, as a last resort the end gaps can be increased by filing the ring ends very carefully with a fine file. Mount the ring in a vice equipped with soft jaws, slip the ring over the file with the ends contacting the file face, and slowly move the ring to remove material from the ends. Take care, as piston rings are sharp and are easily broken.
8 It is equally unlikely that the end gap will be too large. If the gaps are too large, check that you have the correct rings for your engine and for the cylinder bore size.
9 Repeat the checking procedure for each ring in the first cylinder, and then for the rings in the remaining cylinders. Remember to keep rings, pistons and cylinders matched up.
10 Once the ring end gaps have been checked and if necessary corrected, the rings can be fitted to the pistons.
11 Fit the piston rings using the same technique as for removal. Fit the bottom scraper ring first, and work up. Observe the text markings on one side of the top and bottom rings; this must face upwards when the rings are fitted. The middle ring is bevelled,

13.5 Measure the piston ring gap using feeler gauges

and the bevel must face downwards when installed. Do not expand the compression rings too far, or they will break. **Note:** *Always follow any instructions supplied with the new piston ring sets – different manufacturers may specify different procedures. Do not mix up the top and second compression rings, as they have different cross-sections.*
12 When all the rings are in position, arrange the ring gaps 120° apart, with the exception of the 3-part oil scraper ring where the two plain rings should be 90° apart from each other.

14 Pistons and connecting rod assemblies – refitting

1 Before refitting the piston/connecting rod assemblies, the cylinder bores must be perfectly clean, and the crankshaft and intermediate section must be in place.
2 Remove the big-end bearing cap from No 1 cylinder connecting rod (refer to the marks noted or made on removal). Remove the original bearing shells, and wipe the bearing recesses of the connecting rod and cap with a clean, lint-free cloth. They must be kept spotlessly-clean. Ensure that new big-end bearing cap retaining bolts are available.
3 Clean the back of the new upper bearing shell, fit it to No 1 connecting rod, then fit the other shell of the bearing to the big-end bearing cap. Note that shell with the black-coloured size marker on its edge must be fitted to the connecting rod. On 'fractured' type rods and caps, no locating notch for the bearing shell tab is provided. On these rods/caps, simply position the shells as centrally as possible. Where tabs and notches are provided, make sure the tab on each shell fits into the notch in the rod or cap recess.
4 Position the piston ring gaps in their correct positions around the piston, lubricate the piston and rings with clean engine oil, and attach a piston ring compressor to the piston. Leave the skirt protruding slightly, to guide the piston into the cylinder bore. The rings must be compressed until they're flush with the piston.
5 Rotate the crankshaft until No 1 big-end journal is at BDC (Bottom Dead Centre), and

14.8 Tap the piston into the bore using a hammer handle

apply a coat of engine oil to the cylinder walls.
6 Arrange the No 1 piston/connecting rod assembly so that the channel in the base of the piston aligns with the piston cooling jet at the base of the cylinder bore. Gently insert the assembly into the No 1 cylinder bore, and rest the bottom edge of the ring compressor on the engine block.
7 Tap the top edge of the ring compressor to make sure it's contacting the block around its entire circumference.
8 Gently tap on the top of the piston with the end of a wooden hammer handle while guiding the connecting rod big-end onto the crankpin. The piston rings may try to pop out of the ring compressor just before entering the cylinder bore, so keep some pressure on the ring compressor. Work slowly, and if any resistance is felt as the piston enters the cylinder, stop immediately. Find out what is binding, and fix it before proceeding. *Do not*, for any reason, force the piston into the cylinder – you might break a ring and/or the piston. Take great care not to damage the piston cooling jets **(see illustration)**.
9 Make sure the bearing surfaces are perfectly clean, then apply a uniform layer of clean engine oil to both of them. You may have to push the piston back up the cylinder bore slightly to expose the bearing surface of the shell in the connecting rod.
10 Slide the connecting rod back into place on the big-end journal, refit the big-end bearing cap. Lubricate the bolt threads, fit the bolts and tighten them in two stages to the specified torque.
11 Repeat the entire procedure for the remaining piston/connecting rod assemblies.
12 The important points to remember are:
a) *Keep the backs of the bearing shells and the recesses of the connecting rods and caps perfectly clean when assembling them.*
b) *Make sure you have the correct piston/ rod assembly for each cylinder.*
c) *The channel in the base of the piston must align with the piston cooling jet.*
d) *Lubricate the cylinder bores with clean engine oil.*
e) *Lubricate the bearing surfaces before fitting the big-end bearing caps.*
13 After all the piston/connecting rod

14.16 Measure the piston protrusion using a dial gauge

assemblies have been properly installed, rotate the crankshaft a number of times by hand, to check for any obvious binding.
14 If new pistons, connecting rods, or crankshaft are fitted, or if a new short engine is installed, the projection of the piston crowns above the cylinder head surface at TDC must be measured, to determine the correct head gasket required.
15 Fit the sump as described in Section 15.
16 Anchor a DTI gauge to the cylinder block, and zero it on the head gasket mating surface. Rest the gauge probe on No 1 piston crown and turn the crankshaft slowly by hand so that the piston reaches TDC (Top Dead Centre). Measure and record the maximum projection at TDC **(see illustration)**.

17 Repeat the measurement for the remaining pistons and record.
18 If the measurements differ from piston-to-piston, take the highest figure and use this to determine the head gasket type required – refer to Chapter 2A, 2B or 2C for details.

15 Sump – refitting

See the relevant section of Chapter 2A, 2B or 2C.

16 Engine – initial start-up after overhaul and reassembly

1 Refit the remainder of the engine components in the order listed in Section 11. Refit the engine and transmission to the vehicle as described in Section 3 of this Part. Double-check the engine oil and coolant levels and make a final check that everything has been reconnected. Make sure that there are no tools or rags left in the engine compartment.
2 Remove the glow plugs (Chapter 5B).
3 Turn the engine over on the starter motor until the oil pressure warning light goes out. If the light fails to extinguish after several seconds of cranking, check the engine oil level and that the oil filter is fitted securely. Assuming these are correct, check the security of the oil pressure sensor wiring – do not progress any further until you are sure that oil is being pumped around the engine at sufficient pressure.
4 As applicable, refit the glow plugs, and reconnect the camshaft position sensor and fuel injector wiring connectors.
5 Start the engine, noting that this also may take a little longer than usual, due to the fuel system components being empty.
6 While the engine is idling, check for fuel, coolant and oil leaks. Don't be alarmed if there are some odd smells and smoke from parts getting hot and burning off oil deposits. Note also that it may initially be a little noisy until the hydraulic tappets fill with oil.
7 Keep the engine idling until hot water is felt circulating through the top hose, check that it idles reasonably smoothly and at the usual speed, then switch it off.
8 After a few minutes, recheck the oil and coolant levels, and top-up as necessary (see *Weekly checks*).
9 If new components such as pistons, rings or crankshaft bearings have been fitted, the engine must be run-in for the first 500 miles. Do not operate the engine at full-throttle, or allow it to labour in any gear during this period. It is recommended that the oil and filter be changed at the end of this period.

Notes

Chapter 3
Cooling, heating and air conditioning systems

Contents

Degrees of difficulty

Easy, suitable for novice with little experience	Fairly easy, suitable for beginner with some experience	Fairly difficult, suitable for competent DIY mechanic	Difficult, suitable for experienced DIY mechanic	Very difficult, suitable for expert DIY or professional

Specifications

General

System type . . . . Water-based coolant, pump-assisted circulation, thermostatically controlled

Thermostat

4-cylinder engines . . . . Not available
5-cylinder engines:
  Opening commences . . . . 82°C

Torque wrench settings	Nm	lbf ft
Auxiliary heater glow plugs	15	11
Compressor mounting bolts	24	18
Coolant pump bolts:		
4-cylinder engines:		
1.6 litre	10	7
2.0 litre	17	13
5-cylinder engines	10	7
Coolant temperature sensor	22	16
Expansion valve screws	5	4
Radiator-to-condenser bolts	5	4
Radiator support bolts	24	18
Thermostat housing:		
4-cylinder engines:		
1.6 litre	10	7
2.0 litre	17	13
5-cylinder engines:		
2.0 litre	10	7
2.4 litre	17	13

1 General information and precautions

The cooling system is of pressurised semi-sealed type with the inclusion of an expansion tank to accept coolant displaced from the system when hot and to return it when the system cools.

Water-based coolant is circulated around the cylinder block and head by the coolant pump which is driven by the engine timing belt. As the coolant circulates around the engine it absorbs heat as it flows then, when hot, it travels out into the radiator to pass across the matrix. As the coolant flows across the radiator matrix, airflow created by the forward motion of the vehicle cools it, and it returns to the cylinder block. Airflow through the radiator matrix is assisted by a two-speed electric fan, which is controlled by the engine management system ECU.

A thermostat is fitted to control coolant flow through the radiator. When the engine is cold, the thermostat valve remains closed so that the coolant flow which occurs at normal operating temperatures through the radiator matrix is interrupted.

As the coolant warms up, the thermostat valve starts to open and allows the coolant flow through the radiator to resume.

The engine temperature will always be maintained at a constant level (according to the thermostat rating) whatever the ambient air temperature.

Most models have an oil cooler mounted on the sump – this is basically a heat exchanger with a coolant supply, to take heat away from the oil in the sump.

The vehicle interior heater operates by means of coolant from the engine cooling system. Coolant flow through the heater matrix is constant; temperature control being achieved by blending cool air from outside the vehicle with the warm air from the heater matrix, in the desired ratio.

Air entering the passenger compartment is filtered by a pleated paper filter element, sometimes known as a pollen filter. Also available instead of a pollen filer is a multifilter, which is a carbon impregnated filter which absorbs incoming smells, etc. With this system a pollution sensor monitors the quality of the incoming air, and opens and closes the recirculation flaps accordingly.

The standard climate control (air conditioning) systems are described in detail in Section 9.

⚠️ **Warning: Do not attempt to remove the expansion tank filler cap, or to disturb any part of the cooling system, while it or the engine is hot, as there is a very great risk of scalding. If the expansion tank filler cap must be removed before the engine and radiator have fully cooled down (even though this is not recommended) the pressure in the** cooling system must first be released. Cover the cap with a thick layer of cloth, to avoid scalding, and slowly unscrew the filler cap until a hissing sound can be heard. When the hissing has stopped, showing that pressure is released, slowly unscrew the filler cap further until it can be removed; if more hissing sounds are heard, wait until they have stopped before unscrewing the cap completely. At all times, keep well away from the filler opening.

⚠️ **Warning: Do not allow antifreeze to come in contact with your skin, or with the painted surfaces of the vehicle. Rinse off spills immediately with plenty of water. Never leave antifreeze lying around in an open container, or in a puddle in the driveway or on the garage floor. Children and pets are attracted by its sweet smell, but antifreeze is fatal if ingested.**

⚠️ **Warning: Refer to Section 9 for precautions to be observed when working on vehicles equipped with air conditioning.**

2 Cooling system hoses – disconnection and renewal

Note: *Refer to the warnings given in Section 1 of this Chapter before proceeding. Hoses should only be disconnected once the engine has cooled sufficiently to avoid scalding.*

1 If the checks described in Chapter 1 reveal a faulty hose, it must be renewed as follows.

2 First drain the cooling system (see Chapter 1); if the antifreeze is not due for renewal, the drained coolant may be re-used, if it is collected in a clean container.

3 To disconnect any hose, use a pair of pliers to release the spring clamps (or a screwdriver to slacken screw-type clamps), then move them along the hose clear of the union **(see illustration)**. Carefully work the hose off its stubs. The hoses can be removed with relative ease when new – on an older vehicle, they may have stuck.

4 If a hose proves to be difficult to remove, try to release it by rotating it on its unions before attempting to work it off. Gently prise the end of the hose with a blunt instrument (such as a

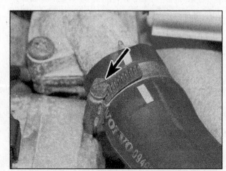

2.3 Screw-type hose clamp (arrowed)

flat-bladed screwdriver), but do not apply too much force, and take care not to damage the pipe stubs or hoses. Note in particular that the radiator hose unions are fragile; do not use excessive force when attempting to remove the hoses.

5 When refitting a hose, first slide the clamps onto the hose, then engage the hose with its unions. Work the hose into position, then check that the hose is settled correctly and is properly routed. Slide each clamp along the hose until it is behind the union flared end, before tightening it securely.

6 Refill the system with coolant (Chapter 1).

7 Check carefully for leaks as soon as possible after disturbing any part of the cooling system.

3 Antifreeze – general information

Note: *Refer to the warnings given in Section 1 of this Chapter before proceeding.*

1 The cooling system should be filled with Volvo antifreeze in a ratio of 50/50 with pure water. At this strength, the coolant will protect against freezing down to -35°C. Antifreeze also provides protection against corrosion, and increases the coolant boiling point. As the engine uses aluminium in its construction, the corrosion protection properties of the antifreeze are critical. Only Volvo antifreeze should be used in the system, and should never be mixed with different antifreeze types.

2 The cooling system should be maintained according to the schedule described in Chapter 1. Old or contaminated coolant mixtures, or antifreeze that is not to Volvo's specification, are likely to cause damage, and encourage the formation of corrosion and scale in the system.

3 Before adding antifreeze, check all hoses and hose connections, because antifreeze tends to leak through very small openings. Engines don't normally consume coolant, so if the level goes down, find the cause and correct it.

4 The specified mixture is 50% antifreeze and 50% clean soft water (by volume). Mix the required quantity in a clean container and then fill the system as described in Chapter 1 and *Weekly checks*. Save any surplus mixture for topping-up.

4 Radiator cooling fan – removal and refitting

Removal

1 Disconnect the battery negative terminal as described in Chapter 5A.

2 Unclip the wiring/pipes on top of the shroud, where fitted.

3 Disconnect the fan wiring plug from the motor. Note that on 2.4 litre engines, the wiring

4.3 Disconnect the fan motor wiring plug

4.4a Use a screwdriver to release the clips (arrowed) at the top of the radiator

4.4b Withdraw the fan assembly upwards from the engine compartment

4.4c Fan motor mounting bolts (arrowed)

5.1 Remove the radiator top mount securing sections

5.5 Undo the radiator-to-condenser fixing bolt and screw (arrowed)

plug is located on the shroud to the left of the fan (see illustration).

4 Using a screwdriver, push back the clips at the top of the radiator on each side that secure the fan shroud to the radiator and withdraw the assembly upwards from the engine bay to remove (see illustrations). On models fitted with an automatic transmission the transmission oil cooler pipes can obstruct the removal of the fans so care is needed to prevent damage to the radiator. We also found that removing the air cleaner housing improved access. If required, the fan motors can be removed from the shroud by undoing the 3 mounting bolts.

Refitting

5 Refitting is the reversal of removal, ensuring that the bottom mountings locate securely in place at the bottom of the radiator.

5 Radiator – removal and refitting

Removal

1 Undo the retaining screws and remove the engine undershield. Undo the screw and remove the triangular plastic sections on top of the lock panel which locate the top of the radiator (see illustration).

2 Drain the cooling system (see Chapter 1) and disconnect the upper and lower radiator hoses.

3 Remove the radiator cooling fan as described in Section 4.

4 Remove the front bumper as described in Chapter 11. Remove the right-hand headlamp as described in Chapter 12.

5 Working through the right-hand side headlamp aperture undo the bolt and screw that attach the condenser to the radiator and secure the condenser to the vehicle body using cable-ties (or similar) (see illustration).

6 Where fitted, undo the screw securing the transmission oil cooler to the radiator, and disconnect the short pipe between the cooler and the radiator. Undo the bolt securing the power steering fluid cooler to the front of the radiator, and secure the cooler to the vehicle body using cable-ties (or similar) (see illustrations).

7 Disconnect the air pipes from the intercooler. To improve access to the pipe clamps, it may be necessary to unclip the plastic air deflectors fitted at either end of the bumper crossbeam. Removing the radiator support brackets on each side by undoing the 2 bolts front and

5.6a Transmission oil cooler bolt (arrowed)

5.6b Disconnect the pipe from the transmission oil cooler (arrowed)

5.6c Secure the power steering oil cooler to the vehicle body

5.7a Undo the clamps for the charge air pipes at the intercooler

5.7b Release the lower clip . . .

5.7c . . . upper clip . . .

rear (noting that the rear bolts are quite tricky to access) can further improve access to the intercooler pipe clamps. Note that the clamps

are crimped to the air pipe and cannot be rotated for refitting (see illustrations).
8 Disconnect the wiring plug for the charge

pressure sensor, located above the left-hand side intercooler pipe. Undo the bolt on each side securing the intercooler, and withdraw the intercooler from beneath the vehicle (see illustrations).
9 At this stage of the process, Volvo use a special tool to support the radiator. However, we used a home-made tool comprising two pieces of metal of 150 mm in length that were bolted to holes in the crossmember and slid beneath the radiator. With the radiator supported in this way, and working from beneath the vehicle, the radiator support beam can be removed by undoing the 2 bolts on each side (see illustrations).
10 Using a screwdriver, push in the 2 clips securing the condenser to the bottom of the radiator. Secure the condenser to the vehicle body using cable-ties (or similar) (see illustration).

5.7d . . . and remove the air deflector

5.7e Support bracket outer bolts (arrowed)

5.8a Charge pressure sensor wiring plug (arrowed)

5.8b Undo the intercooler securing bolts (left-hand side bolt arrowed)

5.9a Home-made radiator support tool bolted to the crossbeam behind the radiator

5.9b Undo the radiator support bolts (left-hand side bolts arrowed) . . .

5.9c . . . and remove the radiator support

5.10 Use a screwdriver to push in the clips at the bottom of the radiator

11 The radiator can now be withdrawn from beneath the car. It is worth noting that a number of items, such as pipes, brackets, and the transmission oil cooler, can obstruct the removal of the radiator so an assistant may be helpful at this stage **(see illustration)**.

Refitting

12 Refit by reversing the removal operations ensuring that the radiator engages with the lugs at the top located beneath the triangular plastic sections on the lock panel. With reference to Chapter 1, refill the cooling system on completion.

6 Coolant temperature sensor – testing, removal and refitting

Testing

1 The coolant temperature sensor is located in the thermostat housing, and is used by both the engine management system and the instrument panel temperature gauge to supply an engine temperature source signal.
2 In the event of a fault in the sensor, or a loss of signal due to poor electrical connections, a fault code will be logged in the engine management system ECU, which can be read out via the diagnostic connector beneath the facia on the driver's side (using a suitable fault code reader).
3 Should a fault code be logged, a careful check should be made of the sensor wiring and the wiring connector. Apart from testing by substitution with a new unit, further checks require the use of Volvo test equipment and should be entrusted to a dealer or suitably-equipped specialist.

Removal

4 Drain the cooling system as described in Chapter 1.
5 Pull the plastic cover on the top of the engine straight up and remove it from the engine compartment.
6 Follow the steps in Section 8 (thermostat removal) for component removal until the sensor becomes accessible. The process is similar for all engines.
7 Disconnect the wiring plug, then unscrew the sensor from the housing **(see illustration)**. Where fitted, discard the seal – a new one must be fitted.

Refitting

8 Screw in the new sensor unit, using a smear of sealant on the threads or a new seal as applicable. Reconnect the wiring connector. Refit the thermostat housing, tightening the screws securely, and reconnect the radiator hose or refit the timing belt cover/engine cover as applicable.
9 Top-up the coolant level as described in *Weekly checks*.

5.11 With an assistant supporting the radiator from above, it can be lowered from beneath the vehicle

7 Coolant pump – removal and refitting

Note: *Refer to the warnings given in Section 1 of this Chapter before proceeding.*

Removal

1 Drain the cooling system as described in Chapter 1.
2 Refer to the relevant Part of Chapter 2A, 2B or 2C and remove the timing belt.
3 Undo the bolts, and remove the coolant pump from its locating dowels **(see illustrations)**. Recover the gasket, and the O-ring seal where applicable, after removing the pump.
4 Thoroughly clean all traces of old gasket from the pump and cylinder block mating faces.

7.3a On 2.4 litre engines, undo the mounting bolts . . .

7.3c On 4-cylinder engines, undo the mounting bolts (arrowed) . . .

6.7 Coolant sensor wiring plug (arrowed)

Refitting

5 Using a new gasket, and O-ring seal where applicable, locate the pump in position.
6 Apply a little thread-locking compound, then tighten the bolts progressively and in a diagonal sequence to the specified torque.
7 Refit the timing belt as described in Chapter 2A, 2B or 2C, and top-up the coolant as described in Chapter 1.

8 Thermostat – removal, testing and refitting

1 As the thermostat ages, it will become slower to react to changes in water temperature. Ultimately, the unit may stick in the open or closed position, and this causes problems. A

7.3a . . . and remove the coolant pump from its locating dowels

7.3d . . . remove the coolant pump, and recover the gasket

8.19 Undo the bolts (arrowed) and remove the thermostat housing

8.24a On 2.0 litre 4-cylinder engines, undo the thermostat securing nuts (arrowed)

8.24b Renew the thermostat housing sealing ring

thermostat which is stuck open will result in a very slow warm-up; a thermostat which is stuck shut will lead to rapid overheating.

2 Before assuming the thermostat is to blame for a cooling system problem, check the coolant level. If the system is draining due to a leak, or has not been properly filled, there may be an air-lock in the system (see Chapter 1).

3 If the engine seems to be taking a long time to warm up (based on heater output or temperature gauge operation), the thermostat is probably stuck open.

4 Equally, a lengthy warm-up period might suggest that the thermostat is missing – it may have been removed or inadvertently omitted by a previous owner or mechanic. Don't drive the vehicle without a thermostat – the engine management system's ECU will stay in warm-up mode for longer than necessary, causing emissions and fuel economy to suffer.

5 If the engine runs hot, use your hand to check the temperature of the radiator top hose. If the hose isn't hot, but the engine is, the thermostat is probably stuck closed, preventing the coolant inside the engine from escaping to the radiator – renew the thermostat. Again, this problem may also be due to an air-lock (see Chapter 1).

6 If the radiator top hose is hot, it means that the coolant is flowing and the thermostat is open. Consult the *Fault diagnosis* section at the end of this manual to assist in tracing possible cooling system faults.

7 To gain a rough idea of whether the thermostat is working properly when the

8.26 Thermostat housing bolts (arrowed) on 2.4 litre engines

engine is warming up, without dismantling the system, proceed as follows.

8 With the engine completely cold, start the engine and let it idle, while checking the temperature of the radiator top hose. Periodically check the temperature indicated on the coolant temperature gauge – if overheating is indicated, switch the engine off immediately.

9 The top hose should feel cold for some time as the engine warms up, and should then get warm quite quickly as the thermostat opens.

10 The above is not a precise or definitive test of thermostat operation, but if the system does not perform as described, remove and test the thermostat as described below.

Removal

Note: *Refer to the warnings given in Section 1 of this Chapter before proceeding.*

11 The engine must be completely cold before starting this procedure – the engine should have been switched off for several hours, and ideally, left to cool overnight.

12 Drain the cooling system as described in Chapter 1

13 Pull the plastic engine cover straight-up and remove it from the engine compartment.

1.6 litre engine

14 Remove the air cleaner housing as described in Chapter 4A.

15 Volvo advise that the fuel filter located at the left-end end of the engine needs to be removed, although we were unable to confirm this in the workshop. If this is the case, the process is as follows. Undo the bolts and remove the engine cover bracket. Release the clips and disconnect the fuel pipes from the top of the filter – be prepared to collect escaping fuel. Undo the 3 bolts and remove the fuel filter mounting bracket, and disconnect the wiring plug. The filter can now be removed

16 The thermostat housing is located at the left-hand end of the cylinder head. Release the clips and disconnect the coolant hoses from the thermostat housing.

17 Disconnect the wiring plug from the engine coolant temperature sensor.

18 Undo the coolant bypass pipe retaining bolt.

19 Undo the 4 retaining bolts and remove the

thermostat housing. Note that the thermostat is integral with the housing. If the thermostat is faulty, the housing must be renewed **(see illustration)**.

2.0 litre 4-cylinder engine

20 Remove the air cleaner housing as described in Chapter 4A.

21 Undo the 2 nuts, disconnect the wiring plug, and remove the actuator for the turbocharger.

22 Undo the 4 bolts and remove the heatshield in front of the thermostat housing.

23 Release the clamps and disconnect the hoses from the thermostat housing.

24 Undo the 4 nuts and remove the thermostat housing from the left-hand end of the cylinder head **(see illustrations)**. Although it may be possible to separate the thermostat from the cover, it would appear that it is not available as a separate part. Check with a Volvo dealer or parts specialist.

5-cylinder engines

25 Disconnect the wiring plug for the coolant temperature sensor.

26 Undo the clamps and disconnect the hoses from the thermostat housing. Undo the 2 retaining bolts and remove the housing from the engine **(see illustration)**.

Testing

27 Check the temperature marking stamped on the thermostat, which will typically be 82°C.

28 Using a thermometer and container of water, heat the water until the temperature corresponds with the temperature marking stamped on the thermostat.

29 Suspend the (closed) thermostat on a length of string in the water, and check that maximum opening occurs within two minutes.

30 Remove the thermostat and allow it to cool down; check that it closes fully.

31 If the thermostat does not open and close as described, or if it sticks in either position, it must be renewed.

Refitting

32 Refitting is a reversal of removal using new gaskets and seals where applicable. Top-up the cooling system as described in Chapter 1.

9 Heating, ventilation and air conditioning systems – general information

Manual climate control

1 On models equipped with a manual climate control system, the heater system is fitted in conjunction with a manually-controlled air conditioning unit.

2 The heater is of the fresh air type. Air enters through a grille in front of the windscreen, and passes to the various vents, a variable proportion of the air passes through the heater matrix, where it is warmed by engine coolant flowing through the matrix.

3 Distribution of air to the vents, and through or around the matrix, is controlled by flaps. These are operated by an electric motor. Separate temperature controls are provided for driver and front passenger, and these are cable-operated.

4 A variable speed electric fan is fitted to boost the airflow through the heater with a pollen filter fitted after the fan.

5 The air conditioning system works in conjunction with the heater to enable any reasonable air temperature to be achieved inside the car. It also reduces the humidity of the incoming air, aiding demisting even when cooling is not required.

6 The refrigeration side of the air conditioning system functions in a similar way to a domestic refrigerator. A compressor, belt-driven from the crankshaft pulley, draws refrigerant in its gaseous state from an evaporator. The compound refrigerant passes through a condenser where it loses heat and enters its liquid state. After dehydration the refrigerant returns to the evaporator where it absorbs heat from air passing over the evaporator fins. The refrigerant becomes a gas again and the cycle is repeated.

7 Various subsidiary controls and sensors protect the system against excessive temperature and pressures. Additionally, engine idle speed is increased when the system is in use, to compensate for the additional load imposed by the compressor.

Automatic climate control

8 On models with automatic climate control, the temperature inside the car can be automatically maintained at the level selected by the operator, irrespective of outside temperature. The computer-controlled system operates the heater, air conditioner and fan functions as necessary to achieve this. The refrigeration side of the system is the same as for models with manual climate control; the fully automatic electronic control operates as follows.

9 An electronic control unit (ECU) receives signal inputs from sensors that detect the air duct temperatures on the driver's and passenger's side, and interior temperature on the driver's and passenger's side. A solar sensor is used to detect the presence of sunlight. Signals are also received from the dampers (air flaps) on their position at any given time. Information on engine temperature, outside temperature, whether or not the engine is running, and if so, the vehicle roadspeed, are also sent to the ECU from the engine management system.

10 When the automatic function is engaged, the ECU can establish the optimum settings needed, based on the sensor signals, for the selected temperature and air distribution. These settings can then be maintained irrespective of driving conditions and weather.

11 Distribution of air to the various vents, and the blending of hot or cold air to achieve the selected temperature, are controlled by dampers (flaps). These are operated by electric motors, which are in turn controlled by the ECU. A variable speed fan which can be manually or automatically controlled is used to boost airflow through the system.

12 Should a fault occur, the ECU stores a series of fault codes for subsequent read-out via the diagnostic connector located in the lower facia panel above the driver's pedals.

Precautions

13 When an air conditioning system is fitted, it is necessary to observe special precautions whenever dealing with any part of the system, or its associated components. If for any reason the system must be discharged, entrust this task to your Volvo dealer or a refrigeration engineer.

⚠ **Warning: The refrigeration circuit contains R134a liquid refrigerant, and it is therefore dangerous to disconnect any part of the system without specialised knowledge and equipment.**

14 The refrigerant is potentially dangerous, and should only be handled by qualified persons. If it is splashed onto the skin, it can cause frostbite. It is not itself poisonous, but in the presence of a naked flame (including a cigarette) it forms a poisonous gas. Uncontrolled discharging of the refrigerant is dangerous, and potentially damaging to the environment.

10 Climate control system components – removal and refitting

Control panel

Note: *The control panel is integral to the centre console and contains the ECU and the temperature sensor for the system. If the control panel assembly is renewed, it will need to be programmed prior to use. This can only be carried out by a Volvo dealer or suitably-equipped specialist.*

1 Remove the ignition remote unit, then wait at least 3 minutes before proceeding.

2 Remove the upper section of the centre console as described in Chapter 11. The ECU is secured to the reverse of the panel by 4 screws **(see illustration)**.

3 Refitting is a reversal of removal.

Heater blower motor

Note: *Volvo say that this task can be carried out with the heater unit in the vehicle. In practice, we found access to be extremely limited and recommend removal of the facia or heater unit (refer to the relevant Section of this Chapter or Chapter 11). The following process was undertaken with the heater unit removed from the vehicle.*

4 Before starting work, set the ventilation system to recirculation mode. This ensures the recirculation flap on the heater unit is in the correct position.

5 Unclip the wiring from the motor housing. Undo the 3 screws and remove the end casing containing the distribution flap motor, to gain access to the blower fan.

6 Release the plastic tab at the motor and turn the complete motor clockwise to release it from the heater housing. Withdraw the motor from the heater housing from the side containing the fan, supporting the fan spindle as it is withdrawn **(see illustrations)**.

10.2 Control panel ECU securing screws (arrowed)

10.6a Release the plastic tab, turn the motor clockwise to release it from the heater housing . . .

10.6b . . . and withdraw the motor

10.7 A hole (arrowed) is provided to insert a securing screw

10.9 Heater blower motor resistor

Air recirculation flap motor

19 The motor is located on the left-hand side of the heater unit and can be accessed by removing the glovebox as described in Chapter 11 (shown with the heater unit removed for clarity).

20 Unclip the operating arm from the motor, undo the 2 screws and remove the motor **(see illustration)**.

21 Refitting is a reversal of removal.

Ventilation flap motor

22 The motor is located on the left-hand side of the heater unit and can be accessed by removing the glovebox as described in Chapter 11.

23 Disconnect the motor wiring connector, undo the 2 screws and remove the motor **(see illustration)**.

24 Refit by reversing the removal operations.

7 Refit by reversing the removal operations. If the plastic tab at the motor breaks on removal, a hole is provided to insert a suitable securing screw **(see illustration)**.

Heater blower motor resistor

8 Remove the glovebox as described in Chapter 11.

9 Disconnect the wiring plug, rotate the resistor anti-clockwise, and remove it from the blower motor housing **(see illustration)**.

10 Refitting is a reversal of removal.

Heater matrix

Note: *Refer to the warnings given in Section 1 of this Chapter before proceeding.*

11 Drain the cooling system as described in Chapter 1.

12 Disconnect the battery negative terminal as described in Chapter 5A.

13 Remove the centre console as described in Chapter 11.

14 Remove the centre air vent and move the rear air vents to one side.

15 Disconnect the wiring plugs **(see illustrations)**, undo the 4 screws, and remove the electric auxiliary heater. Working in the driver's footwell, undo the 2 screws and remove the plastic cover over the coolant pipes.

16 Undo the clamps and disconnect the coolant pipes. Be prepared for coolant spillage **(see illustration)**.

17 Pull the matrix upwards and rearwards to remove **(see illustration)**.

18 Refit by reversing the removal operations. Use new O-rings on the heater pipes and top-up the cooling system as described in *Weekly checks* on completion.

Distribution flap motor

Left-hand side

25 Remove the glovebox compartment as described in Chapter 11.

26 Disconnect the motor wiring connector from the side of the heater housing. Undo the two screws and remove the motor **(see illustration 10.23)**.

27 Refit by reversing the removal operations.

Right-hand side

28 The motor does not appear to be accessible without the removal of the facia or heater unit. Refer to the relevant part of this

10.15a Disconnect the wiring plugs for the electric auxiliary heater . . .

10.15b . . . and remove the plastic cover over the heater pipes

10.16 Remove the coolant pipe clamps

10.17 Remove the heater matrix from the heater housing

10.20 Air recirculation flap motor

10.23 The ventilation flap motor is on the left and the distribution flap motor on the right

10.28 The distribution flap motor is on the left and defroster flap motor is on the right

10.31 Prise off the facia end panel on the passenger side and remove the screw

10.32 Remove the hazard light switch and undo the screw (arrowed)

10.33a Carefully lever out the vent panel . . .

10.33b . . . and remove it from the facia

10.33c Air vent securing screws (arrowed)

Section or entrust this task to a Volvo dealer **(see illustration)**.

Defroster flap motor

29 The motor does not appear to be accessible without the removal of the facia or heater unit. Refer to the relevant part of this Section or entrust this task to a Volvo dealer **(see illustration 10.28)**.

Facia panel vents

Passenger's side and centre vents

30 The passenger side and centre air vents are combined in one panel.
31 Carefully prise off the panel at the end of the facia on the passenger side and undo the exposed screw **(see illustration)**.
32 Remove the hazard light switch as described in Chapter 12 and undo the screw exposed in the aperture **(see illustration)**.
33 Carefully lever the vent panel out of the facia, using a screwdriver with a piece of card beneath it to protect the trim. Disconnect any wiring plugs from the vents as they are withdrawn (where applicable). Once removed, the vents can be separated from the facia trim panel by undoing the screws on the rear of each vent **(see illustrations)**.
34 Refitting is a reversal of removal.

Driver's side vent

35 Remove the headlight switch from the facia panel as described in Chapter 12. Release the two clips on the lower edge of the vent, then push the lower edge rearwards from the facia. Remove the vent **(see illustration)**.
36 Refitting is a reversal of removal.

Driver's windscreen defrost vent

37 Remove the driver's side vent as described previously. Reach through the end of the facia and release the clips and press the defrost vent upwards from the facia.
38 Refitting is a reversal of removal.

Passenger's windscreen defrost vent

39 Remove the glovebox as described in Chapter 11. Reach through the glovebox aperture, release the clips and push the defrost vent upwards from the facia.
40 Refitting is a reversal of removal.

Heater housing

41 Have the air conditioning refrigerant discharged by a suitably-equipped specialist.
42 Remove the centre console and facia as described in Chapter 11.
43 Remove the wiper motor/linkage as

10.35 Release the clips and push the driver's side vent from the facia

described in Chapter 12 to improve access to the expansion valve.
44 Remove the engine electronic control unit (ECU) as described in Chapter 4A and undo the 2 bolts securing the mounting bracket to the bulkhead.
45 Undo the bolt securing the air conditioning pipes to the expansion valve at the bulkhead and pull the pipes towards the front of the vehicle to release them from the expansion valve (note that clearance between the pipes and the secondary bulkhead panel is quite tight). Plug the ends of the pipes to prevent the ingress of dirt, and discard the seals as new ones must be fitted on reconnection **(see illustration)**.
46 Drain the coolant as described in Section 1.
47 Disconnect the heater hoses at the bulkhead, below the expansion valve. Rotate the locking collar on each pipe approximately

10.45 Release the air-conditioning pipes from the expansion valve at the bulkhead

10.47 Rotate the locking collars (arrowed) and disconnect the heater hoses at the bulkhead

10.48a Remove the centre ventilation duct . . .

10.48b . . . and the side ventilation ducts

10.49a Undo the two bolts at the top on each side (right-hand side bolts arrowed) . . .

10.49b . . . the two bolts at the bottom on each side (right-hand side bolts arrowed) . . .

a quarter of a turn anti-clockwise, and pull from the pipe stubs (as with the air conditioning pipes, clearance is quite tight) **(see illustration)**.

48 Working inside the vehicle remove the ventilation ducts from the centre of the heater unit and from the top on each side **(see illustrations)**. Where fitted, disconnect the wiring plugs for the electric auxiliary heater.

49 Remove the alloy frame located in front of the heater unit. There are 2 bolts at the top on each side, 1 bolt each side securing the frame to the lower crossmember, 2 bolts at the bottom on each side, and 2 bolts below the electric auxiliary heater. Unclip any wiring from the frame **(see illustrations)**.

50 Undo the 4 screws, release the clip on each side, and withdraw the electric auxiliary heater/heater matrix cover from the heater unit (this will allow the lower crossmember to be withdrawn) **(see illustration)**.

51 Unclip the wiring loom from the upper crossmember and disconnect the wiring plug from the steering lock unit on the steering column **(see illustrations)**.

52 Make some alignment marks to aid refitting and then remove the facia crossmember. Undo the steering column lower pinch-bolt, the 2 bolts located below the windscreen above the brake servo, and the 2 bolts on each side at the A-pillar. Remove both front doors as described in Chapter 11, and undo the bolt on each side that secure the lower

10.49c . . . and the two bolts below the electric auxiliary heater

10.49d Undo the wiring clips on the frame prior to removal

10.50 Withdraw the auxiliary heater/matrix cover from the heater unit

10.51a Unclip the wiring loom from the upper crossmember . . .

10.51b . . . and disconnect the wiring plug from the steering lock

10.52a Undo the two bolts located above the brake servo . . .

10.52b . . . and the two bolts at the A-pillar on each side

10.52c Undo the lower crossmember bolt . . .

10.52d . . . and withdraw it from the A-pillar

crossmember to the A-pillar. Carefully pull the complete crossmember rearwards from the bulkhead and remove from the vehicle (see illustrations).

53 Disconnect the wiring plugs for the heater control flap motors and disconnect the drain tube from the floorpan on the right-hand side of the heater unit (see illustration).

54 Note their fitted positions, then make a final check to ensure all wiring plugs have been disconnected from the heater housing, and manoeuvre it from the passenger cabin (see illustration).

Evaporator

Note: *Whenever disconnecting air conditioning*

pipes or components, always plug the openings to prevent dirt ingress, and to prevent the receiver/drier from becoming saturated.

55 Remove the heater unit as described in this Section.

56 Remove the foam material around the expansion valve, undo the screws and remove the plastic trim located above the

10.52e Pull the crossmember rearwards and remove it from the vehicle

10.53 Heater unit drain plug

10.54 Pull the heater unit away from the bulkhead

10.56a Remove the foam (arrowed) around the expansion valve

10.56b Undo the pipe clamp screw (arrowed) . . .

10.56c . . . undo the securing screw and remove the pipes

air conditioning pipes. Undo the screw and remove the pipes from the housing **(see illustrations).**

57 Remove the lower section of the heater unit (the part that contains the heater matrix) by undoing the 4 screws and releasing the 3 metal clips **(see illustrations).**

58 Undo the 3 screws and remove the blower motor housing from the heater unit. Release the plastic and metal clips and remove the section of heater unit around the evaporator. The evaporator can now be removed **(see illustrations).**

59 Refitting is a reversal of removal, noting the following points:

a) Fit new O-ring seals to the expansion valve and air conditioning pipe connections at the engine compartment bulkhead.
b) Upon completion have the air conditioning system recharged, and checked for leaks.

Condenser

Note: Whenever disconnecting air conditioning pipes or components, always plug the openings to prevent dirt ingress, and to prevent the receiver/drier from becoming saturated.

60 Have the air conditioning system discharged by a suitably-equipped specialist.

Refer to Section 5 for removal of the radiator (though note that the intercooler should not be separated at this stage), ensuring that the air conditioning pipes to the condenser are also disconnected. Note that the radiator, condenser, and intercooler are removed from the vehicle as one unit. With the units removed, the condenser can be separated.

61 Refitting is a reversal of removal, noting the following points:

a) To aid refitting, disconnect the intercooler air pipes at their locations on the engine and then refit to the intercooler in the correct position. The air deflectors and brackets removed previously can then be refitted before the units are raised into position.
b) The units are raised into position from beneath the vehicle using a suitable jack which should be padded to prevent damage. Ensure that pipes or hoses do not become trapped as the units are raised into position. The aid of an assistant is helpful to support the units while the radiator support is refitted.
c) Fit new O-ring seals to the air conditioning pipe connections.
d) Upon completion, have the air conditioning system recharged, and checked for leaks.
e) Refill the cooling system.

10.57a Undo the securing screws . . .

10.57b . . . and release the metal clips

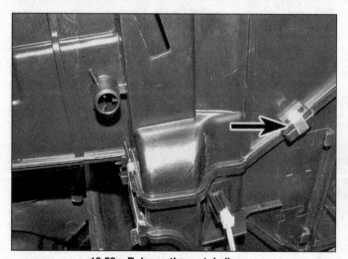

10.58a Release the metal clips . . .

10.58b . . . and remove the section of the heater housing surrounding the evaporator

10.64 Expansion valve securing screws (arrowed)

10.66 Receiver/dryer filter screw

10.73 Undo the three compressor mounting bolts (arrowed)

Expansion valve

Note: *Whenever disconnecting air conditioning pipes or components, always plug the openings to prevent dirt ingress, and to prevent the receiver/drier from becoming saturated.*

62 Have the air conditioning refrigerant discharged by a suitably-equipped specialist.

63 Remove the plenum cover as described in Chapter 12, Section 18, and release the clamps securing the air conditioning pipes to the valve.

64 Undo the two screws securing the expansion valve to the passenger compartment air conditioning pipes, and remove the valve (shown with the heater unit removed for clarity) **(see illustration)**. Discard the O-ring seals, new ones must be fitted.

65 Refitting is a reversal of removal, noting the following points:

a) Tighten the expansion valve screws to the specified torque.

b) Renew all O-ring seals where disturbed.

c) Upon completion, have the air conditioning system recharged and checked for leaks.

Receiver/drier

Note: *Whenever disconnecting air conditioning pipes or components, always plug the openings*

to prevent dirt ingress, and to prevent the receiver/drier from becoming saturated.

66 The receiver/drier is located on the left-hand side of the condenser. To remove the filter, unscrew the cap at the bottom of the unit and withdraw the filter – shown with the unit removed for clarity **(see illustration)**.

67 Refitting is a reversal of removal.

Compressor

Note: *Whenever disconnecting air conditioning pipes or components, always plug the openings to prevent dirt ingress, and to prevent the receiver/drier from becoming saturated.*

68 Have the air conditioning refrigerant discharged by a suitably-equipped specialist.

69 Remove the auxiliary drivebelt as described in Chapter 1.

70 Jack up the front of the vehicle and support it securely on axle stands (see *Jacking and vehicle support*). Undo the clips/screws and remove the engine undershield.

71 Undo the clamps and remove the inlet air pipe at the bottom of the manifold.

72 Undo the screws and detach the air conditioning pipes from the compressor. Discard the O-ring seals, new ones must be fitted.

73 Disconnect the wiring plug, then remove the 3 bolts securing the compressor to the

engine, and manoeuvre it downwards and out from the vehicle **(see illustration)**.

74 Refitting is a reversal of removal, noting the following points:

a) Renew all O-ring seals where disturbed, lubricating them with compressor oil (Volvo 116 1627) before refitting.

b) Upon completion, have the air conditioning system recharged and checked for leaks.

Solar sensor

75 The solar sensor is combined with the anti-theft alarm system diode, and is located on top of the facia cover.

76 Carefully prise up the sensor using a screwdriver inserted under its base at the side **(see illustration)**.

77 Disconnect the wiring connector and remove the sensor.

78 Refitting is a reversal of removal.

Passenger compartment and air temperature sensors

79 The passenger compartment sensor is located on the reverse of the climate control panel **(see illustration)**. Air temperature sensors are located in the heater housing and may only be accessible with the heater housing removed. Refer to this Section for removal.

10.76 Carefully prise the solar sensor from the top of the facia

10.79 Passenger compartment temperature sensor

10.84 Air quality sensor

11.5 Disconnect the wiring plugs for the electric auxiliary heater

Evaporator temperature sensor

80 Remove the left-hand side panel from the centre console.

81 Disconnect the wiring plug and carefully prise the sensor from position.

82 Refitting is a reversal of removal.

In-vehicle humidity sensor

83 The sensor is integral with the interior rear view mirror. At the time of writing, we were unable to verify whether the sensor is available separately. Refer to a Volvo dealer.

Air quality sensor

84 The sensor is located on the left-hand side of the heater blower motor housing and can be accessed by removing the glovebox as described in Chapter 11 **(see illustration)**.

11 Auxiliary heater – general information, removal and refitting

General information

1 Models may be fitted with an auxiliary heater which raises the temperature of the coolant in the system, thus raising the temperature of the engine and passenger cabin. The system consists of an electrically-heated unit located below the heater matrix.

Removal and refitting

2 Disconnect the battery negative lead as described in Chapter 5A.

3 Remove the centre console as described in Chapter 11.

4 Remove the central air vent and move the rear air vents to one side.

5 Disconnect the wiring plugs on the heater unit, undo the screw on each side, and withdraw the unit **(see illustration)**.

6 Refitting is a reversal of removal.

Chapter 4 Part A:
Fuel and exhaust systems

Contents

Degrees of difficulty

Easy, suitable for novice with little experience 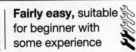 | **Fairly easy,** suitable for beginner with some experience | **Fairly difficult,** suitable for competent DIY mechanic | **Difficult,** suitable for experienced DIY mechanic | **Very difficult,** suitable for expert DIY or professional

Specifications

General

System type:	
1.6 litre engine	Unable to verify
2.0 litre 4-cylinder engine	Direct injection common rail with Siemens high pressure delivery pump
5-cylinder engines	Direct injection common rail with Bosch high pressure delivery pump
Fuel tank pump pressure	Unable to verify
Fuel injection pump	Tandem pump (high pressure and low pressure) driven by the inlet camshaft
Injection pressure:	
1.6 litre engine	Not available
2.0 litre 4-cylinder engine	350 to 1650 bar
5-cylinder engines	Not available
Turbocharger type	Garret – variable nozzle
Turbocharger boost pressure	Not available
Idle speed:*	
1.6 litre engine	780 rpm
2.0 litre 4-cylinder engine	800 rpm
5-cylinder engines	720 rpm

* Not adjustable – controlled by engine control module (ECM)

Torque wrench settings

	Nm	lbf ft
Exhaust manifold-to-EGR pipe nuts (2.0 litre 5-cylinder engine)	24	18
Exhaust manifold to cylinder head:		
1.6 litre engine	24	18
2.0 litre 4-cylinder engine:		
Stage 1	15	11
Stage 2	25	18
2.0 litre 5-cylinder engine:		
End nuts:		
Stage 1	14	10
Stage 2	16	12
Top and bottom nuts:		
Stage 1	12	7
Stage 2	14	10
2.4 litre engine:		
Stage 1	15	11
Stage 2	25	18
Exhaust manifold heat shield (5-cylinder engines only)	24	18
Fuel injector clamp screws:*		
1.6 litre engine:		
Stage 1	4	3
Stage 2	Angle-tighten a further 65°	
2.0 litre 4-cylinder engine:		
Stage 1	4	3
Stage 2	Angle-tighten a further 45°	
5-cylinder engines	13	10
Fuel pressure safety valve	95	70
Fuel pressure sensor:		
2.4 litre engines (D5244 T4 and T5)	70	52
Fuel pressure sensor adapter to common rail	60	44
Fuel pump mounting screws:		
1.6 litre engine	22	16
2.0 litre 4-cylinder engine	20	15
5-cylinder engines	18	13
Fuel rail-to-cylinder head bolts:		
All except 2.0 litre 4-cylinder engine	24	18
2.0 litre 4-cylinder engine	22	16
Fuel sender locking ring	85	63
Fuel tank restraining strap bolts	24	18
Fuel temperature sensor	21	15
High-pressure pipe union nuts:*		
1.6 litre engine:		
Stage 1	20	15
Stage 2	25	18
2.0 litre 4-cylinder engine:		
Stage 1	19	14
Stage 2	30	22
5-cylinder engines	28	21
Manifold absolute pressure sensor (MAP):		
4-cylinder engines	5	4
5-cylinder engines	10	7
Oxygen sensor	45	33
Turbocharger:		
Coolant pipe to turbocharger	38	28
Oil feed to turbocharger:		
1.6 litre engine	18	13
2.0 litre 4-cylinder engine	38	28
2.0 litre 5-cylinder engine	18	13
2.4 litre engine	25	18
Oil feed to cylinder block	38	28
Turbocharger to exhaust manifold:*		
1.6 litre engine	25	18
2.0 litre 4-cylinder engine	24	18
2.0 litre 5-cylinder engine:		
Stage 1	18	13
Stage 2	24	18
2.4 litre engine	Not applicable	

* Do not re-use

1 General information and precautions

General information

The operation of the fuel injection system is described in more detail in Section 5.

Fuel is drawn from a tank under the rear of the vehicle by a tank-immersed electric pump, and then forced through a filter to the injection pump. The inlet camshaft driven injection pump is a tandem pump – a low-pressure gear-type pump which supplies the high-pressure pump with fuel at a constant pressure, and a high-pressure piston-type pump which supplies fuel to the common fuel rail at variable pressure. Fuel is supplied from the common fuel rail to the injectors. Also inside the injection pump assembly is a pressure control valve which regulates the quantity of fuel to the high-pressure pump, and a bypass valve which returns excess fuel back to the low pressure pump. The injectors are operated by solenoids controlled by the ECM, based on information supplied by various sensors. The engine ECM also controls the preheating side of the system – refer to Chapter 5B for more details.

The EDC (electronic diesel control) system fitted, incorporates a 'drive-by-wire' system, where an accelerator pedal position sensor is fitted instead of the traditional accelerator cable. The position and rate-of-change of the accelerator pedal is reported by the position sensor to the ECM, which then adjusts the fuel injectors and fuel pressure to deliver the required amount of fuel, and optimum combustion efficiency.

The exhaust system incorporates a turbocharger, and an EGR. Further detail of the emission control systems can be found in Chapter 4B.

Precautions

● When working on diesel fuel system components, scrupulous cleanliness must be observed, and care must be taken not to introduce any foreign matter into fuel lines or components.
● After carrying out any work involving disconnection of fuel lines, it is advisable to check the connections for leaks; pressurise the system by cranking the engine several times.
● Electronic control units are very sensitive components, and certain precautions must be taken to avoid damage to these units as follows.
● When carrying out welding operations on the vehicle using electric welding equipment, the battery and alternator should be disconnected.
● Although the underbonnet-mounted modules will tolerate normal underbonnet conditions, they can be adversely affected by excess heat or moisture. If using welding equipment or pressure-washing equipment in the vicinity of an electronic module, take care not to direct heat, or jets of water or steam at the module. If this cannot be avoided, remove the module from the vehicle, and protect its wiring plug with a plastic bag.
● Before disconnecting any wiring, or removing components, always ensure that the ignition is switched off.
● Do not attempt to improvise ECM fault diagnosis procedures using a test lamp or multimeter, as irreparable damage could be caused to the module.
● After working on fuel injection/engine management system components, ensure that all wiring is correctly reconnected before reconnecting the battery or switching on the ignition.

2 Air cleaner assembly – removal and refitting

Removal

1.6 litre engine

1 Disconnect the mass airflow meter wiring plug, undo the 2 retaining screws, and remove the meter from the air pipe. Undo the clamp and disconnect the air pipe from the housing.
2 Undo the 2 screws securing the differential pressure sensor to the base of the housing.
3 Pull the housing upwards sharply to release it from the three mounting grommets. Remove the air intake duct as the housing is withdrawn.

2.0 litre 4-cylinder engine

4 Remove the plastic engine cover.
5 Disconnect the mass airflow meter wiring plug, undo the 2 retaining bolts, and remove the meter from the air pipe.
6 Undo the clip and disconnect the air pipe at the rear of the housing, and the pipe leading from the housing to the lock panel.
7 Release the wiring loom securing clips at the base of the housing and pull the housing upwards sharply to release it from the three mounting grommets. Remove the air intake duct as the housing is withdrawn.

5-cylinder engines

8 Undo the screws, remove the top of the assembly, and remove the air filter element. Disconnect the air pipes (see illustrations).
9 Using a pair of pliers, release the clip in the bottom of the housing and withdraw the assembly from the engine bay.

Refitting

10 Refitting is a reversal of removal. Make sure the outlet and intake ducts are clipped securely into position (where applicable).

3 Fuel tank – removal and refitting

Note: *Observe the precautions in Section 1 before working on any component in the fuel system.*

Removal

1 Before the tank can be removed, it must be drained of as much fuel as possible. To avoid the dangers and complications of fuel

2.8a Undo the screws securing the top of the air cleaner housing

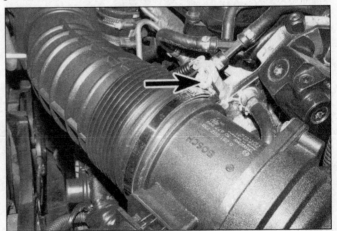
2.8b Undo the clamp (arrowed) and disconnect the air pipe

3.3a Undo the retaining clips for the plastic underbody panel on the right-hand side of the fuel tank . . .

3.3b . . . and remove the panel

3.3c Undo the bolts and remove the heat shield above the exhaust pipe

3.3d Remove the plastic underbody panel on the left-hand side of the fuel tank

3.4 Release the exhaust hanger ahead of the left-hand side rear wheel

3.5 Remove the heat shield to the left of the fuel tank

handling and storage, it is advisable to carry out this operation with the tank almost empty.
2 Disconnect the battery negative lead (see Chapter 5A).
3 Undo the 5 nuts and remove the plastic underbody panel on the right-hand side of the tank. Undo the 6 bolts (2 at the front and 4 at the rear) and remove the centre section of heat shield above the exhaust pipe. Undo the 4 nuts and remove the plastic underbody panel on the left-hand side of the tank (see illustrations).
4 Using a suitable tool, release the exhaust

hangers located ahead of the left-hand side rear wheel, above the front of the rear subframe, and adjacent to the rear exhaust silencer (see illustration).
5 Undo the 2 metal clips and the 4 plastic nuts and remove the heat shield to the left of the tank (see illustration). With the exhaust hangers released, the shield can be fed over the exhaust pipe though this can be quite awkward and care should be taken not to bend the shield excessively.
6 Undo the clamps securing the fuel filler hose to the tank (see illustration).

7 Make a note of the correct positions and undo the fuel pipe unions located ahead of the tank (see illustration). Be prepared to collect escaping fuel.
8 Position a trolley jack under the centre of the tank. Insert a protective wooden pad between the jack head and tank base, then raise the jack to just take the weight of the tank.
9 Undo the clips securing the brake pipes to the tank retaining straps, and undo the strap retaining bolts. Prise out the plastic lugs that secure the straps to the fuel tank and remove the straps. Carefully lower the jack and tank

3.6 Undo the filler hose pipe clamp (arrowed)

3.7 Undo the fuel pipe unions ahead of the fuel tank

3.9a Rear tank strap left-hand side retaining bolt

3.9b Front tank strap left-hand side retaining bolt

3.9c Rear tank strap right-hand side retaining bolt

slightly. Disconnect the fuel pipes adjacent to the fuel filter and undo the wiring plug and pipe connections for the sender unit located on top of the tank, along with the breather hose **(see illustrations)**.

10 Lower the jack and tank, and remove the tank from under the car.

11 If the tank is contaminated with sediment or water, remove the gauge sender unit and the fuel pump. Swill the tank out with clean fuel.

12 The tank is moulded from a synthetic material and if damaged, it should be renewed. However, in certain cases it may be possible to have small leaks or minor damage repaired. Seek the advice of a dealer or suitable specialist concerning tank repair.

13 If a new tank is to be fitted, transfer all the components from the old tank to the new. Always renew the seals and plastic nuts securing the fuel pump and gauge sender unit. Once used, they may not seat and seal properly on a new tank.

Refitting

14 Refitting is a reversal of removal. On completion, refill the tank with fuel and check exhaustively for signs of leakage before driving the car on the road.

4 Accelerator pedal – removal and refitting

Removal

1 Undo the two screws and remove the

trim panel above the pedals in the driver's footwell.

2 Undo the 3 nuts securing the assembly to the bulkhead **(see illustration)**.

3 Release the cable-tie, and disconnect the position sensor wiring plug as the pedal assembly is removed. No further dismantling of the assembly is recommended.

Refitting

4 Refit by reversing the removal operations.

5 Fuel injection system – general information

The system is under the overall control of the electronic diesel control (EDC) system, which also controls the preheating system (see Chapter 5B).

Fuel is supplied from the rear-mounted fuel tank, via an electrically-powered lift pump (controlled by the central electronic module) and fuel filter, to the fuel injection pump. The fuel injection pump supplies fuel under high pressure to the common fuel rail. The fuel rail provides a reservoir of fuel under pressure ready for the injectors to deliver direct to the combustion chamber. The individual fuel injectors incorporate solenoids which, when operated, allow the high-pressure fuel to be injected. The solenoids are controlled by the EDC electric control module (ECM). The fuel injection pump purely provides high pressure fuel. The timing and duration of the injection is controlled by the ECM, based on the

information received from the various sensors. In order to increase combustion efficiency and reduce combustion noise (diesel 'knock'), a small amount of fuel is injected before the main injection takes place – this is known as pre- or pilot-injection. The fuel filter may also incorporate a heater element and a temperature sensor – if so this is activated at temperatures below -3°C and deactivated at 5°C.

Additionally, the engine management ECM activates the preheating system (Chapter 5B), and the exhaust gas recirculation (EGR) system (see Chapter 4B).

The system uses the following sensors.

a) *Crankshaft sensor – informs the ECM of the crankshaft speed and position.*

b) *Coolant temperature sensor – informs the ECM of engine temperature.*

c) *Mass airflow/intake air temperature sensor – informs the ECM of the mass and temperature of air entering the intake tract.*

d) *Wheel speed sensor – informs the ECM of the vehicle speed.*

e) *Accelerator pedal position sensor – informs the ECM of throttle position, and the rate of throttle opening/closing.*

f) *Fuel high-pressure sensor – informs the ECM of the pressure of the fuel in the common rail.*

g) *Camshaft position sensor – informs the ECM of the camshaft position so that the engine firing sequence can be established.*

h) *Brake light switch – informs the ECM when the brakes are being applied.*

3.9d Front tank strap right-hand side retaining bolt and brake pipe clips

3.9e Breather hose connection on top of the fuel tank

4.2 Throttle pedal securing nuts

i) *Manifold absolute pressure sensor – informs the ECM of the boost pressure generated by the turbocharger.*

j) *Air conditioning pressure sensor – informs the ECM of the high-pressure side of the air conditioning circuit, in case a raised idle speed is required to compensate for compressor load.*

On all models, a 'drive-by-wire' throttle control system is used. The accelerator pedal is not physically connected to the fuel injection pump with a traditional cable, but instead is monitored by a dual potentiometer mounted on the pedal assembly, which provides the engine control module (ECM) with a signal relating to accelerator pedal movement.

The signals from the various sensors are processed by the ECM, and the optimum fuel quantity and injection timing settings are selected for the prevailing engine operating conditions.

Catalytic converter(s), a particulate filter (depending on model and market) and an exhaust gas recirculation (EGR) system are fitted, to reduce harmful exhaust gas emissions. Details of this and other emissions control system equipment are given in Chapter 4B.

If there is an abnormality in any of the readings obtained from any sensor, the ECM enters its back-up mode. In this event, the ECM ignores the abnormal sensor signal, and assumes a pre-programmed value which will allow the engine to continue running (albeit at reduced efficiency). If the ECM enters this back-up mode, the warning light on the instrument panel will come on, and the relevant

fault code will be stored in the ECM memory.

If the warning light comes on, the vehicle should be taken to a Volvo dealer or specialist at the earliest opportunity. A complete test of the electronic diesel control (EDC) system can then be carried out, using a special electronic test unit which is simply plugged into the system's diagnostic connector. The connector is located below the driver's side of the facia above the pedals **(see illustration)**.

6 Fuel system – priming and bleeding

1 Volvo state that no priming or bleeding is required, as the system is self-bleeding. However, If the vehicle has run out of diesel, or major parts of the fuel system have been disturbed, replenish the tank or check there is sufficient fuel in the tank (as applicable) then operate the fuel tank-mounted pump for 1 to 2 minutes by inserting the remote unit and briefly pressing the 'start/stop' button, prior to attempting to start the engine. This should ensure sufficient fuel reaches the engine-mounted pump prior to starting.

7 Fuel gauge sender/pump units – removal and refitting

Note: *Observe the precautions in Section 1 before working on any component in the fuel system.*

Removal

1 Disconnect the battery negative lead (see Chapter 5A).

2 Remove the fuel tank as described in Section 3.

3 Make a note of the correct position, then remove the wiring plug and use a screwdriver to depress the clips and disconnect the fuel hoses from the top of the sender unit. Note the position of any seals and be prepared for fuel spillage as the hoses are removed **(see illustration)**.

4 Note the alignment marks between the sender unit and the tank, then remove the locking ring. Volvo use a specific tool (999 7093) but the locking ring can be removed using a suitable home-made tool or a proprietary remover purchased from a motor factors **(see illustrations)**.

5 Carefully withdraw the assembly from the tank, taking care not to bend or damage the float arm. Recover the seal between sender unit and tank **(see illustration)**.

Refitting

6 Refitting is a reversal of removal, bearing in mind the following points:

a) *Use a new seal, ensuring it is seated correctly, smeared with petroleum jelly.*

b) *Take care when lowering the assembly into the tank not to bend or damage the float arm.*

c) *Note the alignment marks when refitting the sender.*

5.9 The diagnostic connector is located on the driver's side of the facia

7.3 Disconnect the fuel hoses on top of the sender unit

7.4a Sender unit alignment marks

7.4b Remove the sender locking ring using a suitable tool . . .

7.4c . . . or a home-made equivalent

7.5 Withdraw the sender unit from the fuel tank

8 Fuel injection system – testing and adjustment

Testing

1 If a fault appears in the fuel injection system, first ensure that all the system wiring connectors are securely connected and free from corrosion. Ensure that the fault is not due to poor maintenance; ie, check that the air cleaner filter element is clean, that the cylinder compression pressures are correct (see Chapter 2A, 2B or 2C), and that the engine breather hoses are clear and undamaged.
2 If the engine will not start, check the condition of the glow plugs (see Chapter 5B).
3 If these checks fail to reveal the cause of the problem, the vehicle should be taken to a Volvo dealer or specialist for testing using special electronic equipment which is plugged into the diagnostic connector. The tester should locate the fault quickly and simply, avoiding the need to test all the system components individually, which is time-consuming, and also carries a risk of damaging the ECM.

Adjustment

4 The engine idle speed, maximum speed and fuel injection pump timing are all controlled by the ECM. Whilst in theory it is possible to check the settings, if they are found to be in need of adjustment, the car will have to be taken to a suitably-equipped Volvo dealer or specialist. They will have access to the necessary diagnostic equipment required to test and (where possible) adjust the settings.

9 Fuel injection pump – removal and refitting

Caution: Be careful not to allow dirt into the injection pump or injector pipes during this procedure.
Note: *Any rigid high-pressure fuel pipes disturbed must be renewed.*

Removal

1 Disconnect the battery negative lead (see Chapter 5A). On 5-cylinder engines, remove the battery as described in Chapter 5A.
2 Remove the plastic cover from the top of the engine, by pulling it straight up from its mountings.
3 Remove the air cleaner assembly as described in Section 2.

1.6 litre engine

4 Remove the timing belt as described in Chapter 2A.
5 Remove the EGR cooler as described in Chapter 4B.
6 Undo the 2 union bolts and remove the pipe at the rear of the engine above the high-pressure fuel pump.
7 Undo the wiring plug and undo the wiring loom bracket bolts.
8 Disconnect the wiring plug from the high-pressure fuel pump. Undo the 4 bolts and remove the plate around the wiring connection,
9 Undo the union nuts and remove the high-pressure fuel pipe between the fuel common rail and the high-pressure pump. Plug the openings to prevent contamination.
10 Undo the 4 bolts and remove the bracket at the rear of the high-pressure fuel pump.
11 Depress the release buttons and disconnect the fuel supply and return hoses from the pump. Note that the hoses may have a release button on each side of the fitting. Plug the openings to prevent contamination.
12 Hold the pump sprocket stationary, and loosen the centre nut securing it to the pump shaft.
13 The fuel pump sprocket is a taper fit on the pump shaft and it will be necessary to make up a tool to release it from the taper. Partially unscrew the sprocket retaining nut, fit the home-made tool, and secure it to the sprocket with two 7.0 mm bolts and nuts. Prevent the sprocket from rotating as before, and screw down the nuts, forcing the sprocket off the shaft taper.
14 Once the taper is released, remove the tool, unscrew the nut fully, and remove the sprocket from the pump shaft.

15 Undo the three bolts, and remove the pump from the mounting bracket.

2.0 litre 4-cylinder engine

16 Remove the vacuum pump as described in Chapter 9.
17 Undo the unions and remove the high-pressure fuel pipe between the pump and the fuel rail (see illustration). Discard the pipe, a new one must be fitted.
18 Note their fitted positions, depress the release tabs, and disconnect the fuel supply and return pipes from the pump (see illustrations). Be prepared for fuel spillage. Plug the openings to prevent contamination.
19 Note their fitted positions, and disconnect the wiring plugs from the pump.
20 Undo the 3 retaining bolts and pull the pump from the cylinder head (see illustration). Discard the gasket.

5-cylinder engines

21 Slacken the unions, then remove the high-pressure fuel pipe between the pump and the common (fuel) rail. Discard the pipe, a new one must be fitted. Plug or cover the fuel rail and pump ports to prevent dirt ingress.
22 Release the clamps and disconnect the supply and return hoses from the pump. If the metal hose clamps are damaged during removal, update them with traditional worm-drive clamps. Plug or seal the pump ports to prevent dirt ingress.
23 Disconnect sensor wiring plugs from the pump.
24 Remove the three retaining screws, and remove the fuel pump. Recover the connecting

9.17 Remove the high-pressure pipe between the pump and the fuel rail

9.18a Disconnect the fuel supply . . .

9.18b . . . and return hoses from the pump

9.20 Fuel pump retaining bolts on 2.0 litre 4-cylinder engines

9.24a Pump retaining screws on 5-cylinder engines

9.24b Recover the connecting piece between the end of the camshaft and the pump drive

piece between the end of the camshaft and the pump drive – this is easily lost as the pump is removed **(see illustrations)**. Discard the seal, a new one must be fitted. With the exception of the swirl control valve (see Section 11), no internal components of the pump are available. If the pump is faulty, the complete unit may have to be renewed – consult a Volvo dealer or specialist.

Caution: Do not rotate the pump once removed – it's important that it retains its original position if refitted.

Refitting

25 Ensure that the mating surfaces of the pump and engine are clean and dry, and fit a new O-ring seal where appropriate. Lubricate the seal with clean engine oil.
26 Position the fuel pump, ensuring any connecting piece is in place, then tighten the mounting screws to the specified torque.
27 Reconnect the fuel supply and return

hoses to the pump, and secure them with new clamps.
28 Fit the new high-pressure fuel pipe between the pump and common rail, then tighten to the specified torque, using a crow's-foot adapter **(see illustration)**.
29 The remainder of refitting is a reversal of removal, bearing in mind the following points:
a) *Prior to starting the engine, insert the remote unit and press the 'Start' button briefly. This activates the tank-mounted pump, and ensures sufficient fuel reaches the injection pump for lubrication purposes prior to starting.*
b) *Depress the accelerator pedal to the floor then start the engine as normal (this may take longer than usual – operate the starter in ten second bursts with 5 seconds rest in between each operation). Run the engine at a fast idle speed for a minute or so to purge any remaining trapped air from the fuel lines. After this time the engine should idle smoothly at a constant speed.*

c) *Once the engine has started, thoroughly check for fuel leaks from the disturbed pipes/hoses.*

10 Fuel injectors – removal and refitting

Caution: Be careful not to allow dirt into the injection pump or injector pipes during this procedure.

Removal

1 Remove the plastic cover from the top of the engine by pulling it straight up from its mountings.
2 Make sure the areas around the high-pressure fuel pipe unions from the fuel rail to the injectors are scrupulously clean and free from debris, etc. If possible, use a vacuum cleaner and a degreaser to clean the area.
3 Depending on the engine fitted, remove

9.24c The pump connecting piece must align with the slots in the end of the inlet camshaft

9.28 Use a crows-foot adapter to tighten the pipe union, and a second spanner to counterhold the pump port. Do not allow the pump port to rotate

10.4 Depress the clip and disconnect the wiring plugs from the injectors

10.5 Prise out the clip and pull the return pipe from each injector

10.6a Undo the pipe union on the common rail

10.6b Use a second spanner to prevent the port on the injector from turning whilst slackening the union

components until the injectors become accessible with reference to the relevant chapters.

4 Disconnect the wiring plugs from the top of each injector **(see illustration)**.

5 Extract the retaining clip and disconnect the leak-off pipe from each injector **(see illustration)**.

6 Undo the unions, then remove the high-pressure fuel pipes from the fuel rail to the injectors. Discard the fuel pipes, new ones

must be fitted. Use a second spanner on the on the injector port to counterhold when slackening the pipe union **(see illustrations)**. Be prepared for fuel spillage, and plug/cover the ports in the injectors and fuel rail to prevent contamination.

7 Unscrew the 2 screws/nuts securing each injector (complete with spacers where fitted) and remove the injectors **(see illustration)**.

8 Slide the washers from the end of each injector. Discard the washers – new ones must be fitted. Cover the injector hole in the cylinder head to prevent dirt ingress **(see illustration)**.

9 If the injectors are to be refitted, plug all openings, and store them upright in their original order. They must be refitted to their original positions **(see illustration)**.

10.7 Injector retaining screws (arrowed)

10.8 Slide the washer from the end of the injector

10.9 The injectors should be stored upright

10.11a Fit the new clamp ring . . .

10.11b . . . and washer

10.11c We fabricated a tool out of sheet metal to allow the circlip to slide over the end of the injector

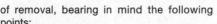

10.11d The circlip must locate in the groove

Refitting

10 Ensure that the injectors and seats in cylinder head are clean, dry and free from soot. It's essential the sealing surfaces are dirt-free, otherwise leakage will occur.

11 Fit new clamp rings, washers, circlips (where applicable) **(see illustrations)** and sealing washers to the injectors, and refit them to the cylinder head.

12 Fit new rigid high-pressure pipes between the common rail and the injectors. Starting at the common rail, tighten the pipe unions to the specified torque. Repeat this procedure on the pipe unions at the injectors. Use a second open-ended spanner to counterhold the injector ports whilst tightening the pipe unions.

13 The remainder of refitting is a reversal

of removal, bearing in mind the following points:

a) Check the condition of the fuel return hoses, and renew if any appear damaged or perished.

b) Depending on the engine fitted, different 'classes' of injector may be available as spare parts. You should refer to a Volvo dealer or parts specialist before purchasing.

c) If new injectors are fitted, new software may need to be downloaded to the engine management ECM from Volvo. Entrust this task to a Volvo dealer or specialist.

d) Depress the accelerator pedal to the floor then start the engine as normal (this may take longer than usual – operate the starter in ten second bursts with

5 seconds rest in between each operation). Run the engine at a fast idle speed for a minute or so to purge any remaining trapped air from the fuel lines. After this time the engine should idle smoothly at a constant speed.

e) Once the engine has started, thoroughly check for fuel leaks from the disturbed pipes/hoses.

11 Electronic diesel control (EDC) system components – removal and refitting

Crankshaft position/ speed sensor

1.6 litre engine

1 Remove the plastic engine cover.

2 Unclip the hoses from their bracket on top of the upper pulley cover.

3 Remove the auxiliary drivebelt as described in Chapter 1.

4 Raise the front of the vehicle and support it securely on axle stands (see *Jacking and vehicle support*). Undo the fasteners and remove the engine undershield.

5 To lock the crankshaft, working underneath the engine, insert Volvo tool No 999 7169 into the hole in the right-hand face of the engine block casting over the lower section of the flywheel. Rotate the crankshaft until the tool engages in the corresponding hole in the flywheel.

6 Remove the crankshaft pulley as described in Chapter 2A.

7 Undo the securing bolts and remove the upper and lower pulley covers.

8 Disconnect the wiring plug, remove the retaining bolt, and carefully remove the sensor **(see illustration)**.

9 Refitting is the reverse of removal.

2.0 litre 4-cylinder engine

10 Slacken the right-hand front road wheel nuts, then raise the front of the vehicle and support it securely on axle stands (see *Jacking and vehicle support*). Remove the roadwheel.

11 Release the fasteners and remove the right-hand front wheel arch liner.

12 The sensor is located adjacent to the crankshaft pulley. Disconnect the sensor wiring plug.

13 Slacken and remove the retaining bolt and carefully remove the sensor **(see illustration)**.

14 Refitting is the reverse of removal, tightening the retaining bolt securely.

5-cylinder engines

15 Remove the EGR cooler and valve assembly, as described in Chapter 4B.

16 The sensor is located above the flywheel. Trace the wiring back from the sensor, and disconnect the wiring plug.

17 Slacken and remove the retaining bolt and

11.8 Crankshaft position sensor – 1.6 litre engine

11.13 Crankshaft position sensor – 2.0 litre 4-cylinder engine carefully remove the sensor from its mounting **(see illustration)**.

18 Refitting is the reverse of removal, tightening the retaining bolt securely.

Mass airflow/ intake air temperature sensor

19 The location of the sensor, in the air intake pipe close to the air cleaner housing, is similar for all models.

20 Ensure the ignition is switched off then release the retaining clip and disconnect the wiring connector from the airflow sensor **(see illustration)**.

21 Undo the screws then remove the airflow sensor from the air intake pipe, along with its sealing ring where fitted.

22 Refitting is the reverse of removal, lubricating the new sealing ring.

Coolant temperature sensor

23 Refer to Chapter 3 for removal and refitting details.

Accelerator pedal position sensor

24 The sensor is secured to the accelerator pedal. Refer to Section 4 of this Chapter on pedal removal. Note that at the time of writing, the sensor was not available separately from the pedal assembly.

Manifold absolute pressure sensor

All except 2.4 litre engines

25 The MAP sensor is mounted on the inlet manifold **(see illustrations)**.

26 Pull the plastic cover on the top of the engine straight up from its mountings at the front and right-hand edges, then pull it forwards.

27 Ensure the ignition is switched off then disconnect the wiring connector from the sensor.

28 Slacken and remove the retaining bolt and remove the sensor from the vehicle.

2.4 litre engines

29 On 2.4 litre engines, the sensor is mounted on the intercooler. Remove the intercooler as described in Section 15, disconnect the wiring plug, remove the retaining bolt, and remove the sensor

30 Refitting is the reverse of removal, tightening the sensor retaining securely.

Turbo boost pressure sensor

31 On 2.4 litre engines the sensor is mounted on the intercooler outer pipe **(see illustration)**. On other engines it is located between the air cleaner assembly and the inlet manifold.

32 Ensure the ignition is switched off then disconnect the wiring connector from the sensor.

33 Slacken and remove the retaining bolt and remove the sensor from the vehicle.

34 Refitting is the reverse of removal, tightening the sensor retaining bolt securely.

11.17 Crankshaft position sensor – 5-cylinder engines

11.25a Manifold absolute pressure sensor on 2.0 litre 4-cylinder engine . . .

Brake light switch

35 The engine control module receives a signal from the brake light switch which indicates when the brakes are being applied. Brake light switch removal and refitting details can be found in Chapter 9.

Electronic control module (ECM)

Note: *If a new control module is fitted, it must be programmed using dedicated Volvo test equipment. Entrust this task to a Volvo dealer or suitably-equipped specialist.*

36 Disconnect the battery negative lead (see Chapter 5A), then wait at least 2 minutes before commencing work, to allow any stored electrical energy to dissipate.

37 The ECM box is located beneath the plenum cover at the rear of the engine bay. Ensure the area around the ECM is clean

11.31 Boost pressure sensor (arrowed)

11.20 Mass airflow sensor wiring plug (arrowed)

11.25b . . . and on the 1.6 litre engine

to avoid debris falling inside when it is removed.

38 To remove the ECM, remove the plenum cover as described in Chapter 12, Section 18. Release the locking catches and remove the wiring plugs – a cover may be fitted over the plugs on some models. Wrap the wiring plugs in clean plastic bags to prevent the ingress of dirt. Undo the 2 retaining bolts at the bulkhead and remove the ECM complete with its bracket **(see illustration)**. **Note:** *Do not touch the control module terminal pins with the bare hands – there is a danger of damage due to static electricity.*

39 Refitting is a reversal of removal.

Fuel pressure sensor

40 Remove the plastic cover from the top of the engine, by pulling it straight up from its mountings.

11.38 Release the locking catches and disconnect the wiring plugs

11.44 Fuel pressure sensor (arrowed)

11.57 Fuel pressure control valve (arrowed)

11.65 Fuel pressure control valve (arrowed) – pump-mounted valve

1.6 litre engine

41 The sensor is located at the left-hand end of the fuel rail. If this component fails it is possible that the fuel rail may need to be renewed so you should refer to a Volvo dealer or parts specialist.

2.0 litre 4-cylinder engine

42 Volvo advise that the sensor should not be loosened or removed. If this component fails it is possible that the fuel rail may need to be renewed so you should refer to a Volvo dealer or parts specialist.

5-cylinder engines

43 Remove the swirl control valve/motor as described in this Section.
44 Disconnect the wiring plug from the sensor, located at the right-hand end of the fuel rail (see illustration).
45 Unscrew the pressure sensor. Plug the openings to prevent contamination.
46 Refitting is a reversal of removal, tightening the sensor to the specified torque, where given.

Fuel pressure control valve

1.6 litre engine

47 It would appear that the valve on this engine is not available separately from the high-pressure pump. Refer to a Volvo dealer.

2.0 litre 4-cylinder engine

48 We were unable to confirm the process for removal on this engine so you should refer to a Volvo dealer.

5-cylinder engines – fuel rail-mounted valve

49 Pull the plastic cover on the top of the engine upwards to remove it.
50 Remove the air intake hose between the bonnet slam panel and the air cleaner.
51 Remove the hose from the EGR valve-to-the inlet manifold, and the inlet manifold hose.
52 Release the clamps/clips and move aside the crankcase breather pipes assembly.
53 Undo the unions and remove the high pressure fuel pipes from the fuel rail to the injectors and the pump. Discard the pipes, new ones must be fitted.
54 Disconnect the wiring plugs from the control valve and pressure sensor on the fuel rail.
55 Release the clamp and disconnect the fuel return hose from the fuel rail. Be prepared for fluid spillage, and plug the openings to prevent contamination.
56 Undo the 2 bolts and remove the fuel rail.
57 Unscrew the control valve from the fuel rail (see illustration).
58 Refitting is a reversal of removal.

2.0 litre 5-cylinder engine – pump-mounted valve

59 Pull the plastic cover on top of the engine upwards to remove it.
60 Clean the area around the valve on the pump, then disconnect the valve wiring plug.
61 Undo the 2 bolts and remove the valve from the pump. Be prepared for fluid

spillage. Plug or cover the opening to prevent contamination.
62 Refitting is a reversal of removal, lubricating the valve O-ring before fitting.

2.4 litre engine – pump-mounted valve

63 Remove the air cleaner assembly as described in Section 2.
64 Clean the area around the valve on the pump, then disconnect the valve wiring plug.
65 Undo the 3 Torx bolts and remove the valve by slowing rotating it and pulling it from the pump. Be prepared for fluid spillage. Plug or cover the openings to prevent contamination (see illustration).
66 Refitting is a reversal of removal, lubricating the valve O-ring before fitting.

Camshaft position sensor

67 Remove the plastic cover from over the top of the engine, by pulling it straight up from its mountings at the front and right-hand edges, then pull it forwards.
68 Ensure that the ignition is switched off, and disconnect the wiring plug from the sensor, located on the right-hand side of the cylinder head cover (see illustrations).
69 Undo the screw and remove the sensor.
70 To refit the sensor, ensure the mating face of the camshaft cover and sensor are clean and that the sensor is properly located on its dowels.
71 Fit the sensor into the cover, position the camshaft sprocket spoke in the upright position, then position the sensor so it's in contact with the camshaft sprocket. Pull the

11.68a Camshaft position sensor location on 1.6 litre engines . . .

11.68b . . . on 2.0 litre 4-cylinder engines . . .

11.68c . . . and on 5-cylinder engines

11.71 Refitting the camshaft position sensor on 2.0 litre 4-cylinder engines

11.73 Swirl valve motor control arm

11.74 Undo the bolts (arrowed) securing the swirl valve control motor

sensor back 1.2 mm and tighten the screw securely **(see illustration)**. To correctly set the distance between the sensor and pulley, new sensors are supplied with a small plastic tab – install the sensor so the tab is against the camshaft pulley.

Swirl control valve/motor

5-cylinder engines

72 Remove the plastic cover from over the top of the engine, by pulling it straight up from its mountings.
73 Pull the control arm from the valve/motor **(see illustration)**.
74 Undo the 2 bolts and remove the control valve/motor **(see illustration)**. Disconnect the wiring plug and No 1 glow plug as the assembly is withdrawn.
75 Refitting is a reversal of removal. Note that if a new valve/motor has been fitted, the values stored in the ECM must be reset using dedicated diagnostic equipment. Entrust this task to a Volvo dealer or suitably-equipped specialist.

Turbocharger boost control motor

76 Depending on the engine fitted the position of the variable vane within the turbocharger (and therefore the boost output) is controlled by an electric motor attached to the vane control arm **(see illustration)**. The motor is controlled by the engine management ECM. We were unable to confirm whether the motor is available separately from the turbocharger

so you should refer to a Volvo dealer or specialist.

Fuel temperature sensor

5-cylinder engines

Note: *We were unable to establish the removal process for other engines so you should refer to a Volvo dealer.*
77 Remove the plastic cover from over the top of the engine, by pulling it straight up from its mountings.
78 The sensor is located on the top/front edge of the high-pressure pump at the left-hand end of the cylinder head. Disconnect the sensor wiring plug **(see illustration)**.
79 Clean the area around the sensor, then unscrew it from the pump. Be prepared for fluid spillage. Plug the opening to prevent contamination.
80 Refitting is a reversal of removal, tightening the sensor to the specified torque.

Throttle body

81 Remove the plastic engine cover. Remove the air cleaner housing on 5-cylinder engines.
82 Slacken the clamps and disconnect the air hoses from the throttle body. Move the hoses to one side.
83 Unscrew any sensors, then undo the retaining bolts and remove the throttle body **(see illustration)**. Discard the gasket, a new one must be fitted.
84 Refitting is a reversal of removal. If a new throttle body has been fitted, the stored values in the engine management ECM must

be reset. Entrust this task to a Volvo dealer or suitably-equipped specialist.

12 Turbocharger – description and precautions

Description

A turbocharger increases engine efficiency by raising the pressure in the inlet manifold above atmospheric pressure. Instead of the air simply being sucked into the cylinders, it is forced in. Additional fuel is supplied by the injection pump in proportion to the increased air intake.

Energy for the operation of the turbocharger comes from the exhaust gas. The gas flows through a specially-shaped housing (the turbine housing) and in so doing spins the turbine wheel. The turbine wheel is attached to a shaft, at the end of which is another vaned wheel known as the compressor wheel. The compressor wheel spins in its own housing and compresses the inducted air on the way to the inlet manifold.

The compressed air passes through an intercooler. This is an air-to-air heat exchanger, mounted with the radiator at the front of the vehicle. The purpose of the intercooler is to remove some of the heat gained in being compressed from the inducted air. Because cooler air is denser, removal of this heat further increases engine efficiency.

The turbocharger has adjustable guide

11.76 Turbocharger boost control motor

11.78 The fuel temperature sensor is located on the high-pressure fuel pump

11.83 Throttle body retaining bolts (top two bolts arrowed)

vanes controlling the flow of exhaust gas into the turbine, the vanes being controlled by the engine management ECM. At lower engine speeds, the vanes close together, giving a smaller exhaust gas entry port, and therefore higher gas speed, which increases boost pressure at low engine speed. At high engine speed, the vanes are turned to give a larger exhaust gas entry port, and therefore lower gas speed, effectively maintaining a reasonably constant boost pressure over the engine rev range. This is known as a variable nozzle turbocharger (VNT).

The turbo shaft is pressure-lubricated by an oil feed pipe from the main oil gallery. The shaft 'floats' on a cushion of oil. A drain pipe returns the oil to the sump.

Precautions

● The turbocharger operates at extremely high speeds and temperatures. Certain precautions must be observed to avoid

premature failure of the turbo or injury to the operator.
● Do not operate the turbo with any parts exposed. Foreign objects falling onto the rotating vanes could cause excessive damage and (if ejected) personal injury.
● Do not race the engine immediately after start-up, especially if it is cold. Give the oil a few seconds to circulate.
● Always allow the engine to return to idle speed before switching it off – do not blip the throttle and switch off, as this will leave the turbo spinning without lubrication.
● Allow the engine to idle for several minutes before switching off after a high-speed run.
● Observe the recommended intervals for oil and filter changing, and use a reputable oil of the specified quality (see *Lubricants and fluids*). Neglect of oil changing, or use of inferior oil, can cause carbon formation on the turbo shaft and subsequent failure.

13 Turbocharger – removal and refitting

Note: *While the location of the turbocharger differs depending on the engine fitted (on the 1.6 litre engine it is mounted at the front of the engine, while on the other engines it is mounted at the rear), the process for removal is essentially similar. It will be necessary to remove components to gain access to the turbocharger, and you should refer to the relevant Chapters.*

Removal

1 Remove the plastic cover from over the top of the engine by pulling it straight up from its mountings.
2 Raise the front of the vehicle and support securely on axle stands (see *Jacking and vehicle support*).
3 Remove the catalytic converter/ particulate filter as described in Chapter 4B. It is secured to the turbocharger by a clamp or by bolts **(see illustrations)**.
4 It will be necessary to remove the air intake pipe at the turbocharger, and to undo the oil pipe unions **(see illustration)**.
5 Depending on the engine fitted, it may also be necessary to remove any heat shields **(see illustrations)**.
6 Disconnect the actuator wiring plug where appropriate, any hose or vacuum pipes at the turbocharger, and unbolt any component support brackets.
7 Undo the securing bolts and separate the turbocharger from the exhaust manifold **(see illustrations)**. Note that on 2.4 litre engines, the turbocharger is integral with the exhaust manifold. Undo the 10 retaining nuts and remove the manifold and turbocharger from beneath the vehicle. Discard the exhaust manifold gasket – a new one must be fitted.

Refitting

8 Refitting is a reversal of removal, noting the following points:
   a) Ensure all mating surfaces are clean and dry.
   b) Renew all O-rings, seals and gaskets.

13.3a Undo the pipe securing clamp . . .

13.3b . . . or securing bolts

13.4 Turbocharger oil pipe union

13.5a Turbocharger heat shield

13.5b Exhaust manifold/turbocharger heat shield

13.7a Turbocharger mounting bolts (arrowed)

13.7b Turbocharger-to-exhaust manifold mounting bolts (arrowed)

c) Tighten all fasteners to the specified torque where available.
d) Fit new exhaust front section/catalytic converter-to-turbocharger nuts/bolts where appropriate.

14 Turbocharger – examination and overhaul

1 With the turbocharger removed, inspect the housing for cracks or other visible damage.
2 Spin the turbine or the compressor wheel to verify that the shaft is intact and to feel for excessive shake or roughness. Some play is normal since in use the shaft is 'floating' on a film of oil. Check that the wheel vanes are undamaged.
3 The wastegate and actuator are integral with the turbocharger, and cannot be checked or renewed separately. Consult a Volvo dealer or other specialist if it is thought that the wastegate may be faulty.
4 If the exhaust or induction passages are oil-contaminated, the turbo shaft oil seals have probably failed. (On the induction side, this will also have contaminated the intercooler, where applicable, which if necessary should be flushed with a suitable solvent.)
5 No DIY repair of the turbo is possible. A new unit may be available on an exchange basis.

15 Intercooler – removal and refitting

1 Raise the front of the car and support securely on axle stands (see *Jacking and vehicle support*) and remove the engine undershield.
2 Support the radiator as described in Chapter 3. Undo the 2 bolts at each end and remove the radiator support beam **(see illustration)**.

3 Disconnect the intercooler pipes from their locations within the engine bay.
4 Undo the 2 mounting bolts at the bottom of the radiator and withdraw the intercooler from beneath the vehicle. Disconnect any wiring plugs as the unit is withdrawn **(see illustrations)**.
5 Refitting is a reversal of removal.

16 Manifolds – removal and refitting

Inlet manifold

1 The inlet manifold is integral with the cylinder head cover – refer to Chapter 2A, 2B or 2C.

Exhaust manifold

Note: *On 2.4 litre engines, the exhaust manifold is integral with the turbocharger and cannot be removed separately. Refer to Section 13 for turbocharger removal.*
2 Disconnect the battery as described in Chapter 5A.
3 Remove the turbocharger as described in Section 13.
4 On the 2.0 litre 4-cylinder engine, remove the EGR cooler as described in Chapter 4B.
5 Slacken and remove the nuts retaining the exhaust manifold, and remove it from the engine. Discard the gasket, a new one must be fitted.
6 Examine all the manifold studs for signs of damage and corrosion; remove all traces of corrosion, and repair or renew any damaged studs.
7 Ensure the mating surfaces of the exhaust manifold and cylinder head are clean and dry. Position a new gasket, and refit the exhaust manifold to the cylinder head. Tighten the nuts to the specified torque.

15.2 Undo the radiator support beam bolts (left-hand side bolts arrowed)

8 The remainder of refitting is a reversal of removal, noting the following points:
a) Tighten all fasteners to their specified torque where available. Note that on the 2.0 litre 5-cylinder engine, the torque value for the 2 nuts at each end of the manifold differ from the those at the top and bottom.
b) Check and, if necessary, top-up the oil level as described in 'Weekly checks'.

17 Exhaust system – general information and component renewal

General information

1 The exhaust system consists of two sections: the front pipe with the catalytic converter, and the rear section with the intermediate and rear silencers. A particulate filter is available on some vehicles depending on the engine fitted.
2 If required, the rear silencer can be renewed independently of the remainder of the system, by cutting the old silencer from the pipe, and slipping the new one over the cut end.
3 The exhaust system is joined together by

15.4a Undo the intercooler mounting bolts (left-hand side bolt arrowed) . . .

15.4b . . . and withdraw the intercooler from beneath the vehicle

a mixture of flanged, or sliding joints. Apply plenty of penetrating fluid to the fasteners prior to removal, undo the fasteners, unhook the rubber mountings, and manoeuvre the system from under the vehicle.

Rear silencer

4 If the rear silencer is the only part of the system requiring renewal, cut the old silencer from the rear section of the system using pipe cutters or a hacksaw. The exact point where the cut is made can differ depending on the engine fitted so you should check with a Volvo dealer before cutting the system. Free the silencer from its mountings, and remove it from the vehicle.

5 Clean up and de-burr the end of the existing exhaust pipe with a file/emery tape, etc.

6 Replacement rear silencers are available which slip over the end of the existing exhaust pipe, and are clamped in place. Slip the new silencer over the pipe, engage the rubber silencer mountings, then tighten the pipe clamp securely.

7 Each section is refitted by reversing the removal sequence, noting the following points:

a) *Ensure that all traces of corrosion have been removed from the flanges and renew all gaskets.*
b) *Inspect the rubber mountings for signs of damage or deterioration, and renew as necessary.*
c) *Prior to tightening the exhaust system fasteners to the specified torque, ensure that all rubber mountings are correctly located, and that there is adequate clearance between the exhaust system and vehicle underbody.*

18 Swirl duct – removal and refitting

Note: *5-cylinder engines only.*

Removal

1 The swirl duct is fitted to the cylinder head to control the flow of air into the inlet tracts. The duct contains valves which alter the flow of air depending on engine speed and load, generating a swirl motion for increased combustion efficiency and lower exhaust

18.2 Swirl valve motor control arm

emissions. To remove the duct, begin by removing the cylinder head cover/inlet manifold as described in Chapter 2C.

2 Disconnect the actuating arm from the swirl control motor **(see illustration)**.

3 Undo the bolts and remove the swirl duct.

Refitting

4 Refitting is a reversal of removal, tightening all fasteners securely.

Chapter 4 Part B:
Emission control systems

Contents

Degrees of difficulty

Easy, suitable for novice with little experience	Fairly easy, suitable for beginner with some experience	Fairly difficult, suitable for competent DIY mechanic	Difficult, suitable for experienced DIY mechanic	Very difficult, suitable for expert DIY or professional

Specifications

Torque wrench settings	Nm	lbf ft
Catalytic converter to turbocharger*	25	18
Exhaust front pipe to intermediate pipe:		
4-cylinder engines	50	37
5-cylinder engines	24	18
Exhaust front pipe-to-flange nuts/bolts*	50	37
Exhaust gas temperature sensor:		
4-cylinder engines	30	22
5-cylinder engines	45	33
EGR valve/cooler:		
M6 bolts	10	7
M8 bolts	24	18
M12 bolts	50	37
Oil separator bolts	20	15
Oxygen sensor	45	33

1 General information

All models covered by this manual have various features built into the fuel and exhaust systems to help minimise harmful emissions. These features fall broadly into three categories; crankcase emission control, evaporative emission control, and exhaust emission control. Additionally, some models may be equipped with a particulate emission filter which uses a porous silicon carbide substrate to trap particulates of carbon as the exhaust gases pass through.

The main features of these systems are as follows.

Crankcase emission control

Crankcase gases are taken via hoses from the cylinder head and the cylinder block, into a cyclone type oil separator. Here, the gases are forced to twist past two cones. As the gases pass the cones, oil is thrown out and condenses on the walls of the separator, where it then returns to the sump. The gases are admitted into the intake system, via a pressure limiting valve.

Exhaust gas recirculation system

This system is designed to recirculate small quantities of exhaust gas into the inlet tract, and therefore into the combustion process. This reduces the level of oxides of nitrogen present in the final exhaust gas which is released into the atmosphere.

The volume of exhaust gas recirculated is controlled by an electrically-operated solenoid valve. The solenoid, valve and cooler is an assembly mounted at the left-hand end of the cylinder head between the inlet and exhaust manifold.

The EGR system is controlled by the engine management ECM, which receives information on engine operating parameters from its various sensors.

Particulate filter system

The particulate filter is combined with the catalytic converter in the exhaust system, and its purpose it to trap particulates of carbon (soot) as the exhaust gases pass through, in order to comply with latest emission regulations.

The filter can be automatically regenerated (cleaned) by the system's ECM on-board the vehicle. The engine's high-pressure injection system is utilised to inject fuel into the exhaust gases during the post-injection period; this causes the filter temperature to increase sufficient to oxidise the particulates, leaving an ash residue.

2 Catalytic converter – general information and precautions

The catalytic converter is a reliable and simple device, which needs no maintenance in itself, but there are some facts of which an owner should be aware if the converter is to function properly for its full service life.

a) *Always keep the fuel system well-maintained in accordance with the manufacturer's schedule (see Chapter 1).*

b) *If the engine develops a misfire, do not drive the vehicle at all (or at least as little as possible) until the fault is cured.*

c) *DO NOT push – or tow-start the vehicle – this will soak the catalytic converter in unburned fuel, causing it to overheat when the engine does start.*

d) *DO NOT switch off the ignition at high engine speeds, ie, do not blip the throttle immediately before switching off.*

e) *DO NOT use fuel or engine oil additives – these may contain substances harmful to the catalytic converter.*

f) *DO NOT continue to use the vehicle if the engine burns oil to the extent of leaving a visible trail of blue smoke.*

g) *Remember that the catalytic converter operates at very high temperatures. DO NOT, therefore, park the vehicle in dry undergrowth, over long grass or piles of dead leaves, after a long run.*

h) *Remember that the catalytic converter is FRAGILE. Do not strike it with tools during servicing work.*

i) *The catalytic converter used on a well-maintained and well-driven vehicle should last for between 50 000 and 100 000 miles. If the converter is no longer effective, it must be renewed.*

3 Crankcase emission control system – checking and component renewal

Checking

1 The components of this system require no attention other than to check that the hoses are clear and undamaged.

Oil separator renewal

2 Where fitted the oil separator is located on the front facing side of the cylinder block, below the inlet manifold.

3 Remove the clips securing the connecting hoses to the separator unit. If the clips are in less than perfect condition, obtain new clips for reassembly.

4 Undo the retaining bolts and remove the unit from the engine.

5 Refit the oil separator using a reversal of removal.

4 Exhaust emission control systems – checking and component renewal

Checking

1 Checking of the system as a whole entails a close visual inspection of all hoses, pipes and connections for condition and security. Apart from this, any known or suspected faults should be attended to by a Volvo dealer or suitably-equipped specialist.

Oxygen sensor

Note: *The sensor is delicate, and will not work if it is dropped or knocked, if its power supply is disrupted, or if any cleaning materials are used on it. The sensor is located in the exhaust manifold or front section of the exhaust system depending on the engine fitted.*

2 Remove the plastic engine cover.

3 Disconnect the oxygen sensor wiring connector, unscrew the sensor and collect the sealing washer (where fitted) **(see illustration)**.

4 On refitting, clean the sealing washer (where fitted) and renew it if it is damaged or worn. Apply a smear of anti-seize compound to the sensor's threads, then refit the sensor, tightening it to the specified torque. Reconnect the wiring and secure with cable-ties where applicable.

Catalytic converter

Note: *The catalytic converter is part of the exhaust system front section, and depending on model, may be combined with a particulate filter. The process for renewal differs slightly depending on the engine fitted, but the following is essentially correct.*

5 Remove the plastic engine cover and the engine undershield.

6 Unscrew the exhaust gas temperature and oxygen sensors from the catalytic convertor, and where appropriate unscrew the pressure

4.3 Oxygen sensor

4.6 Differential pressure pipe

4.9 Exhaust clamp nuts (arrowed)

pipes for the differential pressure sensor **(see illustration)**.

7 On the 1.6 litre engine, remove the air pipe between the air cleaner housing and the turbocharger and the charge air pipe at the front of the engine.

8 Where fitted remove the heat shield over the exhaust manifold/turbocharger.

9 Undo the clamp or nuts and disconnect the exhaust pipe from the turbocharger. Undo the nuts securing the exhaust rear section to the front section **(see illustration)**.

10 On 2.0 and 2.4 litre engines, unhook the exhaust hangers at the rear subframe mounting bracket, undo the 2 bolts each side and remove the crossmember at the rear of the subframe **(see illustration)**.

11 Ensure that all pipes and hoses have been disconnected and that any mounting brackets have been released and withdraw the catalytic converter from beneath the vehicle.

12 Refitting is a reversal of removal, noting the following points:

a) Ensure that all traces of corrosion have

been removed from the flanges and renew all gaskets.

b) Inspect the rubber mountings for signs of damage or deterioration, and renew as necessary.

c) Prior to the tightening the exhaust system fasteners to the specified torque, ensure that all rubber mountings are correctly located, and that there is adequate clearance between the exhaust system and vehicle underbody.

EGR valve/cooler

13 Depending on the engine fitted, the EGR valve/cooler is located at the left-hand end or at the rear of the engine **(see illustration)**.

14 With the plastic engine cover removed, refer to the relevant Chapters for component removal until the EGR valve/cooler becomes accessible.

15 In all cases it will be necessary to disconnect the wiring plug to the EGR actuator and to remove any pipes or hoses connected to the unit along with any pipe clamps **(see illustration)**. Note that on 5-cylinder engines,

4.10 Exhaust hangers at the rear of the front subframe

the EGR valve is integral with the EGR cooler and the cooling system should be drained before removal.

16 Ensuring that no other connections remain, the mounting bolts can now be undone and the unit removed.

17 To remove the EGR cooler, drain the cooling system as described in Chapter 1,

4.13 EGR valve/cooler

4.15 EGR valve pipe clamp (arrowed)

4.17a Disconnect the EGR cooler water pipes (arrowed)

4.17b EGR water cooler pipe fitting (arrowed) on some engines

undo the clips, and release the water pipes from the cooler **(see illustrations)**.

18 Undo the cooler mounting bolts and remove the unit.

19 Refitting of both units is the reversal of removal, renewing any gaskets where applicable. If a new valve is fitted, it may require resetting and this task should be entrusted to a Volvo dealer or suitably-equipped specialist. Refill the cooling system as described in Chapter 1.

Particulate filter

20 See the Section above for catalytic converter renewal.

Particulate filter differential pressure sensor

Note: *After renewing the pressure differential sensor, the values for the sensor stored in the ECM must be adapted. This requires access to dedicated Volvo diagnostic equipment, and should be entrusted to a Volvo dealer or suitably-equipped specialist.*

21 The sensor is located on the side of the air cleaner housing on the 1.6 litre engine, or at the rear of the cylinder head **(see illustration)**.

22 On all engines disconnect the sensor wiring plug, undo the clips and disconnect the hoses. The sensor can now be withdrawn.

4.21 Particulate filter differential pressure sensor (arrowed) located at the rear of the cylinder head

Chapter 5 Part A:
Starting and charging systems

Contents

Degrees of difficulty

Easy, suitable for novice with little experience	**Fairly easy,** suitable for beginner with some experience	**Fairly difficult,** suitable for competent DIY mechanic	**Difficult,** suitable for experienced DIY mechanic	**Very difficult,** suitable for expert DIY or professional

Specifications

System type	12 volt, negative earth

Battery

Type	Low-maintenance or maintenance-free sealed for life
Capacity	60 to 90 Ah (depending on model)

Alternator

Type	Bosch
Output	120 or 140 A
Brush minimum length	5.0 mm

Starter motor

Type	Bosch 1.4, 2.0 or 2.2 kW

Torque wrench settings	Nm	lbf ft
Alternator mounting bolts	24	18
Alternator pulley	80	59
Starter motor mounting bolts:		
1.6 litre engine	35	26
All other engines	50	37

1 General information and precautions

General information

The engine electrical system consists mainly of the charging and starting systems. Because of their engine-related functions, these components are covered separately from the body electrical devices such as the lights, instruments, etc (which are covered in Chapter 12). Information on the diesel preheating system is covered in Chapter 5B.

The electrical system is of the 12 volt negative earth type.

The battery is of the low-maintenance or maintenance-free (sealed for life) type, and is charged by the alternator, which is belt-driven from the crankshaft pulley.

The starter motor is of the pre-engaged type, incorporating an integral solenoid. On starting, the solenoid moves the drive pinion into engagement with the flywheel ring gear before the starter motor is energised. Once the engine has started, a one-way clutch prevents the motor armature being driven by the engine until the pinion disengages from the flywheel.

Further details of the various systems are given in the relevant Sections of this Chapter. While some repair procedures are given, the usual course of action is to renew the component concerned.

Precautions

Warning: It is necessary to take extra care when working on the electrical system to avoid damage to semi-conductor devices (diodes and transistors), and to avoid the risk of personal injury. In addition to the precautions given in 'Safety first!' observe the following when working on the system:
• *Always remove rings, watches, etc before working on the electrical system.* Even with the battery disconnected, capacitive discharge could occur if a component's live terminal is earthed through a metal object. This could cause a shock or nasty burn.
• *Do not reverse the battery connections.* Components such as the alternator, electronic control units, or any other components having semi-conductor circuitry could be irreparably damaged.
• *Never disconnect the battery terminals, the alternator, any electrical wiring or any test instruments when the engine is running.*
• *Do not allow the engine to turn the alternator when the alternator is not connected.*
• *Never test for alternator output by 'flashing' the output lead to earth.*
Always ensure that the battery negative lead is disconnected when working on the electrical system.

• If the engine is being started using jump leads and a slave battery, connect the batteries *positive-to-positive* and *negative-to-negative* (see *Jump starting*). This also applies when connecting a battery charger.
• *Never* use an ohmmeter of the type incorporating a hand-cranked generator for circuit or continuity testing.
• Before using electric-arc welding equipment on the car, *disconnect the battery, alternator and components such as the electronic control units* (where applicable) to protect them from the risk of damage.

2 Battery – testing and charging

Testing

Standard and low-maintenance battery

1 If the vehicle covers a small annual mileage, it is worthwhile checking the specific gravity of the electrolyte every three months to determine the state of charge of the battery. Use a hydrometer to make the check, and compare the results with the following table. Note that the specific gravity readings assume an electrolyte temperature of 15°C; for every 10°C below 15°C subtract 0.007. For every 10°C above 15°C add 0.007.

	Above 25°C	Below 25°C
Fully-charged	1.210 to 1.230	1.270 to 1.290
70% charged	1.170 to 1.190	1.230 to 1.250
Discharged	1.050 to 1.070	1.110 to 1.130

2 If the battery condition is suspect, first check the specific gravity of electrolyte in each cell. A variation of 0.040 or more between any cells indicates loss of electrolyte or deterioration of the internal plates.
3 If the specific gravity variation is 0.040 or more, the battery should be renewed. If the cell variation is satisfactory but the battery is discharged, it should be charged as described later in this Section.

Maintenance-free battery

4 In cases where a sealed for life maintenance-free battery is fitted, topping-up and testing of the electrolyte in each cell may not be possible (see Chapter 1, Section 10). The condition of the battery can therefore only be tested using a battery condition indicator or a voltmeter.
5 Certain models may be fitted with a maintenance-free battery, with a built-in charge condition indicator. The indicator is located in the top of the battery casing, and indicates the condition of the battery from its colour. The charge conditions denoted by the colour of the indicator should be printed on a label attached to the battery – if not, consult a Volvo dealer or automotive electrician for advice.
6 If testing the battery using a voltmeter, connect the voltmeter across the battery and

note the voltage. The test is only accurate if the battery has not been subjected to any kind of charge for the previous six hours. If this is not the case, switch on the headlights for 30 seconds, then wait four to five minutes before testing the battery after switching off the headlights. All other electrical circuits must be switched off, so check that the doors and tailgate are fully shut when making the test.
7 If the voltage reading is less than 12.2 volts, then the battery is discharged, whilst a reading of 12.2 to 12.4 volts indicates a partially-discharged condition.
8 If the battery is to be charged, remove it from the vehicle and charge it as described later in this section.

Charging

Note: *The following is intended as a guide only. Always refer to the manufacturer's recommendations (often printed on a label attached to the battery) before charging a battery.*

Standard and low-maintenance battery

9 Charge the battery at a rate equivalent to 10% of the battery capacity (eg, for a 45 Ah battery charge at 4.5 A) and continue to charge the battery at this rate until no further rise in specific gravity is noted over a four-hour period.
10 Alternatively, a trickle charger charging at the rate of 1.5 amps can safely be used overnight.
11 Especially rapid boost charges which are claimed to restore the power of the battery in 1 to 2 hours are not recommended, as they can cause serious damage to the battery plates through overheating. If the battery is completely flat, recharging should take at least 24 hours.
12 While charging the battery, note that the temperature of the electrolyte should never exceed 38°C.

Maintenance-free battery

13 This battery type takes considerably longer to fully recharge than the standard type, the time taken being dependent on the extent of discharge, but it can take anything up to three days.
14 A constant voltage type charger is required, to be set, when connected, to 13.9 to 14.9 volts with a charger current below 25 amps. Using this method, the battery should be useable within three hours, giving a voltage reading of 12.5 volts, but this is for a partially-discharged battery and, as mentioned, full charging can take far longer.
15 If the battery is to be charged from a fully-discharged state (condition reading less than 12.2 volts), have it recharged by your Volvo dealer or local automotive electrician, as the charge rate is higher, and constant supervision during charging is necessary.

3 Battery – removal and refitting

Caution: Wait at least 5 minutes after turning off the ignition switch before disconnect the battery. This is to allow sufficient time for the various control modules to store information.

Removal

1 Pull up the rubber seal located on the edge of the plenum cover, undo the clips and remove the battery cover **(see illustration)**.
2 Slacken the clamp bolt and disconnect the clamp from the battery negative (earth) terminal.
3 Undo the 2 bolts and disconnect the cables from the positive terminal **(see illustration)**.
4 Unclip the cable from the battery surround box and disconnect the breather pipe.
5 Unscrew the bolt and remove the battery retaining clamp, and lift the battery from its tray **(see illustrations)**.
6 If required, the battery tray can be removed by undoing the 4 retaining bolts **(see illustration)**.

Refitting

7 Position the battery in the tray, refit the retaining clamp and tighten the retaining bolt securely.
8 Reconnect the battery positive lead, followed by the negative lead. Smear a little petroleum jelly on the terminals.
9 Refit the battery cover, and the rubber seal.
10 When switching on the engine for the first time, stand outside the vehicle and reach in to start the engine, keeping clear of the airbag operating areas.

4 Charging system – testing

Note: *Refer to the warnings given in 'Safety first!' and in Section 1 of this Chapter before starting work.*

3.6 Remove the battery tray by undoing the four bolts (arrowed)

3.1 Undo the clips and remove the battery cover

3.5a Undo the battery clamp bolt . . .

1 If the ignition/no-charge warning light fails to illuminate when the ignition is switched on, first check the alternator wiring connections for security. If all is satisfactory, the alternator maybe at fault and should be renewed or taken to an auto-electrician for testing and repair.
2 If the ignition warning light illuminates when the engine is running, stop the engine and check that the drivebelt is correctly tensioned (see Chapter 1) and that the alternator connections are secure. If all is so far satisfactory, have the alternator checked by an auto-electrician for testing and repair.
3 If the alternator output is suspect even though the warning light functions correctly, the regulated voltage may be checked as follows.
4 Connect a voltmeter across the battery terminals and start the engine.
5 Increase the engine speed until the

5.5 Disconnect the wiring plugs (arrowed) from the alternator, and undo the lower mounting bolts (arrowed) . . .

3.3 Disconnect the cables from the battery positive terminal

3.5b . . . and lift the battery from its tray

voltmeter reading remains steady; the reading should be between 13.5 and 14.8 volts.
6 Switch on as many electrical accessories (eg, the headlights, heated rear window and heater blower) as possible, and check that the alternator maintains the regulated voltage between 13.5 and 14.8 volts.
7 If the regulated voltage is not as stated, the fault may be due to worn brushes, weak brush springs, a faulty voltage regulator, a faulty diode, a severed phase winding, or worn or damaged slip-rings. The brushes and slip-ring may be checked (see Section 6), but if the fault persists the alternator should be renewed or taken to an auto-electrician for testing and repair.

5 Alternator and pulley – removal and refitting

Alternator

1 Disconnect the battery negative lead (see Section 3)
2 Remove the plastic cover from the top of the engine.
3 Remove the auxiliary drivebelt as described in Chapter 1.
4 Disconnect the various wiring plugs and move the wiring loom to one side. Remove any components, with reference to the relevant chapter, until the alternator becomes accessible.
5 Disconnect the wiring multiplug and the lead from the terminal stud at the rear of the alternator **(see illustration)**

5.6 . . . and the upper mounting bolt

5.10a Use a special tool that engages with the splines in the shaft and pulley centre

5.10b Counterhold the shaft whilst unscrewing the pulley centre

6 Undo the upper and lower mounting bolts and remove the alternator **(see illustration)**.
7 Refitting is a reversal of removal, remembering to tighten the various fasteners to their specified torque where given.

Drive pulley

8 The alternator drive pulley is fitted with a one-way clutch to reduced wear and stress on the auxiliary drivebelt. In order to remove the pulley, a special tool (Volvo No 999 5760) will be required to hold the alternator shaft whilst unscrewing the pulley. An equivalent to this tool should be available from auto electrical specialists/automotive tool specialists.
9 Prise the plastic cap from the pulley.
10 Insert the special tool into the splines of the pulley, engaging the central Torx bit with the alternator shaft **(see illustrations)**. Unscrew the pulley anti-clockwise whilst

holding the shaft with the Torx bit, and remove the pulley.
11 Refitting is a reversal of removal, but tighten it securely using the special tool.

---

6 Alternator brush holder/ regulator module – renewal

1 Remove the alternator (see Section 5).
2 Place the alternator on a clean work surface, with the pulley facing down.
3 Undo the cover nuts and screws (there may be 2 or 3 depending on model), then lift the plastic cover from the rear of the alternator **(see illustration)**.
4 Undo the screws (3 or 4 depending on model) and carefully remove the voltage regulator/brush holder from the alternator **(see illustrations)**.

6.3 Prise off the plastic cap, undo the two nuts and one screw (arrowed), then lift off the plastic cover

6.4a Undo the three screws (arrowed) . . .

6.4b . . . and lift away the voltage regulator/brush holder

6.5 Measure the free length of the brushes

5 Measure the free length of the brushes **(see illustration)**. Check the measurement with the Specifications; renew the module if the brushes are worn below the minimum limit.
6 Clean and inspect the surfaces of the slip-rings, at the end of the alternator shaft. If they are excessively worn, or damaged, the alternator must be renewed.
7 Reassemble the alternator by following the dismantling procedure in reverse. On completion, refer to Section 5 and refit the alternator.

---

7 Starting system – testing

Note: *Refer to the precautions given in 'Safety first!' and in Section 1 of this Chapter before starting work.*
1 If the starter motor fails to operate when the 'Start' button is pressed, the following possible causes may be to blame:
  a) *The battery is faulty.*
  b) *The electrical connections between the switch, solenoid, battery and starter motor are somewhere failing to pass the necessary current from the battery through the starter to earth.*
  c) *The solenoid is faulty.*
  d) *The starter motor is mechanically or electrically defective.*
2 To check the battery, switch on the headlights. If they dim after a few seconds, this indicates that the battery is discharged – recharge (see Section 2) or renew the battery. If the headlights glow brightly, operate the ignition switch and observe the lights. If they dim, then this indicates that current is reaching the starter motor, therefore the fault must lie in the starter motor. If the lights continue to glow brightly (and no clicking sound can be heard from the starter motor solenoid), this indicates that there is a fault in the circuit or solenoid – see following paragraphs. If the starter motor turns slowly when operated, but the battery is in good condition, then this indicates that either the starter motor is faulty, or there is considerable resistance somewhere in the circuit.
3 If a fault in the circuit is suspected,

8.4 Undo the starter motor mounting bolts (arrowed)

10.3 Starter control unit securing bolts (arrowed)

disconnect the battery leads (including the earth connection to the body), the starter/solenoid wiring and the engine/transmission earth strap. Thoroughly clean the connections, and reconnect the leads and wiring, then use a voltmeter or test light to check that full battery voltage is available at the battery positive lead connection to the solenoid, and that the earth is sound. Smear petroleum jelly around the battery terminals to prevent corrosion – corroded connections are amongst the most frequent causes of electrical system faults.

4 If the battery and all connections are in good condition, check the circuit by disconnecting the wire from the solenoid blade terminal. Connect a voltmeter or test light between the wire end and a good earth (such as the battery negative terminal), and check that the wire is live when the ignition switch is turned to the start position. If it is, then the circuit is sound – if not, the circuit wiring can be checked as described in Chapter 12.

5 The solenoid contacts can be checked by connecting a voltmeter or test light between the battery positive feed connection on the starter side of the solenoid, and earth. When the ignition switch is turned to the start position, there should be a reading or lighted bulb, as applicable. If there is no reading or lighted bulb, the solenoid is faulty and should be renewed.

6 If the circuit and solenoid are proved sound,

the fault must lie in the starter motor. In this event, it may be possible to have the starter motor overhauled by a specialist, but check on the cost of spares before proceeding, as it may prove more economical to obtain a new or exchange motor.

8 Starter motor – removal and refitting

Removal

1 Remove the plastic cover on top of the engine.
2 Disconnect the battery negative lead and on models fitted with the 1.6 litre engine remove the battery and battery tray (see Section 3).
3 For the 1.6 litre engine, it is also necessary to remove the engine undershield and to remove other components in order to access the starter motor.
4 Disconnect the wiring from the starter motor solenoid, undo the mounting bolts, and remove the unit **(see illustration)**. Note the position of any locating dowels and ensure they are in position when refitting.

Refitting

5 Refitting is a reversal of removal. Tighten all fasteners to their specified torque where given.

9 Starter motor – testing and overhaul

If the starter motor is thought to be suspect, it should be removed from the vehicle and taken to an auto-electrician for testing. Most auto-electricians will be able to supply and fit brushes at a reasonable cost. However, check on the cost of repairs before proceeding, as it may prove more economical to obtain a new or exchange motor.

10 Starter control unit – removal and refitting

1 The starter control unit is located behind the facia at the rear of the remote unit aperture/start-stop button.
2 Disconnect the battery negative terminal as described in Section 3.
3 Remove the instrument panel as described in Chapter 12. Undo the 3 bolts, shown with the facia removed for clarity **(see illustration)**, disconnect the wiring plug, and withdraw the unit from the facia.
4 Refitting is a reversal of removal.

Chapter 5 Part B:
Preheating system

Contents

Degrees of difficulty

Easy, suitable for novice with little experience	**Fairly easy,** suitable for beginner with some experience	**Fairly difficult,** suitable for competent DIY mechanic	**Difficult,** suitable for experienced DIY mechanic	**Very difficult,** suitable for expert DIY or professional

Specifications

Torque wrench setting	Nm	lbf ft
Glow plugs	8	6

1 General information

To assist cold starting, diesel engine models are fitted with a preheating system, which comprises a relay, and glow plugs. The system is controlled by the electronic diesel control (EDC) system, using information provided by the coolant temperature sensor (see Chapter 3).

The glow plugs are miniature electric heating elements, encapsulated in a metal case with a probe at one end, and an electrical connection at the other. The combustion chambers have a glow plug threaded into it. When the glow plug is energised, it heats up rapidly causing the temperature of the air charge drawn into each of the combustion chambers to rise. Each glow plug probe is positioned directly in line with the incoming spray of fuel from the injector. Hence the fuel passing over the glow plug probe is also heated, allowing its optimum combustion temperature to be achieved more readily.

The duration of the preheating period is governed by the electronic diesel control (EDC) system control module (ECM), using information provided by the coolant

temperature sensor. The ECM alters the preheating time (the length for which the glow plugs are supplied with current) to suit the prevailing conditions.

A warning light informs the driver that preheating is taking place. The lamp extinguishes when sufficient preheating has taken place to allow the engine to be started, but power will still be supplied to the glow plugs for a further period, known as post-heating, to reduce exhaust emissions. If no attempt is made to start the engine, the power supply to the glow plugs is switched off to prevent battery drain and glow plug burn-out.

2 Preheating system – testing

1 Full testing of the system can only be carried out using specialist diagnostic equipment which is connected to the engine management system diagnostic wiring connector (see Chapter 4A). If the preheating system is thought to be faulty, some preliminary checks of the glow plug operation may be made as described in the following paragraphs.

2 Connect a voltmeter or 12 volt test lamp between the glow plug supply cable, and a good earth point on the engine. *Caution: Make sure that the live connection is kept well clear of the engine and bodywork.*

3 Have an assistant activate the preheating system by inserting the remote unit and briefly pressing the 'start/stop' button, and check that battery voltage is applied to the glow plug electrical connection. **Note:** *The supply voltage will be less than battery voltage initially, but will rise and settle as the glow plug heats up. It will then drop to zero when the preheating period ends and the safety cut-out operates.*

4 If no supply voltage can be detected at the glow plug, then the glow plug relay or the supply cable may be faulty.

5 To locate a faulty glow plug, measure the electrical resistance between the glow plug terminal and the engine earth, and compare it with the figures that should be available from a Volvo dealer. If the reading is significantly different from that specified, the glow plug is probably defective.

6 If no problems are found, take the vehicle to a Volvo dealer or specialist for testing using the appropriate diagnostic equipment.

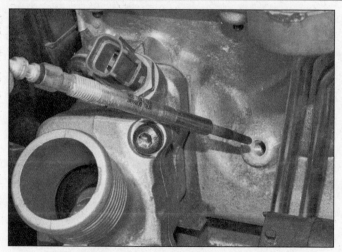

3.3 Unscrew each glow plug from the cylinder head

4.1 The glow plug relay is located on the right-hand side of the radiator/cooling fan on 5-cylinder engines

3 Glow plugs – removal, inspection and refitting

Removal

1 The glow plugs are fitted into the front or rear face of the cylinder head depending on the engine fitted. Remove the engine cover and remove components with reference to the relevant chapter until the glow plugs become accessible.

2 Unplug the wiring connector from each glow plug and where appropriate remove the wiring bracket.

3 Unscrew each plug from the cylinder head using a deep socket **(see illustration)**.

Inspection

4 Inspect the glow plugs for signs of damage. Burnt or eroded glow plug tips can be caused by a bad injector spray pattern. Have the injectors checked if this sort of damage is found.

5 If the glow plugs are in good condition, check them electrically, as described in Section 2.

Refitting

6 Thoroughly clean the glow plugs, and the glow plug seating areas in the cylinder head.

7 Apply a smear of anti-seize compound to the glow plug threads, then refit the glow plug and tighten it to the specified torque.

8 Reconnect the wiring to the glow plug.

9 The remainder of refitting is a reversal of removal.

4 Glow plug relay – removal and refitting

1 The location of the relay differs depending on the engine fitted. We were unable to confirm the location on 4-cylinder engines so if you suspect the component may be faulty you should refer to a Volvo dealer. On 5-cylinder engines it is located on the right-hand side of the radiator/cooling fan shroud **(see illustration)**. Disconnect the wiring plug and unclip the relay from its bracket. Refitting is a reversal of removal.

Chapter 6
Clutch

Contents
Section number

Degrees of difficulty

Easy, suitable for novice with little experience	**Fairly easy,** suitable for beginner with some experience	**Fairly difficult,** suitable for competent DIY mechanic	**Difficult,** suitable for experienced DIY mechanic	**Very difficult,** suitable for expert DIY or professional

Specifications

General
Clutch type. . . . .   Single dry plate, diaphragm spring, self-adjusting, hydraulic actuation

Pressure plate
Warp limit . . . .   0.2 mm

Torque wrench settings

	Nm	lbf ft
Clutch cover retaining bolts	24	18
Master cylinder retaining nuts	24	18
Pedal retaining screws.	24	18
Release bearing and slave cylinder mounting bolts.	10	7

1 General information

A single dry plate diaphragm spring clutch is fitted to all manual transmission models. The clutch is hydraulically-operated via a master and slave cylinder. All models have an internally-mounted slave cylinder and release bearing combined into one unit.

The main components of the clutch are the clutch cover and pressure plate, the driven plate (sometimes called the friction plate or disc) and the release bearing. The pressure plate is bolted to the flywheel, with the driven plate sandwiched between them. The centre of the driven plate carries female splines which mate with the splines on the transmission input shaft. The release bearing acts on the diaphragm spring fingers of the pressure plate.

When the engine is running and the clutch pedal is released, the diaphragm spring clamps the pressure plate, driven plate and flywheel firmly together. Drive is transmitted through the friction surfaces of the flywheel and pressure plate to the linings of the driven plate, and thus to the transmission input shaft.

The slave cylinder is incorporated into the release bearing – when the slave cylinder operates, the release bearing moves against the diaphragm spring fingers. As the spring pressure on the pressure plate is relieved, the flywheel and pressure plate spin without moving the driven plate. As the pedal is released, spring pressure is restored and the drive is gradually taken up.

The clutch hydraulic system consists of a master cylinder, a slave cylinder and the associated pipes and hoses. The fluid reservoir is shared with the brake master cylinder.

All models are fitted with a self-adjusting clutch, which compensates for driven plate wear by altering the attitude of the diaphragm spring fingers by means of a sprung mechanism within the pressure plate cover. This ensures a consistent clutch pedal 'feel' over the life of the clutch.

2 Clutch pedal – removal and refitting

1 Removal and refitting of the clutch pedal is included in the master cylinder removal and refitting procedure described below.

3 Clutch master cylinder – removal and refitting

⚠️ *Warning: Hydraulic fluid is poisonous; wash off immediately and thoroughly in the case of skin contact, and seek immediate medical advice if any fluid is swallowed or gets into*

the eyes. Certain types of hydraulic fluid are inflammable, and may ignite when allowed into contact with hot components; when servicing any hydraulic system, it is safest to assume that the fluid IS inflammable, and to take precautions against the risk of fire as though it is petrol that is being handled. Hydraulic fluid is also an effective paint stripper, and will attack plastics; if any is spilt, it should be washed off immediately, using copious quantities of clean water. Finally, it is hygroscopic (it absorbs moisture from the air) – old fluid may be contaminated and unfit for further use. When topping-up or renewing the fluid, always use the recommended type, and ensure that it comes from a freshly-opened sealed container.

Note: *At the time of writing, it would appear that master cylinder internal components are not available separately, and therefore no repair or overhaul of the cylinder is possible. In the event of a hydraulic system fault, or any sign of visible fluid leakage on or around the master cylinder or clutch pedal, the unit should be renewed – consult a Volvo dealer or specialist.*

Removal

1 Remove the plenum cover as described in Chapter 12, Section 18.
2 Disconnect the wiring plug for the clutch position sensor, located on the side of the master cylinder.
3 Prise out the clip and disconnect the pressure pipe union from the master cylinder **(see illustration)**. Be prepared for further fluid spillage. Cover the open pipe union with a piece of polythene and a rubber band to keep dirt out.
4 Release the fluid supply hose from the retaining clip, then use a clamp on the hose before disconnecting it from the master cylinder. Be prepared for further fluid spillage. Cover the open pipe union with a piece of polythene and a rubber band to keep dirt out.
5 Undo the two screws, and remove the trim panel above the pedals. At this stage of the process, Volvo advise that the steering column be removed, although it may be possible just to undo the steering column lower pinch-bolt and move the steering shaft to one side. If this does not provide adequate access, remove the steering column as described in Chapter 10.
6 Prise off the retaining clip, and pull the master cylinder pushrod from the pedal **(see illustration)**.
7 Remove the start inhibit switch located at the top of the pedal. Disconnect the wiring plug, release the retaining clips, and remove the switch.
8 Working under the facia, undo the 3 nuts securing the master cylinder to the bulkhead.
9 Rotate the master cylinder anti-clockwise (from the cabin) and separate the master cylinder from the pedal bracket. Volvo

3.3 Prise out the clip (arrowed) and disconnect the pressure pipe union from the master cylinder

technicians use a special tool (999 7172) to rotate the master cylinder. In the absence of this tool, use a suitable wrench or adjustable spanner.
10 Manoeuvre the assembly from under the facia. No further dismantling is recommended. If faulty, the pedal and bracket must be renewed as an assembly.

Refitting

11 Refit by reversing the removal operations, noting the following points:
  a) *If a new master cylinder is being fitted, transfer the fluid supply hose from the old cylinder to the new one prior to installation.*
  b) *Tighten the master cylinder retaining nuts to the specified torque.*
  c) *Before refitting the start inhibit switch, ensure the plunger is fully extended.*
  d) *A new clip must be used when reattaching the master cylinder pushrod to the pedal.*
  e) *A new seal is required where the master cylinder meets the bulkhead.*
  f) *Bleed the clutch hydraulic system on completion (Section 5).*

4 Clutch slave cylinder – removal and refitting

Note: *Slave cylinder internal components*

4.3 Slave cylinder fluid pipe clip

3.6 Master cylinder pushrod clip at the clutch pedal

are not available separately, and no repair or overhaul of the cylinder is possible. In the event of a hydraulic system fault, or any sign of fluid leakage, the unit should be renewed.
Note: *Refer to the warning at the beginning of Section 3 before proceeding.*

Removal

1 Remove the transmission as described in Chapter 7A. The internal slave cylinder cannot be removed with the transmission in place.
2 Release the rubber seal from the transmission, and move it inwards down the pipe.
3 Prise out the clip and disconnect the fluid pipe junction from the pipe **(see illustration)**.
4 Remove the 3 mounting bolts (picture shows 2 bolts but process for removal is as set out here) securing the cylinder and release bearing assembly to the transmission, and remove the assembly, feeding the fluid pipe in through the transmission aperture **(see illustration)**.

Refitting

5 Refit by reversing the removal operations, noting the following points:
  a) *Tighten the release bearing assembly mounting bolts to the specified torque.*
  b) *Volvo recommend the use of new seals when refitting the quick-release pipe connections.*

4.4 Undo the bolts and remove the slave cylinder

c) Refit the transmission as described in Chapter 7A.
d) Bleed the clutch hydraulic system on completion (Section 5).

5 Clutch hydraulic system – bleeding

Note: Refer to the warning at the beginning of Section 3 before proceeding.

1 Top-up the hydraulic fluid reservoir on the brake master cylinder with fresh clean fluid of the specified type (see Weekly checks).
2 Remove the dust cap, and fit a length of clear hose over the bleed screw on the slave cylinder **(see illustration)**. Place the other end of the hose in a jar containing a small amount of hydraulic fluid.
3 Slacken the bleed screw, then have an assistant depress the clutch pedal. Tighten the bleed screw when the pedal is depressed. Have the assistant release the pedal, then slacken the bleed screw again.
4 Repeat the process until clean fluid, free of air bubbles, emerges from the bleed screw. Tighten the screw at the end of a pedal downstroke, and remove the hose and jar. Refit the dust cover.
5 Top-up the hydraulic fluid reservoir.
6 Pressure bleeding equipment may be used if preferred – refer to the information in Chapter 9, Section 2.

6 Clutch assembly – removal, inspection and refitting

Warning: Dust created by clutch wear and deposited on the clutch components may contain asbestos, which is a health hazard. DO NOT blow it out with compressed air or inhale any of it. DO NOT use petrol or petroleum-based solvents to clean off the dust. Brake system cleaner or methylated spirit should be used to flush the dust into a suitable receptacle. After the clutch components are wiped clean with rags, dispose of the contaminated rags and the used cleaner in a sealed, marked container.

Note: Volvo tools 999 7068 and 999 5662 may be required to reset the self-adjusting mechanism and compress the diaphragm spring prior to clutch removal, although it is possible to successfully carry out the procedure using improvised home-made tools. Volvo also use a tool (999 7120), bolted to the engine mating face, to lock the flywheel in place. Again, a home-made tool or the assistance of another person will suffice.

Removal

1 Access to the clutch may be gained in one

5.2 Prise off the cap (arrowed) to access the bleed screw

of two ways. Either the engine/transmission assembly can be removed as described in Chapter 2D, and the transmission then separated from the engine, or the engine may be left in the car and the transmission removed independently as described in Chapter 7A. If the clutch is to be refitted, use paint or marker pen to mark the position of the clutch cover relative to the flywheel.

With Volvo special tools

2 Fit Volvo 'counterhold' tool 999 7068 to the clutch cover to reset the self-adjusting mechanism. The pins of the tool must engage in the groove in front of the adjuster springs, then hold the tool against the plate. Engage the hooks at the end of the tool springs in the centre of the three holes, located at 120° intervals along the circumference of the clutch cover.
3 Fit the Volvo compression tool 999 5662 to the clutch cover, and compress the diaphragm spring so that the self-adjusting spring is not under tension. Ensure that hooks on the underside of the compressor engage correctly without clamping the adjuster mechanism springs. Continue to screw in the compression tool spindle until the diaphragm spring has pressed the pressure plate to a 'free' position. A distinct 'click' will be heard when the pressure plate is in the 'free' position.

With or without Volvo special tools

4 Undo the screws and remove the clutch cover/pressure plate, followed by the driven plate **(see illustration)**. Note the orientation of the driven plate.
5 It is important that no oil or grease is allowed to come into contact with the friction material or the pressure plate and flywheel faces during inspection and refitting. **Note:** If the clutch cover/pressure plate is to be refitted, do not allow the diaphragm spring to remain in the compressed state for a long period of time, or the spring may be permanently weakened.

Inspection

6 With the clutch assembly removed, clean off all traces of clutch dust using a dry cloth. This is best done outside or in a well-ventilated area.

6.4 Undo the clutch pressure plate screws

7 Examine the linings of the driven plate for wear and loose rivets, and the rim for distortion, cracks, broken torsion springs and worn splines. The surface of the friction linings may be highly glazed, but, as long as the friction material pattern can be clearly seen, this is satisfactory.
8 If there is any sign of oil contamination, indicated by a continuous or patchy, shiny black discolouration, the plate must be renewed and the source of the contamination traced and rectified. This will be either a leaking crankshaft oil seal or transmission input shaft oil seal – or both.
9 The driven plate must also be renewed if the lining thickness has worn down to, or just above, the level of the rivet heads. Given the amount of dismantling work necessary to gain access to the driven plate, it may be wise to fit a new plate regardless of the old one's condition.
10 Check the machined faces of the flywheel and pressure plate. If either is grooved, or heavily scored, renewal is necessary. Providing the damage is not too serious, the flywheel can be removed as described in the Chapter 2A, 2B or 2C, and taken to an engineering works, who may be able to clean up the surface by machining.
11 The pressure plate must be renewed if any cracks are apparent, if the diaphragm spring is damaged or its pressure suspect, or if there is excessive warpage of the pressure plate face.
12 With the transmission removed, check the condition of the release bearing, as described in Section 7.

Refitting

13 It is advisable to refit the clutch assembly with clean hands, and to wipe down the pressure plate and flywheel faces with a clean dry rag before assembly begins.
14 Fit an appropriate centering tool into the hole at the end of the crankshaft. The tool must be a sliding fit in the crankshaft hole and the driven plate centre.
15 Place the driven plate in position with the longer side of the centre boss towards the flywheel, or as noted on removal. Note that the new driven plate will be marked to

indicate which side faces the flywheel **(see illustrations)**.

With Volvo special tools

16 Fit the counterhold tool 999 7068 to the clutch cover, ensuring the three pins engage in the grooves in front of the adjuster springs, then hold the tool against the plate. Engage the hooks at the end of the tool springs in the centre of the three holes, located at 120° intervals along the circumference of the clutch cover.

17 Fit the Volvo compression tool 999 5662 to the clutch cover, and compress the diaphragm spring so that the self-adjusting springs are not under tension. Ensure that hooks on the underside of the compressor engage correctly without clamping the adjuster mechanism springs. From the initial 'loose' state, the compressor spindle should be turned no more 5.0 turns and a distinct 'click' will be heard when the pressure plate is in the 'free' position.

Without Volvo special tools

18 Using a length of threaded rod, and some circular spacers and two nuts, compress the diaphragm spring fingers and the pressure plate together as shown. Once the fingers are compressed, use a screwdriver to move and hold the adjusting ring anti-clockwise until the pointers align with the marks by the adjustment springs **(see illustrations)**.

19 Slowly undo the nuts to uncompress the pressure plate assembly. The self-adjusting ring/spring marks should remain in the same place (see paragraph 18). Remove the threaded rod, etc.

With or without Volvo special tools

20 Position the clutch cover/pressure plate assembly over the dowels on the flywheel, aligning the previously-made marks (where applicable).

21 Working in a diagonal pattern, fit and evenly tighten the cover retaining bolts to the specified torque.

22 Slowly release the compressor, then

6.15a The driven plate should be marked (arrowed) to indicate which side faces the flywheel

6.15b Fit the driven plate with the longer side of the centre boss towards the flywheel

remove the counterhold tool from the clutch – where applicable.

23 Pull the centering tool from the plate/crankshaft, and check visually that the driven plate appears centrally located.

24 Remove the flywheel locking tool if used.

25 The engine and/or transmission can now be refitted by referring to the appropriate Chapter of this manual.

| 7 | Clutch release bearing – removal, inspection and refitting | |

Removal

1 Access to the clutch release bearing may be gained in one of two ways. Either the engine/transmission assembly can be removed as described in Chapter 2D, and the transmission then separated from the engine, or the engine may be left in the car and the transmission removed independently as described in Chapter 7A.

2 The release bearing and slave cylinder are combined into one unit, and cannot be separated. Refer to the slave cylinder removal procedure in Section 4.

Inspection

3 Check the bearing for smoothness of operation, and renew it if there is any roughness or harshness as the bearing is spun. It is a good idea to renew the bearing as a matter of course during clutch overhaul, regardless of its apparent condition, considering the amount of dismantling work necessary to gain access to it.

Refitting

4 Refer to Section 4.

| 8 | Clutch pedal position sensor – renewal | |

1 The sensor is located on the side of the master cylinder. Remove the battery and battery tray as described in Chapter 5A.

2 Disconnect the sensor wiring plug.

3 Volvo use a special tool (999 7402) to engage with the body of the switch and pull it from the master cylinder. However, a screwdriver or suitable flat-bladed tool can be used instead.

4 Refitting is a reversal of removal.

6.18a Compress the diaphragm spring fingers and the pressure plate together . . .

6.18b . . . then rotate the adjuster ring anti-clockwise . . .

6.18c . . . until the pointers align with the marks by the adjustment springs (arrowed)

Chapter 7 Part A:
Manual transmission

Contents

Degrees of difficulty

Easy, suitable for novice with little experience	**Fairly easy,** suitable for beginner with some experience	**Fairly difficult,** suitable for competent DIY mechanic	**Difficult,** suitable for experienced DIY mechanic	**Very difficult,** suitable for expert DIY or professional

Specifications

General
Designation .... MTX75, M66 or MMT6
Transmission type:
  MTX75 .... Five forward gears and one reverse. Synchromesh on all gears
  M66 and MMT6 .... Six forward gears and one reverse. Synchromesh on all gears

Lubrication
Lubricant type .... See *Lubricants and fluids*
Capacity:
  5-speed (MTX75) .... 2.1 litres
  6-speed:
    M66 .... 1.9 litres
    MMT6 .... 1.65 litres

Torque wrench settings

	Nm	lbf ft
Auxiliary heater mounting nuts.	25	18
Engine mounting nuts/bolts (including torque rod)	See Chapter 2A, 2B or 2C	
Gear lever housing bolts	10	7
Oil filler/drain plugs.	35	26
Reversing light switch	24	18
Roadwheel bolts.	140	103
Starter motor mounting bolts.	See Chapter 5A	
Subframe mounting bolts.	See Chapter 10	
Transmission-to-engine bolts.	50	37

* Do not re-use

1 General information

The manual transmission and final drive are housed in an aluminium casing, bolted directly to the left-hand side of the engine. Gear selection is by a remotely-sited lever assembly, operating the transmission selector mechanism via cables.

On 5-speed transmissions, the internal components comprise the input shaft, the upper and lower layshafts, the final drive differential and the selector mechanism. The input shaft contains the fixed 1st, 2nd and 5th gears, the freewheeling 3rd and 4th gearwheels and the 3rd/4th synchro unit. The upper layshaft contains the freewheeling 5th and reverse gearwheels, the 5th/reverse synchro unit and a final drive pinion. The lower layshaft contains the fixed 3rd and 4th gears, the freewheeling 1st, 2nd and reverse intermediate gearwheels, the 1st/2nd synchro unit and a final drive pinion.

On 6-speed transmissions, the input shaft contains the 6th, 5th gear idler wheels, and the 4th, 1st, and 3rd gearwheels. The two intermediate shafts contain the 5th and 6th gearwheels, 1st, 2nd, 3rd and 4th gear idler wheels, and the final drive gearwheels.

Drive from the engine is transmitted to the input shaft by the clutch. The gears on the input shaft are permanently meshed with the gears on the two layshafts, but when drive is transmitted, only one gear at a time is actually locked to its shaft, with the others freewheeling. The selection of gears is by sliding synchro units; movement of the gear lever is transmitted to selector forks, which slide the appropriate synchro unit towards the gear to be engaged, and lock it to the relevant shaft. In neutral, none of the gears are locked, all are freewheeling.

Reverse gear is obtained by locking the reverse gearwheel to the upper layshaft. Drive is transmitted through the input shaft to the reverse intermediate gearwheel on the lower layshaft, then to the reverse gearwheel and final drive pinion on the upper layshaft. Reverse is therefore obtained by transmitting power through all three shafts, instead of only two as in the case of the forward gears. By eliminating the need for a separate reverse idler gear, synchromesh can also be provided on reverse gear.

2 Gear lever housing – removal and refitting

Removal

1 Remove the centre console and dismantle as described in Chapter 11.
2 Squeeze the gaiter at the base of the gearknob to release the clips and pull the gaiter downwards. Prise out the 2 locking tabs at the base of the knob and pull the knob straight upwards and remove it.
3 Undo the four bolts securing the housing assembly to the floor.
4 Lift up the housing, and prise off the selector inner cable socket joints from the base of the gear lever. Note that the cable ends may be secured by clips.
5 Release the retaining clips securing the selector outer cables to the housing, and remove the assembly from the car.

Refitting

6 Refit by reversing the removal operations. Tighten the four securing bolts to the specified torque. Refit the centre console as described in Chapter 11.

3 Selector cables – removal and refitting

Removal

1 Refer to the relevant part of Chapter 4A and 5A and remove the air cleaner assembly, battery, and battery tray.
2 Working underneath the vehicle remove the heat shield panel at the rear of the engine bay and above the front section of the exhaust. Unclip the cable from the bulkhead.
3 Undo the clips and remove the cable-ends from the selector arms on the transmission. Slide the locking collar forwards and unclip the cables from the bracket on the transmission **(see illustrations)**.
4 Remove the centre console as described in Chapter 11. Remove the central air vent and move the rear air vents to one side.
5 Disconnect the cables from the selector housing.
6 Undo the nuts securing the grommet/cable entry plate to the bulkhead **(see illustration)**.
7 Note the routing of the cables under the facia, and in the engine compartment, as an aid to refitting, then attach welding rod (or similar) to the ends of the cables in the engine compartment. Release any adjacent components as necessary, then pull the cables one at a time into the passenger compartment, then unhook the welding rods leaving them in place to assist refitting. Remove the cables from the car.

Refitting

8 From inside the car, hook the cable ends onto the welding rod, then carefully feed/pull the cables through into the engine compartment, ensuring that they are routed correctly.
9 Reconnect the cables to the gear lever housing, and refit the housing as described in Section 2.
10 Refit the grommet/cable entry plate, and the carpet.
11 Refit the centre console (see Chapter 11).
12 Refit the battery tray, battery and air cleaner assembly as described in Chapter 5A and 4A.

Cable adjustment

13 We were unable to confirm the process for adjusting the selector cables so you should entrust this task to a Volvo dealer

4 Oil seals – renewal

Driveshaft seals

1 Remove the left- or right-hand driveshaft (as appropriate) with reference to Chapter 8.
2 Using a large screwdriver or suitable lever, carefully prise the oil seal out of the

3.3a Remove the cable-ends from the selector arms

3.3b Slide the locking collar forwards and unclip the cables from the bracket

3.6 Undo the nuts (arrowed) at the grommet/cable entry at the bulkhead

4.2 Use a piece of wood to protect the casing when levering out the driveshaft oil seal(s)

4.5 Use a socket or tubular spacer to drive in the oil seal

4.9a Drill a small hole in the hard outer edge of the oil seal, then insert a self-tapping screw . . .

4.9b . . . and use pliers to pull the seal from place

4.10 Use a suitable tube to drive in the seal

transmission casing, taking care not to damage the casing **(see illustration)**.

3 Wipe clean the oil seal seating in the transmission casing.

4 Apply a small amount of general-purpose grease to the new seal lips, then press it a little way into the casing by hand, making sure that it is square to its seating.

5 Using suitable tubing or a large socket, carefully drive the oil seal fully into position until it is flush with the casing edge **(see illustration)**.

6 Refit the driveshaft(s) as described in Chapter 8.

Input shaft oil seal

7 Remove the transmission as described in Section 7.

8 Remove the clutch release bearing/slave cylinder as described in Chapter 6.

9 Note its fitted depth, then drill a small hole in the hard outer surface of the seal, insert a self-tapping screw, and use pliers to extract the seal **(see illustrations)**.

10 Lubricate the new seal with grease and fit it to the bellhousing, lips pointing to the gearbox side. Use a deep socket or suitable tubing to seat it **(see illustration)**.

11 Refit the release bearing/slave cylinder using a reversal of removal.

12 Refit the transmission as described in Section 7.

5 Reversing light switch – removal and refitting

Removal

1 The reversing light switch is located on the upper face of the transmission. Remove the air cleaner assembly as described in the relevant part of Chapter 4A.

2 Disconnect the wiring plug and unscrew the switch from the transmission housing **(see illustration)**.

Refitting

3 Refit by reversing the removal operations.

6 Manual transmission oil – draining and refilling

Note: *Renewal of the transmission oil is not a service requirement and will normally only be necessary if the unit is to be removed for overhaul or renewal. However, if the car has completed a high mileage, or is used under arduous conditions (eg, extensive towing or taxi work), it would be advisable to change the oil as a precaution, especially if the gearchange quality has deteriorated.*

Draining

1 Slacken the left-hand front roadwheel bolts, then jack up the front of the vehicle and support it securely on axle stands (see *Jacking and vehicle support*). Remove the roadwheel.

5.2 Disconnect the reversing light switch wiring plug (arrowed)

2 Release the screws and remove the engine undershield, then position a suitable container beneath the transmission.

3 On the side of the transmission casing, you will see the filler/level plug and the drain plug. Unscrew and remove the drain plug (the lower of the two) and allow the oil to drain into the container **(see illustration)**. Check the condition of the drain plug sealing washer, and renew if necessary.

4 When all the oil has drained, refit the drain plug and tighten it to the specified torque.

Refilling

Note: *For the level check to be accurate, the car must be completely level. If the front of the car has been jacked up, the rear should be jacked up also.*

5 Wipe clean the area around the filler/level plug, and unscrew the plug from the casing.

6.3 Oil drain plug – 5-speed transmission

6 Fill the transmission through the filler/level plug hole with the correct type of oil until the oil begins to run out of the hole.
7 Refit the filler/level plug with a new seal, and tighten it to the specified torque.
8 Dispose of the old oil safely in accordance with environmental regulations.

7 Manual transmission – removal and refitting

Note: *Arrangements must be made to support the engine from above, to allow the subframe to be detached on the left-hand side. The best way to support the engine is with a bar resting in the bonnet channels with an adjustable hook appropriately placed. Trolley jacks and the help of an assistant will also be required throughout the procedure.*

Removal

1 Put the gear lever in neutral.
2 Refer to Section 6 and drain the transmission oil. This is not absolutely essential, but will remove the potential problem of oil spillage when the driveshafts are removed, or when the transmission is moved out of the car.
3 Disconnect the battery negative lead as described in Chapter 5A.
4 Drain the cooling system as described in Chapter 1 (not required for 1.6 litre models with the 5-speed transmission).
5 On models with the 5-speed transmission, remove the catalytic converter as described in Chapter 4B, then undo the bolts and remove the support bracket.
6 Disconnect the gearchange cables from the transmission as described in Section 3.
7 Remove the left-hand side engine mounting as described in Chapter 2C. On models with the 5-speed transmission, remove the rear lower torque rod.
8 Disconnect the wiring plug and undo the nut/clip securing the selector cable to the transmission housing.
9 Undo the nut securing the earth cable to

the transmission housing, and remove any brackets.
10 Clamp the fluid supply hoses from the reservoir to the brake and clutch master cylinders, then extract the circlip and withdraw the slave cylinder supply pipe from the transmission. Have ready a container and rags to catch the fluid which will spill. Cover the open pipe union with a piece of polythene and a rubber band to keep dirt out.
11 Remove the starter motor as described in Chapter 5A.
12 Undo the retaining screws and remove the wheel arch liners.
13 Remove both driveshafts as described in Chapter 8.
14 Remove the front subframe as described in Chapter 10.
15 Use a trolley jack to support the transmission and remove the 7 bolts securing the transmission to the engine. Withdraw the transmission squarely off the engine dowels, taking care not to allow the weight of the unit to hang on the input shaft.
16 Lower the jack and remove the unit from under the car.

Refitting

17 Refitting is a reversal of removal, noting the following points:
a) *Ensure the mating surfaces between the engine and transmission are clean and free of any debris.*
b) *Apply a small amount of wheel bearing grease (Volvo 1161689) to the dowel mounting points on the engine mating surface*
c) *Ensure the input shaft is clean and free of any debris. Wipe clean if necessary and apply a small amount of grease (Volvo 30759651).*
d) *Tighten all fasteners to the their specified torque where given.*
e) *Top-up the gearbox oil as described in Section 6 of this Chapter.*
f) *Top-up the cooling system as described in Chapter 1.*
g) *Bleed the clutch hydraulic system (if necessary) as described in Chapter 6.*

h) *Reconnect the battery negative lead as described in Chapter 5A.*

8 Manual transmission overhaul – general information

Overhauling a manual transmission is a difficult job for the do-it-yourselfer. It involves the dismantling and reassembly of many small parts. Numerous clearances must be precisely measured and, if necessary, changed with selected spacers and circlips. As a result, if transmission problems arise, while the unit can be removed and refitted by a competent do-it-yourselfer, overhaul should be left to a transmission specialist. Rebuilt transmissions may be available – check with your dealer parts department, motor factors, or transmission specialists. At any rate, the time and money involved in an overhaul is almost sure to exceed the cost of a rebuilt unit.

Nevertheless, it's not impossible for an experienced mechanic to rebuild a transmission, providing the special tools are available, and the job is done in a deliberate step-by-step manner, so nothing is overlooked.

The tools necessary for an overhaul include: internal and external circlip pliers, a bearing puller, a slide hammer, a set of pin punches, a dial test indicator, and possibly a hydraulic press. In addition, a large, sturdy workbench and a vice or transmission stand will be required.

During dismantling of the transmission, make careful notes of how each part comes off, where it fits in relation to other parts, and what holds it in place.

Before taking the transmission apart for repair, it will help if you have some idea what area of the transmission is malfunctioning. Certain problems can be closely tied to specific areas in the transmission, which can make component examination and renewal easier. Refer to the *Fault finding* section at the rear of this manual for information regarding possible sources of trouble.

Chapter 7 Part B:
Automatic transmission

Contents

Degrees of difficulty

Easy, suitable for novice with little experience	Fairly easy, suitable for beginner with some experience	Fairly difficult, suitable for competent DIY mechanic	Difficult, suitable for experienced DIY mechanic	Very difficult, suitable for expert DIY or professional

Specifications

General

Type	Computer-controlled six-speed, one reverse, with torque converter lock-up on 5 highest gears
Designation:	TF-80SC

Lubrication

Lubricant type	See *Lubricants and fluids*
Capacity (drain and refill)	7.0 litres (approx)

Torque wrench settings

	Nm	lbf ft
Engine mounting nuts/bolts (including torque rod)	See Chapter 2A, 2B or 2C	
Engine rear mounting bracket to transmission.	50	37
Fluid drain plug.	35	26
Gear lever housing bolts	25	18
Reversing light switch	25	18
Roadwheel bolts.	140	103
Starter motor mounting bolts.	See Chapter 5A	
Subframe mounting bolts.	See Chapter 10	
Torque converter-to-driveplate bolts*.	60	44
Transmission-to-engine bolts.	50	37

* Do not re-use

1 General information

The TF-80SC is a computer-controlled automatic transmission with 6 forward speeds, and torque converter lock-up on the 5 highest speeds. It is equipped with a Geartronic function that allows the driver to manually shift between transmission speeds in a sequential fashion – lever forward to change up, and backward to change down.

The unit is controlled by a transmission control module (TCM) which receives signal inputs from various sensors relating to transmission operating conditions. Information on engine parameters are also sent to the TCM from the engine management system. From this data, the TCM can establish the optimum gear shifting speeds and lock-up engagement points according to the driving mode selected.

Drive is taken from the engine to the transmission by a torque converter. This is a type of fluid coupling which, under certain conditions, has a torque multiplying effect. The torque converter is mechanically locked to the engine, under the control of the TCM, when the transmission is operating in the three highest gears. This eliminates losses due to slip, and improves fuel economy.

The engine can only be started in position P, thanks to a safety/security feature called Shiftlock. With this system, the ignition key can only be removed from the ignition/steering lock if the selector lever is placed in position P. On restarting the car, the selector lever can only be moved from the P position once the ignition is placed in position II.

Most models with automatic transmission feature a Winter mode selector, with the switch located alongside the selector lever. In this mode, the transmission will allow starting off from rest in a higher than normal gear to avoid wheelspin in poor road conditions. This mode can also be used to restrict gearchanging when road conditions dictate the need for more direct control of gear selection.

A kickdown facility causes the transmission to shift down a gear (subject to engine speed) when the throttle is fully depressed. This is useful when extra acceleration is required. Kickdown, like the other transmission functions, is controlled by the TCM.

In addition to control of the transmission, the TCM incorporates a built-in fault diagnosis facility. If a transmission fault occurs, the transmission warning light on the instrument panel will flash; the TCM will revert to an emergency (limp-home) programme which ensures that two forward gears and reverse will always be available, but gearchanging must be performed manually. If a fault of this nature does occur, the TCM stores a series of signals (or fault codes) which can be read and interpreted using suitable diagnostic equipment, for quick and accurate fault diagnosis (see Section 8). The TCM also has a facility for recording the amount of time the gearbox fluid spends above 150°C – normally this temperature is only achieved by taxi-use, or use as a towing vehicle.

Once a predetermined amount of time at or above this temperature is exceeded, the TCM will store a fault code, and illuminate a warning light on the instrument cluster, indicating that the fluid must be changed. However, changing the fluid will not extinguish the warning light – this must be carried out using dedicated Volvo test equipment.

The automatic transmission is a complex unit, but if it is not abused, it is reliable and long-lasting. Repair or overhaul operations are beyond the scope of many dealers, let alone the home mechanic; specialist advice should be sought if problems arise which cannot be solved by the procedures given in this Chapter.

2 Selector cable – removal and refitting

Removal

1 Park the car on a level surface (with the transmission selector lever in position P), then refer to the relevant part of Chapter 4A and 5A and remove the air cleaner assembly, the battery, and the battery tray.
2 Working beneath the vehicle, remove the heat shields at the rear of the engine bay and above the front section of the exhaust. Release the cable from the securing clip. Extract the locking clip and washer securing the selector inner cable to the transmission selector lever (see illustration). Slide the locking collar forward and remove the outer cable up from the bracket on the transmission, and release the inner cable end from the selector lever (see illustration).
3 Remove the centre console as described in Chapter 11. Remove the centre air vent and move the rear air vents to one side.
4 Extract the retaining clip securing the selector inner cable to the gear selector lever, and slide the selector outer cable from the gear selector housing (see illustrations).
5 Undo the bolts securing the cable entry cover plate to the bulkhead (see illustration). Where applicable, release the shift lock cable from the selector cable.
6 Note the routing of the cable under the facia,

2.2a Release the locking clip and disconnect the cable from the selector lever

2.2b Slide the locking collar forward and remove the outer cable from the bracket

2.4a Depress the retaining clip and release the cable from the gear selector

2.4b Slide the outer cable from the gear selector housing

2.5 Undo the bolts (arrowed) securing the cable entry cover plate to the bulkhead

3.2a Undo the front bolts (arrowed) . . .

3.2b . . . and the rear bolts (arrowed) and remove the gear selector housing

3.3a Twist the locking collar clockwise by approximately 45°

3.3b Press in the detent button and pull the gear knob upwards to remove

3.3c Release the clips on each side . . .

3.3d . . . and remove the selector panel

and in the engine compartment, as an aid to refitting. Release any adjacent components as necessary, then pull the cable into the passenger compartment and remove it from the car.

Refitting

7 Refitting is a reversal of removal, carefully feeding the cable through into the engine compartment from inside the car, ensuring that it is correctly routed.

3 Selector housing – removal and refitting

Removal

1 Remove and dismantle the centre console as described in Chapter 11.
2 Undo the 4 bolts and withdraw the housing from the centre console frame **(see illustrations)**.
3 If required, the selector indicator panel can be removed from the housing. Remove the gear knob by twisting the locking collar clockwise by approximately 45 degrees, pressing in the detent button, and pulling the knob upwards. Release the 2 clips on each side and removal the panel, disconnecting any wiring plugs as it is separated from the selector housing **(see illustrations)**.

Refitting

4 Refitting is a reversal of removal.

4 Transmission control module (TCM) – removal and refitting

Note: *If a new control module is fitted, it must be programmed using dedicated Volvo test equipment. Entrust this task to a Volvo dealer or suitably-equipped specialist.*

Removal

1 Disconnect the battery negative terminal as described in Chapter 5A.
Caution: Wait at least two minutes after the battery negative lead has been disconnected for any residual energy to dissipate from the main system relay.
2 The transmission control module (TCM) is located on the top of the transmission casing. Remove the air cleaner assembly as described in the relevant Part of Chapter 4A.
3 Disconnect the wiring plug from the TCM **(see illustration)**.
4 Undo the nut securing the selector lever to the shaft and pull the lever upwards from position. Note the alignment marks on the TCM and selector shaft.
5 Undo the 3 bolts and remove the TCM **(see illustration 4.3)**.

Refitting

6 Ensure the selector lever is in the N (Neutral) position. Refit the TCM to the transmission casing ensuring the arrow on the shaft aligns with the arrow on the TCM **(see**

illustration 4.3)**. Tighten the retaining bolts securely.
7 Refit the lever to the shaft, and tighten the retaining nut securely.
8 Reconnect the wiring plug.
9 Refit the air cleaner assembly.
10 Reconnect the battery negative lead as described in Chapter 5A.

5 Gear shift position sensor – removal and refitting

Note: *This operation can be undertaken in the vehicle but was carried out in the workshop with the centre console removed for clarity.*

4.3 Disconnect the wiring plug (arrowed) from the TCM. Also arrowed are the selector lever and TCM securing bolts

5.2a Carefully prise up the selector rail . . .

5.2b . . . and remove it from the position sensor

5.2c Remove the lower wiring plug . . .

Removal

1 Ensure the selector lever is in the Park position and disconnect any wiring plugs to gain access to the position sensor.
2 Carefully prise out the white plastic guide rail and disconnect the 2 wiring plugs from the position sensor. Using a small screwdriver, carefully push in the 2 upper and 2 lower clips and remove the position sensor **(see illustrations)**.

Refitting

3 Push the position sensor back into place and refit the 2 wiring plugs.
4 Remove the small black section from the guide rail and then refit so that it can slide fore and aft in the grooves in the guide rail (note that on removal the plastic lugs on the black section sit over the grooves and not within them) **(see illustrations)**.
5 Refit the guide rail inserting the left-hand end first and leaving the right-hand end unclipped. Slide the black section on the rail until the lines at the top align, then push the right-hand end of the guide rail into place, ensuring that the tab on the rear of the black section locates in the slot in the position sensor **(see illustrations)**.

5.2d . . . and the upper wiring plug . . .

5.2e . . . and release the sensor retaining clips

6 Fluid seals – renewal

Driveshaft seals

1 The procedure is the same as that described for the manual transmission in Chapter 7A.

Input shaft/torque converter seal

2 Remove the transmission (see Section 7).
3 Pull the torque converter squarely out of the transmission. Be careful, as it is full of fluid.
4 Pull or lever out the old seal. Clean the seat and inspect the seal rubbing surface on the torque converter.

5.4a Note that the black section sits over the grooves prior to removal . . .

5.4b . . . but within the grooves when refitted

5.5a Refit the guide rail inserting the left-hand end first

5.5b Slide the black section on the guide rail until the marks at the top align

5.5c Push the right-hand end of the guide rail into place

5 Lubricate the new seal with transmission fluid and fit it, lips inwards. Seat it with a piece of tube.

6 Lubricate the torque converter sleeve with transmission fluid, and slide the converter into place, pushing it in as far as it will go.

7 Check that the torque converter is fully seated by measuring the distance from the edge of the transmission housing face to the retaining bolt tabs on the converter. The dimension should be approximately 13 mm.

8 Refit the transmission as described in Section 7.

Gear shift linkage rod seal

9 Remove the transmission control module (TCM) as described in Section 4.

10 Carefully prise the old oil seal from position using a small screwdriver. Take care not to damage the linkage rod.

11 Smear the lips of the new oil seal with clean automatic transmission fluid, the guide the seal over the rod (lips towards the transmission), and seat it in place using a suitable tubular spacer.

12 Refit the TCM as described in Section 4.

All seals

13 Check the transmission fluid level as described in Chapter 1 on completion.

---

7 Automatic transmission –
removal and refitting

Note: *Arrangements must be made to support the engine from above, to allow the left-hand engine supports to be removed. The best way to support the engine is with a bar resting in the bonnet channels with an adjustable hook appropriately placed. Trolley jacks and the help of an assistant will also be required throughout the procedure.*

Removal

1 Disconnect the battery negative lead as described in Chapter 5A.

2 Slacken the front roadwheel bolts, then jack up the front of the vehicle, and support it securely on axle stands (see *Jacking and vehicle support*). Remove both front roadwheels.

3 Undo the screws and remove the engine undershield and wheel arch liners.

4 Refer to Chapter 1 and drain the transmission fluid. This is not absolutely essential, but will remove the potential problem of fluid spillage when the driveshafts are removed, or when the transmission is moved out of the car.

5 Remove both driveshafts as described in Chapter 8.

6 Remove the starter motor as described in Chapter 5A.

7 Remove the front subframe as described in Chapter 10.

8 Disconnect the transmission control module wiring plug, undo the nut and disconnect the selector cable from the selector shaft as described in Section 4.

9 Undo the 2 bolts securing the exhaust/catalytic converter bracket to the transmission housing and undo the bolt securing the earth cable to the transmission housing **(see illustration)**.

10 Undo the bolts securing the transmission cooler fluid pipe unions to the transmission housing. Be prepared for some fluid leakage **(see illustration)**.

11 Securely and safely support the transmission from below on a trolley jack.

12 Rotate the crankshaft, using a socket on the pulley nut, until one of the torque converter-to-driveplate retaining bolts becomes accessible through the opening on the rear facing side of the engine. Working through the opening, undo the bolt. Rotate the crankshaft as necessary and remove the remaining bolts in the same way. Note that new bolts will be required for refitting.

13 Lower the engine/transmission by approximately 60 mm and remove the remaining 8 bolts securing the transmission to the engine. Note that the bolts are of differing length.

14 With the aid of an assistant, draw the transmission squarely off the engine dowels making sure that the torque converter remains in position on the transmission. Use the access hole in the transmission housing to hold the converter in place.

15 Lower the jack and remove the unit from under the car.

Refitting

16 Clean the contact surfaces on the torque converter and driveplate, and the transmission and engine mating faces. Lightly lubricate the torque converter guide projection and the engine/transmission locating dowels with grease.

17 Check that the torque converter is fully seated by measuring the distance from the edge of the transmission housing face to the retaining bolt tabs on the converter. The dimension should be approximately 13 mm.

18 The remainder of refitting is a reversal of removal, noting the following points:

a) *Tighten all fasteners to the specified torque where given.*

b) *Flushing of the transmission oil cooler is advised by Volvo, and while not essential, it is a worthwhile precaution to prevent against future contamination. Undo the lower pipe from the oil cooler and place the end in a suitable tray or container. Use an oil syringe or similar to flush fresh oil through the cooler from the upper pipe connection.*

c) *Top-up the transmission fluid as described in Chapter 1.*

d) *Note that if a new transmission is fitted, a software download from Volvo's diagnostic system may be required. Entrust this task to a Volvo dealer or suitably-equipped specialist.*

7.9 Undo the exhaust/catalytic converter bracket bolts (arrowed)

7.10 Undo the bolts (arrowed) securing the fluid pipes to the transmission housing

9.2 Remove the rubber mat behind the centre console panel

9.3 Insert the blade into the hole and depress while moving the gear selector to neutral

8 Automatic transmission – fault diagnosis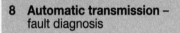

The automatic transmission electronic control system incorporates an on-board diagnostic facility as an aid to fault finding and system testing. The diagnostic system is a feature of the transmission control module (TCM) which continually monitors the system components and their operation. Should a fault occur, the TCM stores a series of signals (or fault codes) for subsequent read-out.

If a fault occurs, indicated by the flashing of the warning light on the instrument panel, the on-board diagnostics can be accessed using a fault code reader for quick and accurate diagnosis. A Volvo dealer will obviously have such a reader, but they are also available from other suppliers. It is unlikely to be cost-effective for the private owner to purchase a fault code reader, but a well-equipped local garage or auto-electrical specialist will have one.

In many instances, the fault may be nothing more serious than a corroded, trapped or loose wiring connection, or a loose, dirty, or badly-fitted component. Remember that if the fault has appeared only a short time after any part of the vehicle has been serviced or overhauled, the first place to check is where that work was carried out, however unrelated it may appear, to ensure that no carelessly-refitted components are causing the problem.

Even if the source of the problem is found and fixed, diagnostic equipment may still be required, to erase the fault code from the TCM memory, and stop the warning light flashing.

If the fault cannot be easily cured, the only alternatives possible at this time are the substitution of a suspect component with a known good unit (where possible), or entrusting further work to a Volvo dealer or suitably-equipped specialist.

9 Emergency release of the selector lever

1 If the vehicle's battery is disconnected or discharged, it is possible to release the selector lever from its locked position. First, ensure the handbrake is fully applied or chock the rear wheels if it is not possible to apply the handbrake.

2 Withdraw the plastic key blade from the remote control unit, and remove the rubber mat from behind the centre console switch panel **(see illustration)**.

3 Insert the blade into the hole revealed by the removal of the mat, and holding the blade down, move the gear lever to the neutral position **(see illustration)**.

Chapter 8
Driveshafts

Contents

Degrees of difficulty

Easy, suitable for novice with little experience	**Fairly easy,** suitable for beginner with some experience	**Fairly difficult,** suitable for competent DIY mechanic	**Difficult,** suitable for experienced DIY mechanic	**Very difficult,** suitable for expert DIY or professional

Specifications

General

Driveshaft type	Equal-length solid-steel shafts, splined to inner and outer constant velocity joints. Intermediate shaft incorporated in right-hand driveshaft assembly
Outer constant velocity joint type.	Ball-and-cage
Inner constant velocity joint type	Tripod

Lubrication

Lubricant type	Special grease supplied in repair kit, or suitable molybdenum disulphide grease – consult a Volvo dealer

Torque wrench settings

	Nm	lbf ft
ABS wheel speed sensor	See Chapter 9	
Brake caliper mounting bolts	See Chapter 9	
Driveshaft bolt:*		
Stage 1	35	26
Stage 2	Angle-tighten a further 90°	
Hub carrier to suspension strut	See Chapter 10	
Lower arm balljoint to hub carrier*	80	59
Right-hand driveshaft support bearing cap bolts	24	18
Roadwheel bolts.	140	103

* Do not re-use

1 General information

Drive is transmitted from the differential to the front wheels by means of two solid-steel, equal-length driveshafts equipped with constant velocity (CV) joints at their inner and outer ends. Due to the position of the transmission, an intermediate shaft and support bearing are incorporated into the right-hand driveshaft assembly.

A ball-and-cage type CV joint is fitted to the outer end of each driveshaft. The joint has an outer member which is splined at its outer end to accept the wheel hub, and is threaded so that it can be fastened to the hub by a large bolt. The joint contains six balls within a cage, which engage with the inner member. The complete assembly is protected by a flexible gaiter secured to the driveshaft and joint outer member.

At the inner end, the driveshaft is splined to engage with a tripod type CV joint, containing needle roller bearings and cups. On the left-hand side, the driveshaft inner CV joint engages directly with the differential sun wheel. On the right-hand side, the inner joint is integral with the intermediate shaft, the inner end of which engages with the differential sun wheel. As on the outer joints, a flexible gaiter secured to the driveshaft and CV joint outer member protects the complete assembly.

2.2 Slacken the driveshaft bolt

2.5 Some models have a rubber seal between the driveshaft and the hub carrier

2.7 Undo the two bolts (arrowed) and remove the intermediate shaft support bearing cap

2 Driveshafts – removal and refitting

Removal

1 Loosen the front wheel bolts, then jack up the front of the car and support it on axle stands (see *Jacking and vehicle support*). Remove the appropriate front roadwheel, then undo the screws and remove the engine undershield. Removing the wheel arch liner may also improve access.

2 Undo the driveshaft retaining bolt. Discard the bolt – a new one must be fitted **(see illustration)**.

3 Free the driveshaft CV joint from the hub flange by tapping it inwards approximately 10 to 15 mm with a plastic or copper mallet. If this fails to free the driveshaft from the hub, the joint will have to be released using a suitable tool bolted to the hub.

4 Undo the nut securing the hub carrier lower balljoint to the suspension control arm (noting the explanation in Chapter 10). Pull down on the suspension arm using a stout bar to release the balljoint shank from the control arm. Take care not to damage the balljoint dust cover during and after disconnection.

5 Swivel the suspension strut and hub carrier assembly outwards, and withdraw the driveshaft CV joint from the hub flange. **Note:** *Some models may have a rubber seal*

on the CV joint adjacent to the ABS signal ring – take care not to damage the seal **(see illustration)**.

6 If removing the left-hand driveshaft, free the inner CV joint from the transmission by levering between the edge of the joint and the transmission casing with a large screwdriver or similar tool. Take care not to damage the transmission oil seal or the inner CV joint gaiter. Withdraw the driveshaft from under the wheel arch.

7 If removing the right-hand driveshaft, undo the two bolts and remove the cap from the intermediate shaft support bearing **(see illustration)**. Pull the intermediate shaft out of the transmission, and remove the driveshaft assembly from under the wheel arch. **Note:** *Do not pull the outer shaft from the intermediate shaft – the coupling will separate.*

Refitting

8 Refitting is a reversal of removal, but observe the following points.

   a) *Prior to refitting, remove all traces, rust, oil and dirt from the splines of the outer CV joint, and lubricate the splines of the inner joint with wheel bearing grease.*
   b) *Renew the rubber seal on the CV joint adjacent to the ABS signal ring (where applicable) if it shows any signs of wear or damage. Note that the seal will only fit properly on the driveshaft one way around.*

   c) *If working on the left-hand driveshaft, ensure that the inner CV joint is pushed fully into the transmission, so that the retaining circlip locks into place in the differential gear.*
   d) *Always use a new driveshaft-to-hub retaining bolt* **(see illustration)**.
   e) *Tighten all nuts and bolts to the specified torque (see Chapter 10 for suspension component torque settings). When tightening the driveshaft bolt, tighten first using a torque wrench, then further, through the specified angle, using an angle-tightening gauge.*
   f) *Tighten the roadwheel bolts to the specified torque.*

3 Outer constant velocity joint gaiter – renewal

1 Remove the driveshaft (Section 2).

2 Cut off the gaiter retaining clips, then slide the gaiter down the shaft to expose the outer constant velocity joint **(see illustration)**.

3 Scoop out as much grease as possible from the joint, then measure and note the distance from the inner groove on the shaft to the inner face of the outer CV joint **(see illustration)**.

4 Tap the exposed face of the inner ball hub with a hammer and brass drift to separate the

2.8 Always renew the driveshaft bolt

3.2 Cut the old clips from the gaiter

3.3 Measure the distance from the inner groove on the shaft to the inner face of the CV joint

3.4 Use a brass drift and hammer to drive the inner joint hub from the driveshaft

3.6a Remove the balls one at a time . . .

3.6b . . . then rotate the cage 90° and lift it out

joint from the driveshaft **(see illustration)**. Slide the gaiter off the driveshaft.

5 With the constant velocity joint removed from the driveshaft, clean the joint using paraffin, or a suitable solvent, and dry it thoroughly. This is especially important if the old gaiter was badly split, as dust and grit may be embedded in the lubricating grease, which will otherwise cause rapid wear of the joint. Remove the retaining circlip from the shaft, and obtain a new one for reassembly (normally supplied in the gaiter kit).

6 Move the inner splined driving member from side-to-side, and remove each ball in turn, then rotate the ball cage 90° to the upright position and lift it from the outer part of the joint **(see illustrations)**. Examine the balls for cracks, flat spots or signs of surface pitting.

7 Inspect the ball tracks on the inner and outer members. If the tracks have widened, the balls will no longer be a tight fit. At the same time, check the ball cage windows for wear or cracking between the windows. At the time of writing, it would appear that only complete exchange driveshafts are available – if the joints appear worn, complete renewal may be the only option – check with a Volvo dealer or specialist.

8 If the joint is in satisfactory condition, obtain a repair kit from your Volvo dealer, consisting of a new gaiter, retaining clips, driveshaft bolt, circlip and grease.

9 Refit the inner driving member and cage into the outer part of the joint, and insert the balls one at a time.

10 Pack the joint with the half of the grease supplied, working it well into the ball tracks,

3.10 Pack the joint with half the grease supplied in the gaiter kit

and into the driveshaft opening in the inner member **(see illustration)**.

11 Slide the rubber gaiter onto the shaft, fit the new circlip to the end of the shaft **(see illustration)**.

12 Engage the constant velocity joint with the driveshaft splines, and tap it onto the shaft until the internal circlip locates in the driveshaft groove. This can by verified by comparing the dimension with that obtained in paragraph 3.

13 Check that the circlip holds the joint securely on the driveshaft, then apply the remaining grease to the joint and the inside of the gaiter **(see illustration)**.

14 Locate the outer lip of the gaiter in the groove on the joint outer member, then fit the two retaining clips. Remove any slack in the clips by carefully compressing the raised section using a pair of pincers **(see illustrations)**.

3.11 Fit the new circlip to the end of the shaft

15 Check that the constant velocity joint moves freely in all directions, then refit the driveshaft as described in Section 2.

16 Volvo recommend lubricating the gaiter once the driveshaft is refitted by applying a small amount of spray wax (Volvo 30787812) to the outside of the gaiter.

4 Inner constant velocity joint gaiter – renewal

Renewal

1 Remove the driveshaft(s) as described in Section 2.

2 Cut through the metal clips, and slide the gaiter from the inner CV joint.

3 Clean out some of the grease from the joint, then make alignment marks between the

3.13 Apply the remaining grease to the inside of the gaiter

3.14a Use pincers to compress the raised section of the outer clip . . .

3.14b . . . and the inner clip

4.3 Make alignment marks between the shaft and housing

4.6a Remove the circlip from the end of the shaft . . .

4.6b . . . then carefully drive the tripod from the shaft

housing and the shaft, to aid reassembly **(see illustration)**.

4 Carefully pull the housing from the tripod, twisting the housing so the tripod rollers come out one at a time. If necessary, use a soft-faced hammer or mallet to tap the housing off.

5 Clean the grease from the tripod and housing.

6 Remove the circlip, and carefully drive the tripod from the end of the shaft **(see illustrations)**. Discard the circlip, a new one (supplied in the repair kit) must be fitted. Remove the gaiter if still on the shaft.

7 Slide the new gaiter onto the shaft along with the smaller clip **(see illustration)**.

8 Refit the tripod with the bevelled edge towards the driveshaft, and drive it fully into

place, until the new circlip can be installed **(see illustrations)**.

9 Lubricate the tripod rollers with some of the grease supplied in the gaiter kit, then fill the housing and gaiter with the remainder.

10 Refit the housing to the tripod, tapping it gently into place using a soft-faced hammer or mallet if necessary.

11 Slide the new gaiter into place ensuring the smaller diameter of the gaiter locates over the grooves in the shaft **(see illustration)**.

12 Fit the new retaining clips and refit the driveshaft **(see illustration)**.

13 Volvo recommend lubricating the gaiter once the driveshaft is refitted by applying a small amount of spray wax (Volvo 30787812) to the outside of the gaiter.

5 Right-hand driveshaft support bearing – removal and refitting

Note: *Renewal of the bearing requires the use of special tools. This task is best entrusted to a Volvo dealer or suitably-equipped specialist.*

6 Driveshaft overhaul – general information

Road test the car, and listen for a metallic clicking from the front as the car is driven slowly in a circle with the steering on full lock. Repeat the check on full-left and full-right lock. This noise may also be apparent when pulling away from a standstill with lock applied. If a clicking noise is heard, this indicates wear in the outer constant velocity joints.

If vibration, consistent with roadspeed, is felt through the car when accelerating, there is a possibility of wear in the inner constant velocity joints.

If the joints are worn or damaged, it would appear at the time of writing that no parts are available, other than boot kits, and the complete driveshaft must be renewed. Exchange driveshafts are available – check with a Volvo dealer or specialist.

4.7 Slide the new gaiter and smaller diameter clip onto the shaft

4.8a Fit the tripod with the bevelled edge (arrowed) towards the shaft . . .

4.8b . . . then fit the new circlip

4.11 The smaller diameter of the gaiter must locate over the groove in the shaft (arrowed)

4.12 Equalise the air pressure before tightening the gaiter clip

Chapter 9
Braking system

Contents

Degrees of difficulty

Easy, suitable for novice with little experience	**Fairly easy,** suitable for beginner with some experience	**Fairly difficult,** suitable for competent DIY mechanic	**Difficult,** suitable for experienced DIY mechanic	**Very difficult,** suitable for expert DIY or professional

Specifications

General

System type:

Footbrake . . . . Dual-circuit hydraulic with servo assistance. Disc brakes front and rear. Anti-lock braking (ABS) on all models

Handbrake . . . . Electrically-operated

Front brakes

Type   Ventilated disc, with single-piston sliding calipers

Brake pad friction material minimum thickness	2.0 mm
Disc diameter	286, 305 or 320 mm
Disc thickness:	
All except 305 mm diameter discs:	
New	26.0 mm
Wear limit	23.0 mm
305 mm diameter discs:	
New	28.0 mm
Wear limit	25.0 mm
Maximum disc run-out	0.04 mm
Maximum disc thickness variation	0.008 mm

Rear brakes

Type   Solid disc, with single-piston sliding calipers

Brake pad minimum lining thickness	2.0 mm
Disc diameter	295 mm
Disc thickness:	
New	13.0 mm
Wear limit	10.0 mm
Maximum disc run-out	0.08 mm
Maximum disc thickness variation	0.008 mm

Torque wrench settings

	Nm	lbf ft
ABS unit mounting bolts	10	7
ABS unit pipe unions:		
6 mm diameter	14	10
8 mm diameter	18	13
ABS wheel sensor mounting bolts	5	4
Brake disc retaining bolt	35	26
Brake pedal bolts	24	18
Flexible hose unions	18	13
Front caliper:		
Guide pins*	28	21
Bracket bolts*	200	148
Handbrake actuator bolts	10	7
Handbrake control module mounting bolts	7	5
Master cylinder mounting nuts	25	18
Rear caliper:		
Guide pin bolts*	35	26
Caliper bracket bolts*	110	81
Rigid pipe unions	14	10
Roadwheel bolts	140	103
Steering column joint pinch-bolt	See Chapter 10	
Subframe mounting bolts:*	See Chapter 10	
Vacuum pump bolts	See Chapter 2A, 2B or 2C	
Vacuum servo unit mounting nuts	24	18

* Do not re-use

1 General information

The brake pedal operates disc brakes on all four wheels by means of a dual circuit hydraulic system with servo assistance. The handbrake is electrically-operated and acts on the rear brake pads by means of an actuator. An anti-lock braking system (ABS) is fitted to all models, and is described in further detail in Section 17.

The hydraulic system is split into two circuits, so that in the event of failure of one circuit, the other will still provide adequate braking power (although pedal travel and effort may increase). An axle-split system is employed, in which one circuit serves the front brakes and the other circuit the rear brakes.

The brake servo is of the direct-acting type, being interposed between the brake pedal and the master cylinder. The servo magnifies the effort applied by the driver. It is vacuum-operated with a camshaft-driven vacuum pump.

Instrument panel warning lights alert the driver to low fluid level by means of a level sensor in the master cylinder reservoir. Other warning lights remind when the handbrake is applied, and indicate the presence of a fault in the ABS system.

Note: *When servicing any part of the system, work carefully and methodically; also observe scrupulous cleanliness when overhauling any part of the hydraulic system. Always renew components (in axle sets, where applicable) if in doubt about their condition, and use only genuine Volvo parts, or at least those of known good quality. Note the warnings given* in 'Safety first!' and at relevant points in this Chapter concerning the dangers of asbestos dust and hydraulic fluid.

2 Hydraulic system – bleeding

⚠ *Warning: Hydraulic fluid is poisonous; wash off immediately and thoroughly in the case of skin contact, and seek immediate medical advice if any fluid is swallowed or gets into the eyes. Certain types of hydraulic fluid are inflammable, and may ignite when allowed into contact with hot components; when servicing any hydraulic system, it is safest to assume that the fluid IS inflammable, and to take precautions against the risk of fire as though it is petrol that is being handled. Hydraulic fluid is also an effective paint stripper, and will attack plastics; if any is spilt, it should be washed off immediately, using copious quantities of clean water. Finally, it is hygroscopic (it absorbs moisture from the air). The more moisture is absorbed by the fluid, the lower its boiling point becomes, leading to a dangerous loss of braking under hard use. Old fluid may be contaminated and unfit for further use. When topping-up or renewing the fluid, always use the recommended type, and ensure that it comes from a freshly-opened sealed container.*

General

1 The correct functioning of the brake hydraulic system is only possible after removing all air from the components and circuit; this is achieved by bleeding the system.

2 During the bleeding procedure, add only clean, fresh hydraulic fluid of the specified type; never re-use fluid that has already been bled from the system. Ensure that sufficient fluid is available before starting work.

3 If there is any possibility of incorrect fluid being used in the system, the brake lines and components must be completely flushed with uncontaminated fluid and new seals fitted to the components.

4 If brake fluid has been lost from the master cylinder due to a leak in the system, ensure that the cause is traced and rectified before proceeding further.

5 Park the car on level ground, apply the handbrake, and switch off the ignition.

6 Check that all pipes and hoses are secure, unions tight, and bleed screws closed. Remove the dust caps and clean any dirt from around the bleed screws.

7 Unscrew the master cylinder reservoir cap, and top-up the reservoir to the MAX level line. Refit the cap loosely, and remember to maintain the fluid level at least above the MIN level line throughout the procedure, otherwise there is a risk of further air entering the system.

8 There is a number of one-man, do-it-yourself, brake bleeding kits currently available from motor accessory shops. It is recommended that one of these kits is used wherever possible, as they greatly simplify the bleeding operation, and also reduce the risk of expelled air and fluid being drawn back into the system. If such a kit is not available, the basic (two-man) method must be used, which is described in detail below.

9 If a kit is to be used, prepare the car as described previously, and follow the kit manufacturer's instructions, as the procedure may vary slightly according to the type being used; generally, they are as outlined below in the relevant sub-section.

10 Whichever method is used, the same sequence must be followed (paragraphs 11 and 12) to ensure the removal of all air from the system.

Bleeding sequence

11 If the hydraulic system has only been partially disconnected and suitable precautions were taken to minimise fluid loss, it should only be necessary to bleed that part of the system (ie, the primary or secondary circuit).

12 If the complete system is to be bled, then it should be done in the following sequence:
  a) *Front left-hand brake*
  b) *Front right-hand brake.*
  c) *Rear brakes (in any order).*

Bleeding

Basic (two-man) method

13 Collect a clean glass jar of reasonable size, a suitable length of plastic or rubber tubing which is a tight fit over the bleed screw, and a ring spanner to fit the screws. The help of an assistant will also be required.

14 If not already done, remove the dust cap from the bleed screw of the first wheel to be bled **(see illustration)**, and fit the spanner and bleed tube to the screw. Place the other end of the tube in the jar, and pour in sufficient fluid to cover the end of the tube.

15 Ensure that the master cylinder reservoir fluid level is maintained at least above the MIN level line throughout the procedure.

16 Have the assistant fully depress the brake pedal several times to build-up pressure, then maintain it on the final downstroke.

17 While pedal pressure is maintained, unscrew the bleed screw (approximately one turn) and allow the compressed fluid and air to flow into the jar. The assistant should maintain pedal pressure, following it down to the floor if necessary, and should not release it until instructed to do so. When the flow stops, tighten the bleed screw again have the assistant release the pedal slowly, and recheck the reservoir fluid level.

18 Repeat the steps given in paragraphs 16 and 17 until the fluid emerging from the bleed screw is free from air bubbles. If the master cylinder has been drained and refilled, and air is being bled from the first screw in the sequence, allow approximately five seconds between cycles for the master cylinder passages to refill.

19 When no more air bubbles appear, tighten the bleed screw securely, remove the tube and spanner, and refit the dust cap. Do not overtighten the bleed screw.

20 Repeat these procedures on the remaining calipers in sequence until all air is removed from the system and the brake pedal feels firm again.

Using a one-way valve kit

21 As their name implies, these kits consist of a length of tubing with a one-way valve fitted,

2.14 Pull the dust cap (arrowed) from the bleed screw

to prevent expelled air and fluid being drawn back into the system; some kits include a translucent container, which can be positioned so that the air bubbles can be more easily seen flowing from the end of the tube.

22 The kit is connected to the bleed screw, which is then opened **(see illustration)**. The user returns to the driver's seat, depresses the brake pedal with a smooth steady stroke, and slowly releases it; this is repeated until the expelled fluid is clear of air bubbles.

23 Note that these kits simplify work so much that it is easy to forget the master cylinder fluid level; ensure that this is maintained at least above the MIN level line at all times.

Using a pressure-bleeding kit

Note: *This is the method recommended by Volvo if the hydraulic system has been either wholly or partially drained.*

24 These kits are usually operated by the reserve of pressurised air contained in the spare tyre. However, note that it will probably be necessary to reduce the pressure to a lower level than normal; refer to the instructions supplied with the kit.

25 By connecting a pressurised, fluid-filled container to the master cylinder reservoir, bleeding is then carried out by simply opening each bleed screw in turn (in the specified sequence) and allowing the fluid to run out, until no more air bubbles can be seen in the expelled fluid.

26 This method has the advantage that the large reservoir of fluid provides an additional safeguard against air being drawn into the system during bleeding.

27 Pressure-bleeding is particularly effective when bleeding difficult systems, or when bleeding the complete system at the time of routine fluid renewal.

All methods

28 When bleeding is complete, and firm pedal feel is restored, wash off any spilt fluid, tighten the bleed screws securely, and refit their dust caps.

29 Check the hydraulic fluid level in the master cylinder reservoir, and top-up if necessary.

30 Discard any hydraulic fluid that has been bled from the system; it will not be fit for re-use.

2.22 Connect the kit and open the bleed screw

31 Check the feel of the brake pedal. If it feels at all spongy, air must still be present in the system, and further bleeding is required. Failure to bleed satisfactorily after a reasonable repetition of the bleeding operations may be due to worn master cylinder seals.

32 Check the operation of the clutch. Any problems noted would indicate a need to bleed the clutch system also – see Chapter 6.

---

3 Hydraulic pipes and hoses – renewal

Note: *Before starting work, refer to the warning at the beginning of Section 2 concerning the dangers of hydraulic fluid.*

1 If any pipe or hose is to be renewed, minimise hydraulic fluid loss by removing the master cylinder reservoir cap, placing a piece of plastic film over the reservoir and sealing it with an elastic band. Alternatively, flexible hoses can be sealed, if required, using a proprietary brake hose clamp; metal brake pipe unions can be plugged (if care is taken not to allow dirt into the system) or capped immediately they are disconnected. Place a wad of rag under any union that is to be disconnected, to catch any spilt fluid.

2 If a flexible hose is to be disconnected, unscrew the brake pipe union nut before removing the spring clip which secures the hose to its mounting, where applicable. Some of the flexible hose unions are protected by a rubber cover – in this case, the pipe will have to be removed from its mounting bracket first, and the cover slid down the pipe, before the nut can be unscrewed.

3 To unscrew the union nuts, it is preferable to obtain a brake pipe spanner of the correct size; these are available from most large motor accessory shops. Failing this, a close-fitting open-ended spanner will be required, though if the nuts are tight or corroded, their flats may be rounded-off if the spanner slips. In such a case, a self-locking wrench is often the only way to unscrew a stubborn union, but it follows that the pipe and the damaged nuts must be renewed on reassembly.

4 Always clean a union and surrounding area before disconnecting it. If disconnecting a

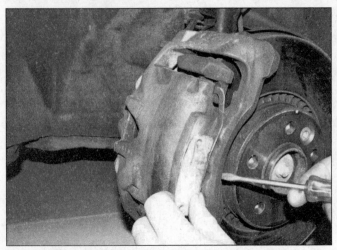

4.2a Carefully prise the spring clip from the caliper

4.2b Remove the plastic caps from the rear of the caliper . . .

4.2c . . . and unscrew the guide pins using an Allen key

4.2d Lift the caliper from the bracket

4.2e Lift out the outer brake pad . . .

4.2f . . . and unclip the inner brake pad from the caliper piston component with more than one union, make a careful note of the connections before disturbing any of them.

5 If a brake pipe is to be renewed, it can be obtained, cut to length and with the union nuts and end flares in place from Volvo dealers. All that is then necessary is to bend it to shape, following the line of the original, before fitting it to the car. Alternatively, most motor accessory shops can make up brake pipes from kits, but this requires very careful measurement of the original, to ensure that the new one is of the correct length. The safest answer is usually to take the original to the shop as a pattern.

6 Before refitting, blow through the new pipe or hose with dry compressed air. Do not overtighten the union nuts. It is not necessary to exercise brute force to obtain a sound joint.

7 If flexible rubber hoses are renewed, ensure that the pipes and hoses are correctly routed, with no kinks or twists, and that they are secured in the clips or brackets provided. Original equipment flexible hoses have white lines along their length which clearly show if the hose is twisted.

8 After fitting, bleed the hydraulic system as described in Section 2, wash off any spilt fluid, and check carefully for fluid leaks.

4 Front brake pads – renewal

⚠️ **Warning: Disc brake pads must be renewed on both front wheels at the same time – never renew the pads on only one wheel, as uneven braking may result. Dust created by wear of the pads may contain asbestos, which is a health hazard. Never blow it out with compressed air and do not inhale any of it. DO NOT use petroleum-based solvents to clean brake parts. Use brake cleaner or methylated spirit only. DO NOT allow any brake fluid, oil or grease to contact the brake pads or disc. Also refer to the warning at the start of Section 2 concerning the dangers of hydraulic fluid.**

1 Loosen the front wheel bolts and chock the rear wheels. Jack up the front of the car and support it on axle stands (see *Jacking and vehicle support*). Remove the front roadwheels.

2 Follow the accompanying photos **(illustrations 4.2a to 4.2k)** for the pad renewal procedure. Be sure to stay in order and read the caption under each illustration, and note the following points:

a) *Measure the thickness of the pad friction material (see illustration 4.2g). If any one pad has worn down to the specified minimum, all four front pads must be renewed. Do not interchange pads in an attempt to even out wear (uneven pad wear may be due to the caliper sticking on the guide pins).*

b) *Thoroughly clean the caliper guide surfaces, and apply a little silicone grease (Volvo 116 1688) to the caliper bracket where the pads contact the bracket, and to the corresponding point on the pads.*

c) *When pushing the caliper piston back to accommodate new pads, keep a close eye on the fluid level in the reservoir.*

Caution: Pushing back the piston causes a reverse-flow of brake fluid, which has been known to 'flip' the master cylinder rubber seals, resulting in a total loss of braking. To avoid this, clamp the caliper flexible hose and open the bleed screw – as the piston is pushed back, the fluid can be directed into a suitable container using a hose attached to the bleed screw. Close the screw just before the piston is pushed fully back, to ensure no air enters the system.

4.2g If the thickness of the pads is less than 2 mm, all the pads should be renewed

4.2h Press the piston back into the caliper using a piston retraction tool

4.2i Insert the new outer brake pad into the caliper bracket . . .

4.2j . . . and clip the new inner brake into the caliper piston

4.2k Refit the caliper, insert new guide pins, and tighten them to the specified torque

3 Depress the brake pedal repeatedly, until the pads are pressed into firm contact with the brake disc, and normal (non-assisted) pedal pressure is restored.

4 Repeat the above procedure on the remaining front brake caliper.

5 Refit the roadwheels, then lower the vehicle to the ground and tighten the roadwheel bolts to the specified torque.

6 Check the hydraulic fluid level as described in *Weekly checks*.

Caution: New pads will not give full braking efficiency until they have bedded-in. Be prepared for this, and avoid hard braking as far as possible for the first hundred miles or so after pad renewal.

5 Rear brake pads – renewal

⚠ *Warning: Disc brake pads must be renewed on both rear wheels at the same time – never renew the pads on only one wheel as uneven braking may result. Dust created by wear of the pads may contain asbestos, which is a health hazard. Never blow it out with*

compressed air and do not inhale any of it. *DO NOT use petroleum-based solvents to clean brake parts. Use brake cleaner or methylated spirit only. DO NOT allow any brake fluid, oil or grease to contact the brake pads or disc. Also refer to the warning at the start of Section 2 concerning the dangers of hydraulic fluid.*

1 Loosen the rear wheel bolts and chock the front wheels. Jack up the rear of the car and support it on axle stands (see *Jacking and vehicle support*). Remove the rear roadwheels.

2 Activate the handbrake service mode. You will need a tool similar to the one shown **(see illustration)**, which can be purchased from specialist suppliers. Alternatively, the task of changing the rear brake pads will need to be entrusted to a Volvo dealer or suitably-equipped specialist.

3 Follow the accompanying photos **(illustrations 5.2 to 5.3k)** for the pad renewal procedure. Be sure to stay in order and read the caption under each illustration, and note the following points:

a) *Thoroughly clean the caliper guide surfaces, and apply a little silicone grease (Volvo 116 1688) to the bracket where the*

5.2 Activate the handbrake service mode using a suitable tool

pads contact it, and to the corresponding point on the pads.

b) *When pushing the caliper piston back to accommodate new pads, keep a close eye on the fluid level in the reservoir.*

c) *Note that the top and bottom metal clips that secure the brake pads differ slightly so note the correct position on removal.*

Caution: Pushing back the piston causes a reverse-flow of brake fluid, which has been known to 'flip' the master cylinder rubber seals, resulting in a total loss of braking. To avoid this, clamp the caliper flexible hose

5.3a Undo the caliper guide pin bolts

5.3b Move the caliper from the bracket

5.3c Remove the outer brake pad . . .

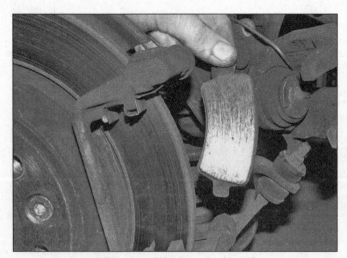

5.3d . . . and the inner brake pad

5.3e Remove the lower clip . . .

5.3f . . . and the upper clip

5.3g Clean the caliper surfaces using a suitable brake cleaning agent

5.3h Fit the new upper clip . . .

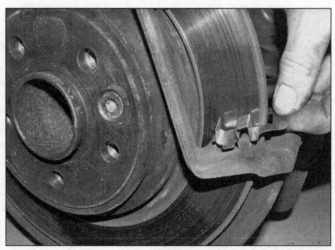

5.3i . . . and lower clip

5.3j Apply a little silicone grease where the brake pads contact the bracket

5.3k Insert the new pads and fit the caliper using new bolts tightened to the specified torque

6.4 Measure the disc thickness using a micrometer

6.5 Undo the bolts (arrowed) and remove the brake caliper bracket

6.6 Front brake disc securing screw

and open the bleed screw – as the piston is pushed back, the fluid can be directed into a suitable container using a hose attached to the bleed screw. Close the screw just before the piston is pushed fully back, to ensure no air enters the system.

4 Depress the brake pedal repeatedly, until the pads are pressed into firm contact with the brake disc, and normal (non-assisted) pedal pressure is restored.

5 Repeat the above procedure on the remaining rear brake caliper.

6 Deactivate the handbrake service mode (see the note above)

7 Refit the roadwheels, then lower the vehicle to the ground and tighten the roadwheel bolts to the specified torque.

8 Check the hydraulic fluid level as described in *Weekly checks*.

Caution: New pads will not give full braking efficiency until they have bedded-in. Be prepared for this, and avoid hard braking as far as possible for the first hundred miles or so after pad renewal.

6 Front brake disc – inspection, removal and refitting

Note: Before starting work, refer to the warning at the beginning of Section 4 concerning the dangers of asbestos dust.

Inspection

Note: If either disc requires renewal, BOTH

7.3 Undo the caliper bracket bolts (arrowed)

should be renewed at the same time, to ensure even and consistent braking. New brake pads should also be fitted.

1 Remove the front brake pads as described in Section 4.

2 Inspect the disc friction surfaces for cracks or deep scoring (light grooving is normal and may be ignored). A cracked disc must be renewed; a scored disc can be reclaimed by machining, provided that the thickness is not reduced below the specified minimum.

3 Check the disc run-out using a dial test indicator with its probe positioned near the outer edge of the disc. If the run-out exceeds the figures given in the Specifications, machining may be possible, otherwise disc renewal will be necessary.

4 Excessive disc thickness variation can also cause judder. Check this using a micrometer (see illustration).

Removal

5 With the brake pads and caliper removed (Section 8), undo the two mounting bolts and remove the brake caliper bracket (see illustration). Note that new bolts will be required for refitting.

6 Check whether the position of the disc in relation to the hub is marked, and if not, make your own mark as an aid to refitting. Remove the screw which holds the disc to the hub, and lift off the disc (see illustration). Tap it with a soft-faced mallet if necessary to free it.

Refitting

7 Ensure that the hub and disc mating faces are spotlessly clean. Clean any rustproofing

7.4 Rear brake disc securing screw

compound off a new disc with degreaser and a rag.

8 Locate the disc on the hub with the orientation marks aligned, then refit and tighten the retaining screw.

9 Refit the brake caliper bracket and limiter bracket, then tighten the new bolts to the specified torque.

10 Refit the brake pads as described in Section 4.

7 Rear brake disc – inspection, removal and refitting

Note: Before starting work, refer to the warning at the beginning of Section 5 concerning the dangers of asbestos dust.

Inspection

Note: If either disc requires renewal, BOTH should be renewed at the same time, to ensure even and consistent braking. New brake pads should also be fitted.

1 With the rear brake pads removed (Section 5), the inspection procedures are the same as for the front brake disc, and reference should be made to Section 6.

Removal

2 If not already done, remove the rear brake pads as described in Section 5. Suitably support the caliper, or suspend it using string or wire tied to a convenient suspension component.

3 Undo the two caliper bracket bolts, and withdraw the bracket (see illustration). Note that new bolts will be required for refitting.

4 Unscrew the disc retaining screw (see illustration).

5 Mark the position of the disc in relation to the hub, then pull off the disc. Tap it with a soft-faced mallet if necessary to free it.

Refitting

6 Ensure that the hub and disc mating faces are spotlessly clean. Clean any rustproofing compound off a new disc with degreaser and a rag.

7 Locate the disc on the hub with the orientation marks aligned, and refit the retaining screw.

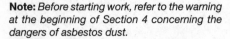

8 Refit the brake caliper bracket and tighten the new bolts to the specified torque.
9 Refit the brake pads as described in Section 5.

8 Front brake caliper – removal, overhaul and refitting

Note: *Before starting work, refer to the warning at the beginning of Section 2 concerning the dangers of hydraulic fluid, and to the warning at the beginning of Section 4 concerning the dangers of asbestos dust.*

Removal

1 Apply the handbrake and chock the rear wheels. Loosen the front wheel bolts, then jack up the front of the car and support it on axle stands (see *Jacking and vehicle support*). Remove the roadwheel.
2 To minimise fluid loss, unscrew the master cylinder reservoir filler cap and place a piece of polythene over the filler neck. Secure the polythene with an elastic band ensuring that an airtight seal is obtained. Preferably, use a brake hose clamp, a G-clamp, or a similar tool with protected jaws, to clamp the front flexible hydraulic hose **(see illustration)**.
3 Clean the area around the hydraulic hose-to-caliper union, then slacken the hose union half a turn. Be prepared for fluid spillage.
4 Remove the brake pads as described in Section 4.
5 Unscrew the caliper from the hydraulic hose, and wipe up any spilled brake fluid immediately. Plug or cap the open unions.
6 If required, remove the caliper bracket by undoing the two bolts which secure it to the hub carrier. Note that new bolts will be required for refitting.

Overhaul

Note: *At the time of writing it was unclear whether overhaul kits were available for the calipers. Check with a Volvo dealer or specialist prior to dismantling the caliper.*

Refitting

7 If removed, refit the caliper bracket using new bolts tightened to the specified torque.

8 Refit the brake pads as described in Section 4, but screw the caliper onto the flexible hose before refitting it to the caliper bracket.
9 Tighten the flexible hose union ensuring that the hose is not kinked.
10 Remove the brake hose clamp or polythene, where fitted, and bleed the hydraulic system as described in Section 2.
11 Apply the footbrake two or three times to settle the pads, then refit the roadwheel and lower the car. Tighten the wheel bolts in a diagonal sequence to the specified torque.

9 Rear brake caliper – removal, overhaul and refitting
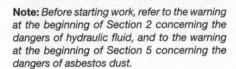

Note: *Before starting work, refer to the warning at the beginning of Section 2 concerning the dangers of hydraulic fluid, and to the warning at the beginning of Section 5 concerning the dangers of asbestos dust.*

Removal

1 To minimise fluid loss, unscrew the master cylinder reservoir filler cap, and place a piece of polythene over the filler neck. Secure the polythene with an elastic band, ensuring that an airtight seal is obtained. Preferably, use a brake hose clamp, a G-clamp, or a similar tool with protected jaws, to clamp the rear flexible hydraulic hose.
2 Activate the handbrake service mode.
3 Clean around the hydraulic union on the caliper, and undo. Be prepared for fluid spillage and plug or cap the open unions.
4 Disconnect the wiring plug from the parking brake actuator.
5 Undo the 2 caliper guide pin bolts.

Overhaul

Note: *At the time of writing it was unclear whether overhaul kits were available for the calipers. Check with a Volvo dealer or specialist prior to dismantling the caliper.*

Refitting

6 Refit the brake caliper using new guide pin bolts.
7 Refit the brake pipe to the caliper, and tighten the union securely.

8 Remove the brake hose clamp or polythene, where fitted, and bleed the hydraulic system as described in Section 2.
9 Deactivate the handbrake service mode.
10 Apply the footbrake two or three times to settle the pads, then refit the roadwheel and lower the car. Tighten the wheel bolts in a diagonal sequence to the specified torque.

10 Brake master cylinder – removal and refitting

Note: *Before starting work, refer to the warning at the beginning of Section 2 concerning the dangers of hydraulic fluid.*
Note: *Overhaul of the master cylinder is not possible, and internal components are not available separately. In the event of a fault in the master cylinder, the unit must be renewed.*

Removal

1 Disconnect the battery negative lead (see Chapter 5A).
2 Depress the brake pedal repeatedly to collapse any residual vacuum in the servo, then siphon as much fluid as possible from the master cylinder reservoir, using a hydrometer or old poultry baster.
Caution: Do not siphon the fluid by mouth – it is poisonous.
3 Disconnect any wiring connectors from the reservoir/master cylinder.
4 Remove the reservoir.
5 Disconnect the hydraulic pipe unions from the master cylinder. Be prepared for further fluid spillage. Cap the open unions to keep dirt out.
6 Remove the nuts which secure the master cylinder to the servo **(see illustrations)**. Pull the master cylinder off the servo studs and remove it. Discard the O-ring seal, a new one must be fitted. Be careful not to spill hydraulic fluid on the paintwork.

Refitting

7 Place the master cylinder (with a new seal) in position on the servo unit, and secure with the nuts tightened to the specified torque.
8 Refit the brake pipes, but do not tighten the union nuts fully at this stage.
9 Refit the reservoir.

8.2 Clamp the flexible brake hose

10.6a Undo the upper master cylinder nut (arrowed) . . .

10.6b . . . and the lower master cylinder nut

11.2 Brake pedal servo rod retaining clip (arrowed)

11.3 Brake pedal securing nuts (arrowed)

d) Check and, if necessary, bleed the hydraulic system as described in Section 2 on completion.

10 Reconnect the reservoir/master cylinder electrical connectors.
11 Place absorbent rags under the brake pipe unions on the master cylinder, then fill the reservoir with clean hydraulic fluid of the specified type.
12 Tighten the brake pipe unions securely when hydraulic fluid can be seen seeping out.
13 Bleed the hydraulic system as described in Section 2 on completion.
14 After the system has been bled, pressure test the master cylinder by depressing the brake pedal hard and holding it down for 30 seconds. Release the pedal and check for leaks around the master cylinder pipe unions.

6 Refit the facia trim panel.
7 Check the operation of the brake lights.

12 Vacuum servo unit – removal and refitting

Removal

1 Disconnect the battery negative lead (see Chapter 5A), then depress the brake pedal several times to dissipate any vacuum in the servo unit.
2 Remove the master cylinder as described in Section 10.
3 Disconnect the vacuum hose from the servo and, noting their fitted positions, disconnect any wiring connectors.
4 Remove the trim panel under the facia on the driver's side as described in Chapter 11.
5 Disconnect the servo pushrod and linkage from the brake pedal by removing the retaining clip **(see illustration 11.2)**.
6 Undo the four nuts securing the servo unit to the bulkhead and withdraw the unit from the engine bay.

Refitting

7 Refitting is a reversal of removal bearing in mind the following points:
   a) *Ensure that the seal is in position before fitting the servo.*
   b) *The nuts securing the servo to the bulkhead should be renewed. Tighten all nuts and bolts to the specified torque.*
   c) *Refit the master cylinder as described in Section 10.*

13 Handbrake actuator – removal and refitting

1 Loosen the rear wheel bolts and chock the front wheels. Jack up the rear of the car and support it on axle stands (see *Jacking and vehicle support*). Remove the rear roadwheels.
2 Activate the handbrake service mode (see the note in Section 5).
3 Disconnect the wiring plug from the actuator **(see illustration)**.
4 Undo the 2 screws and remove the actuator from the brake caliper **(see illustration)**.
5 Refitting is a reversal of removal. Deactivate the handbrake service mode.

14 Handbrake switch – removal and refitting

1 The switch is located to the right-hand side of the steering wheel, below the main light switch.
2 To remove, undo the 2 screws and remove the trim panel containing the switch **(see illustration)**. Undo the wiring plug as the panel is withdrawn.
3 Refitting is a reversal of removal.

15 Handbrake module – removal and refitting

1 The module is located behind the left-hand side trim panel in the luggage area. Remove the panel as described in Chapter 11.
2 Undo the 2 bolts, disconnecting the wiring plug, and remove.
3 Refitting is a reversal of removal. Note that if a new unit is fitted, suitable software will need to be downloaded and installed from Volvo. Entrust this task to a Volvo dealer of suitably-equipped specialist.

11 Brake pedal – removal and refitting

Removal

1 Remove the trim panel under the facia on the driver's side as described in Chapter 11.
2 Release the retaining clip and disconnect the servo pushrod from the pedal **(see illustration)**.
3 Undo the nuts securing the pedal bracket to the brake servo **(see illustration)**.

Refitting

4 Manoeuvre the pedal into position. Renew all retaining bolts and tighten to the specified torque.
5 Reconnect the servo pushrod to the pedal, and secure it with the retaining clip.

13.3 Handbrake actuator wiring plug

13.4 Undo the two actuator securing screws (arrowed)

14.2 Handbrake switch securing screws (arrowed)

16.2 The brake light switch (arrowed) is located to the right of the brake pedal

16 Brake light switch – removal and refitting

Removal

1 Ensure the ignition is switched off.
2 Remove the trim panel under the facia on the driver's side as described in Chapter 11. The brake light switch is located immediately to the right of the brake pedal, adjacent to the brake diagnosis switch **(see illustration)**. Note that both units must be removed before the brake light switch can be renewed or refitted.
3 Disconnect the wiring plugs from both switches.
4 Remove the brake diagnosis switch by twisting anti-clockwise and pulling it from place. Then remove the brake light switch by twisting clockwise and pulling it from place.

Refitting

5 With the brake pedal in the rest position, insert the brake light switch and twist anti-clockwise to lock in position.
6 Insert the brake diagnosis switch and twist clockwise to lock in position. Use a feeler gauge to check the clearance between the

plunger and the bracket at the rear – the gap should be between 0.5 and 1.5 mm
7 Reconnect the wiring plugs and refit the panels removed for access.

17 Anti-lock braking system (ABS) – general information

The anti-lock braking system, fitted as standard equipment on all models, monitors the rotational speed of the wheels under braking. Sudden deceleration of one wheel, indicating that lock-up is occurring, causes the hydraulic pressure to that wheel's brake to be reduced or interrupted momentarily.

The main components of the system are the wheel sensors, the electronic control module (ECM) and the hydraulic modulator assembly.

One sensor is fitted to each wheel, together with a pulse wheel carried on the wheel/driveshaft hub. The sensors monitor the rotational speeds of the wheels, and are able to detect when there is a risk of wheel locking (low rotational speed). The wheel sensors also provide vehicle speed information to the speedometer.

Information from the sensors is fed to the ECM, which operates solenoid valves in the hydraulic modulator. The solenoid valves restrict the hydraulic fluid supply to any caliper detected to be on the verge of locking.

Should a fault develop in the system, the ECM illuminates a warning light on the instrument panel and disables the system. Normal braking will still be available, but without the anti-lock function. In the event of a fault, the ECM stores a series of signals (or fault codes) for subsequent read-out using diagnostic equipment (see Section 19).

Electronic brake force distribution (EBD) is incorporated into the ABS system, and regulates the proportion of braking force applied to the front and rear wheels.

On cars equipped with a traction control system, the ABS system performs a dual role.

In addition to detecting when a wheel is locking under braking, the system also detects a wheel that is spinning under acceleration. When this condition is detected, the brake on that wheel is momentarily applied to reduce, or eliminate, the wheelspin. When the rotational speed of the spinning wheel is detected to be equal to the other wheels, the brake is released. On vehicles equipped with stability control the same sensors, solenoids and pipes are used. However, vehicles are also equipped with a combined yaw rate and lateral acceleration sensor, and a steering wheel angle sensor.

18 Anti-lock braking system (ABS) components – removal and refitting

Removal

Front wheel sensor

1 Loosen the appropriate front wheel bolts and chock the rear wheels. Jack up the front of the car and support it on axle stands (see *Jacking and vehicle support*). Remove the roadwheel.
2 Undo the screw which secures the sensor to the hub carrier **(see illustration)** and disconnect the wiring plug. Withdraw the sensor, and unclip the wiring from any brackets.

Rear wheel sensor

3 Loosen the appropriate rear wheel bolts and chock the front wheels. Jack up the rear of the car and support it on axle stands (see *Jacking and vehicle support*). Remove the roadwheel.
4 Undo the screw which secures the sensor to the hub carrier **(see illustration)** and disconnect the wiring plug. Withdraw the sensor, and unclip the wiring from any brackets.

Hydraulic modulator

Note: *Before starting work, refer to the warning at the beginning of Section 2 concerning the dangers of hydraulic fluid.*

18.2 Front ABS sensor securing screw (arrowed)

18.4 Rear ABS sensor securing screw (arrowed)

18.9 Disconnect the wiring plug (arrowed) from the side of the hydraulic modulator

18.13 Brake pedal position sensor

5 Remove the battery and battery tray as described in Chapter 5A. Where fitted, undo the mounting bolts and remove the bracket below the battery tray.

6 Remove the plenum cover as described in Chapter 12, Section 18.

7 Wipe clean all the brake pipe unions at the hydraulic modulator. Place absorbent rags beneath the pipe unions to catch any spilt fluid.

8 Before disconnecting the fluid pipes from the hydraulic modulator, mark them for position (eg, by wrapping labels around the pipes). Undo the union nuts on the brake pipes on the top of the hydraulic modulator. Carefully withdraw the pipes, and cover the open unions and pipe ends.

9 Release the connector locking clip and disconnect the wiring plug on the side of the modulator **(see illustration)**.

10 Undo the bolts securing the hydraulic modulator mounting bracket to the bulkhead. Move the wiring aside, and lift out the modulator assembly and bracket.

11 Note that the modulator is a sealed precision assembly, and must not under any circumstances be dismantled. If the unit is knocked or dropped, it must be renewed. If a new unit is being fitted, do not remove any blanking plugs until the pipes are ready for reconnection.

Brake pedal position sensor

12 Depress the brake pedal two or three times to dissipate any vacuum remaining in the servo unit.

13 Disconnect the wiring connector from the pedal sensor located on the front face of the vacuum servo unit **(see illustration)**.

14 Open the circlip and withdraw the sensor from the servo. Recover the O-ring and spacer sleeve from the sensor if fitted.

Refitting

15 In all cases, refitting is a reversal of the removal operations but note the following points:

a) Clean off all dirt from the wheel sensors and mounting locations before refitting with a stiff brush.

b) Bleed the hydraulic system as described in Section 2 after refitting the hydraulic modulator.

c) Where fitted use a new O-ring on the brake pedal position sensor, and ensure that the colour-coded spacer sleeve matches the colour code of the servo unit.

19 Anti-lock braking system (ABS) – fault diagnosis

General information

1 The anti-lock braking system incorporates an on-board diagnostic system to facilitate fault finding and system testing. Should a fault occur, the ECM stores a series of signals (or fault codes) for subsequent read-out via the diagnostic plug located under the facia, above the pedals.

2 If problems have been experienced, the on-board diagnostic system can be used to pinpoint any problem areas, but this requires special test equipment. Once this has been done, further tests may often be necessary to determine the exact nature of the fault; ie, whether a component itself has failed, or whether it is a wiring or other inter-related problem. Apart from visually checking the wiring and connections, any testing will require the use of a fault code reader at least. A Volvo dealer will obviously have such a reader, but they are also available from other suppliers. It is unlikely to be cost-effective for the private owner to purchase a fault code reader, but a well-equipped local garage or auto-electrical specialist will have one.

Preliminary checks

Note: *When carrying out these checks to trace a fault, remember that if the fault has*

appeared only a short time after any part of the vehicle has been serviced or overhauled, the first place to check is where that work was carried out, however unrelated it may appear, to ensure that no carelessly-refitted components are causing the problem.

Note: *Remember that any fault codes which have been logged will have to be cleared from the ECM memory using a dedicated fault code reader (see paragraph 2) before you can be certain the cause of the fault has been fixed.*

3 Check the condition of the battery connections – remake the connections or renew the leads if a fault is found. Use the same techniques to ensure that all earth points in the engine compartment provide good electrical contact through clean, metal-to-metal joints, and that all are securely fastened.

4 Next work methodically around the engine compartment, checking all visible wiring, and the connections between sections of the wiring loom. What you are looking for at this stage is wiring that is obviously damaged by chafing against sharp edges, or against moving suspension/transmission components and/or the auxiliary drivebelt, by being trapped or crushed between carelessly-refitted components, or melted by being forced into contact with hot engine castings, coolant pipes, etc. In almost all cases, damage of this sort is caused in the first instance by incorrect routing on reassembly after previous work has been carried out (see the note at the beginning of this sub-Section).

5 Wires can break or short together inside the insulation so that no visible evidence betrays the fault, but this usually only occurs where the wiring loom has been incorrectly routed so that it is stretched taut or kinked sharply; either of these conditions should be obvious on even a casual inspection. If this is thought to have happened and the fault proves elusive, the suspect section of wiring should be checked very carefully during the more detailed checks which follow.

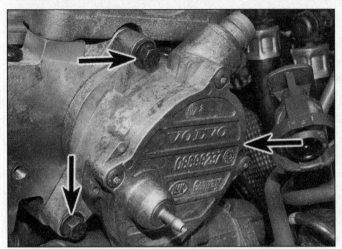

20.5 Vacuum pump retaining bolts (arrowed)

20.6a Renew the vacuum pump O-rings (arrowed)

20.6b Ensure the drive lugs align with the slots in the end of the exhaust camshaft

6 Depending on the extent of the problem, damaged wiring may be repaired by rejoining the break or splicing-in a new length of wire, using solder to ensure a good connection, and remaking the insulation with adhesive insulating tape or heat-shrink tubing, as desired. If the damage is extensive, given the implications for the vehicle's future reliability, the best long-term answer may well be to renew that entire section of the loom, however expensive this may appear.

7 When the actual damage has been repaired, ensure that the wiring loom is re-routed correctly, so that it is clear of other components, is not stretched or kinked, and is secured out of harm's way using the plastic clips, guides and ties provided.

8 Check all electrical connectors, ensuring that they are clean, securely fastened, and that each is locked by its plastic tabs or wire clip, as appropriate. If any connector shows external signs of corrosion (accumulations of white or green deposits, or streaks of 'rust'), or if any is thought to be dirty, it must

be unplugged and cleaned using electrical contact cleaner. If the connector pins are severely corroded, the connector must be renewed; note that this may mean the renewal of that entire section of the loom.

9 If the cleaner completely removes the corrosion to leave the connector in a satisfactory condition, it would be wise to pack the connector with a suitable material which will exclude dirt and moisture, and prevent the corrosion from occurring again; a Volvo dealer may be able to recommend a suitable product.

10 Working methodically around the engine compartment, check carefully that all vacuum hoses and pipes are securely fastened and correctly routed, with no signs of cracks, splits or deterioration to cause air leaks, or of hoses that are trapped, kinked, or bent sharply enough to restrict airflow. Check with particular care at all connections and sharp bends, and renew any damaged or deformed lengths of hose.

11 Check the brake lines, and renew any that are found to be leaking, corroded or crushed. Check particularly the flexible hoses at the brake calipers.

12 It is possible to make a further check of the electrical connections by wiggling each electrical connector of the system in turn as the engine is idling; a faulty connector will be immediately evident from the engine's response (or that of the warning light) as contact is broken and remade. A faulty connector should be renewed to ensure that the future reliability of the system; note that this may mean the renewal of that entire section of the loom.

13 Ensure that the wiring and connections to the wheel sensors are thoroughly checked –

the wheel sensors are subjected to water, road salt and general dirt, and are often responsible for the ABS warning light coming on.

14 If the preliminary checks have failed to reveal the fault, the car must be taken to a Volvo dealer or suitably-equipped garage for diagnostic testing using electronic test equipment.

20 Vacuum pump – removal and refitting

Removal

1 Pull the plastic cover from over the engine straight up from its mountings.

2 On 2.0 litre 4-cylinder engines, undo the retaining bolt and remove the bracket above the vacuum pump.

3 On 5-cylinder engines, remove the battery and battery tray as described in Chapter 5A.

4 Note their fitted positions and disconnect the vacuum hoses from the pump.

5 Undo the retaining bolts and remove the pump from the cylinder head (see illustration). Be prepared for fluid spillage. Discard the O-ring seals, new ones must be fitted. No dismantling of the pump is recommended.

Refitting

6 Fit new O-ring seals to the pump mating face, then align the pump drive lugs with the slots in the end of the exhaust camshaft, and fit the pump to the cylinder head – tighten the bolts to the specified torque (see illustrations).

7 The remainder of refitting is a reversal of removal.

Notes

Chapter 10
Suspension and steering

Contents

Degrees of difficulty

Easy, suitable for novice with little experience	Fairly easy, suitable for beginner with some experience	Fairly difficult, suitable for competent DIY mechanic	Difficult, suitable for experienced DIY mechanic	Very difficult, suitable for expert DIY or professional

Specifications

Front suspension
Type . . . . Independent, with MacPherson struts incorporating coil springs and telescopic shock absorbers. Anti-roll bar fitted to all models

Rear suspension
Type . . . . Fully-independent, multi-link with coil springs and hydraulic telescopic shock absorbers. Anti-roll bar fitted to all models

Steering
Type . . . . Power-assisted rack-and-pinion
Steering fluid type . . . . See *Lubricants and fluids*

Wheel alignment and steering angles
Front wheel:
  Camber angle. . . . . -0.3° ± 0.9°
  Castor angle . . . . 4.0° ± 1.0°
  Toe setting . . . . 0.10° ± 0.10° toe-in
Rear wheel:
  Camber angle. . . . . 0.0° ± 1.0°
  Toe setting . . . . 0.20° ± 0.20° toe-in

Roadwheels
Type . . . . Aluminium alloy
Size . . . . 7J x 16, 7J x 17, 7.5J x 17 and 8J x 18

Tyres
Tyre pressures . . . . See sticker on the driver's-side B-pillar
Tyre sizes (dependent on model, market and territory) . . . . 195/65 R 15, 205/65 R 16, 215/55 R 16, 225/45 R 17, 235/40 R 18 and T125/80 R 17 (temporary spare)

Torque wrench settings

	Nm	lbf ft
Front suspension		
ABS wheel sensor	See Chapter 9	
Anti-roll bar clamp bolts	175	129
Anti-roll bar connecting link nuts*	70	52
Anti-roll bar connecting link-to-front strut bolt	60	44
Balljoint-to-hub carrier bolts*	40	30
Brake caliper mounting bracket bolts	See Chapter 9	
Control arm to subframe:*		
Front bolt:		
Stage 1	140	103
Stage 2	Angle-tighten a further 45°	
Rear bolts	175	129
Driveshaft bolt	See Chapter 8	
Hub carrier balljoint-to-control arm nut*	100	74
Subframe front and rear mounting bolts:*		
Stage 1	150	111
Stage 2	Angle-tighten a further 90°	
Subframe rear mounting brackets to body	24	18
Suspension strut to hub carrier*	110	81
Suspension strut piston nut	50	37
Suspension strut upper mounting to body*	30	22
Rear suspension		
Anti-roll bar-to-subframe bolts	50	37
Anti-roll bar connecting link to anti-roll bar	60	44
Brake caliper bolts	See Chapter 9	
Hub bearing to carrier*	90	66
Hub to vehicle body	180	133
Lower control arm to hub carrier and subframe*	90	66
Shock absorber:		
Lower mounting bolt	175	129
Upper mounting bolt	30	22
Subframe mounting bolts*	110	81
Tie-rod-to-subframe bolts*	110	81
Upper control arm to hub carrier and subframe*	110	81
Steering		
Power steering pipes to steering rack	18	13
Power steering pump mounting bolts	24	18
Steering column mounting bolts	24	18
Steering rack-to-subframe nuts/bolt*	140	103
Steering shaft universal joint pinch-bolts*	25	18
Steering wheel bolt*	48	35
Track rod end balljoint nuts*	80	59
Track rod locknuts	90	66
Roadwheels		
Wheel bolts	140	103

* Do not re-use

1 General information

The independent front suspension is of the MacPherson strut type, incorporating coil springs and integral telescopic shock absorbers. The struts are located by transverse control arms, which are attached to the front subframe via rubber bushes at their inner ends, and incorporate a balljoint at their outer ends. The hub carriers, which carry the hub bearings, brake calipers and the hub/disc assemblies, are bolted to the MacPherson struts, and connected to the control arms through the balljoints. A front anti-roll bar is fitted to all models, and is attached to the subframe and to the MacPherson struts via link arms.

The rear suspension is of the fully independent, multilink type, consisting of an upper and lower control arm mounted via rubber bushes, to the hub carrier and rear subframe. The hub carrier is located by a lateral link arm and an upper stay each side. Coil springs are fitted between the lower control arm and the vehicle body, and there are hydraulic shock absorbers.

Power-assisted rack and pinion steering is fitted as standard equipment. Power assistance is derived from a hydraulic pump, belt-driven from the crankshaft pulley.

Note: *Some of the components described in this Chapter are secured by nuts and bolts tightened by the angle-tightening method. These particular nuts and bolts are indicated in the torque wrench settings section of the specifications. When these fastenings are disturbed, it is often required that **new** nuts and/or bolts are always used when refitting, as indicated in the Specifications. Self-locking nuts are also used in many areas, and these should also be renewed, particularly if resistance cannot be felt when the locking portion passes over the bolt or stud thread.*

2.2 Undo the driveshaft bolt

2.4a Undo the brake caliper bracket bolts . . .

2.4b . . . and hang the caliper from the suspension strut

2 Front hub carrier and bearing – removal and refitting

Removal

1 Loosen the appropriate front wheel bolts, then jack up the front of the car and support it on axle stands (see *Jacking and vehicle support*). Remove the front roadwheel.

2 Slacken and remove the bolt securing the driveshaft to the hub **(see illustration)**. Have an assistant depress the brake pedal to prevent the hub from rotating. Discard the bolt, a new one must be used.

3 Working from the rear undo the bolt securing the control arm to the hub. Disconnect the lower arm balljoint using Volvo tool 999 7310.

4 Undo the two bolts securing the brake caliper bracket to the hub carrier. Note that new bolts will be required for refitting. Slide the caliper assembly, complete with brake pads off the disc and suspend it from the coil spring using string or wire **(see illustrations)**.

5 Check whether the position of the brake disc in relation to the hub is marked, and if not, make your own mark as an aid to refitting. Remove the screw which holds the disc to the hub and lift off the disc, and undo the 3 bolts and remove the backplate **(see illustration)**.

6 Free the driveshaft CV joint from the hub flange by tapping it inwards approximately 10 to 15 mm with a plastic or copper mallet.

7 Undo the retaining nut, then disconnect the steering track rod end balljoint from the hub carrier. If necessary, use a balljoint separator tool.

8 Remove the bolt securing the hub carrier to the strut, and pull the hub carrier downwards from the shock absorber. Note which way the bolts are inserted – from the front **(see illustration)**.

9 Swivel the hub carrier assembly outwards, and withdraw the driveshaft CV joint from the hub flange.

10 With the hub carrier removed, the bearing can be pressed from place **(see illustrations)**. Note that this task (and subsequent renewal of the bearing) requires specialist tools and

2.5 Undo the three bolts (arrowed) and remove the brake backplate

should be entrusted to a Volvo dealer or suitably-equipped specialist.

Refitting

11 With the new bearing in place and prior to refitting the hub carrier, remove all traces of metal adhesive, rust, oil and dirt from the splines and threads of the driveshaft outer CV joint.

12 Refit the lower arm balljoint first, then use a stout metal bar to lever down the lower arm and refit the driveshaft to the rear of the hub. Refit the hub to the bottom of the suspension strut, ensuring that the tab on the rear of the strut engages with the slot in the hub as it is refitted.

13 The remainder of refitting is a reversal of removal, but observe the following points:

2.8 With the bolt removed, pull the hub carrier downwards from the bottom of the suspension strut

a) Ensure that the hub and brake disc mating faces are spotlessly clean, and refit the disc with any orientation marks aligned.

b) Have the front suspension geometry checked and adjusted by a Volvo dealer or suitably-equipped specialist.

c) Lubricate the threads of the CV joint and the driveshaft retaining bolt with engine oil before refitting the bolt. A new bolt should be used.

d) Tighten all nuts and bolts to the specified torque (see Chapter 9 for brake component torque settings). When tightening the driveshaft bolt, tighten first using a torque wrench, then further, through the specified angle, using an angle-tightening gauge.

2.10a Pressing the bearing from place

2.10b Pressing the new bearing into place

3.3 Undo the nut (arrowed) securing the anti-roll bar connecting link to the suspension strut

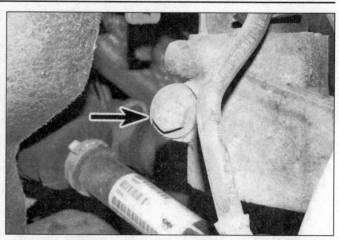

3.6 Hub carrier-to-suspension strut clamping bolt (arrowed)

3.7 Upper strut mounting bolts (arrowed)

3.8 Manoeuvre the strut from the wheel arch

3 Front strut – removal and refitting

Removal

1 Loosen the appropriate front wheel bolts. Chock the rear wheels and apply the handbrake, then jack up the front of the car and support it on axle stands (see *Jacking and vehicle support*). Remove the roadwheel.
2 Remove the ABS wheel sensor wiring from the hub carrier bracket.
3 Undo the retaining nut, and separate the

4.2 Slacken the strut mounting nut half a turn, holding the piston rod with a Torx bit

anti-roll bar connecting link from the bracket on the suspension strut. Use a Torx key to counterhold the nut **(see illustration)**. Discard the nut, a new one must be fitted.
4 Undo the lower control arm balljoint at the hub carrier (refer to process at Section 5).
5 Position a jack beneath the suspension control arm, and raise the jack to just take the weight of the suspension assembly.
6 Undo the clamping bolt securing the suspension strut to the hub carrier. Note that a new nut will be required for refitting **(see illustration)**.
7 From within the engine compartment, remove the plenum cover and undo the three

4.3 Fit the spring compressor

nuts securing the strut upper mounting to the body – **do not** attempt to loosen the centre nut **(see illustration)**. Note that new nuts will be required for refitting.
8 Free the suspension strut from the hub carrier, and manoeuvre the strut out from underneath the wheel arch **(see illustration)**.

Refitting

9 Refitting is a reversal of removal, but observe the following points:
 a) *Ensure that the ABS sensor and the sensor location in the hub carrier are perfectly clean before refitting.*
 b) *Tighten all nuts and bolts to the specified torque, using new nuts/bolts where necessary.*
 c) *Have the suspension geometry check and adjusted by a dealer or suitably-equipped specialist.*

4 Front strut – dismantling, inspection and reassembly

> **Warning: Before attempting to dismantle the suspension strut, a suitable tool to hold the coil spring in compression must be obtained.** Adjustable coil spring compressors which can be positively secured to the spring coils are readily available, and are recommended for this operation. Any attempt to dismantle the strut without such a tool is likely to result in damage or personal injury.

Dismantling

1 Remove the strut from the car as described in Section 3.
2 Slacken the strut mounting nut 1/2 a turn, while holding the protruding portion of the piston rod with a Torx bit **(see illustration)**. Do not remove the nut at this stage.
3 Fit the spring compressors to the coil springs, and tighten the compressors until the load is taken off the spring seats **(see illustration)**.
4 Remove the piston nut, top bearing and

4.4a Remove the piston nut

4.4b With the upper mounting and coil spring removed, the lower rubber mount can be removed

4.4c If required, the gaiter can be separated from the upper mounting . . .

gaiter followed by the spring and lower spring rubber mount. The upper spring rubber mount can be removed, and the gaiter separated from the top mount if required (see illustrations).

Inspection

5 With the strut assembly now completely dismantled, examine all the components for wear, damage or deformation. Renew any of the components as necessary.

6 Examine the shock absorber for signs of fluid leakage, and check the strut piston for signs of pitting along its entire length. Test the operation of the shock absorber, while holding it in an upright position, by moving the piston through a full stroke and then through short strokes of 50 to 100 mm. In both cases, the resistance felt should be smooth and continuous. If the resistance is jerky, or uneven, or if there is any visible sign of wear or damage, renewal is necessary.

7 If any doubt exists about the condition of the coil spring, gradually release the spring compressor, and check the spring for distortion and signs of cracking. Since no

4.4d . . . and the bump stop removed

4.4e if required, the upper spring rubber mount can be removed

minimum free length is specified by Volvo, the only way to check the tension of the spring is to compare it to a new component. Renew the spring if it is damaged or distorted, or if there is any doubt as to its condition.

8 Inspect all other components for signs of damage or deterioration, and renew any that are suspect.

9 If a new shock absorber is being fitted, hold it vertically and pump the piston a few times to prime it.

Reassembly

10 Reassembly is a reversal of dismantling, but ensure that the spring is fully compressed before fitting. Make sure that the spring ends are correctly located in the upper and lower seats and that the two plastic lugs align. Tighten the shock absorber piston retaining nut and strut mounting nuts to the specified torque (see illustrations).

4.10a Ensure that the spring is fully compressed before refitting and that the spring ends are correctly located in their rubber mounts

4.10b When refitting the top mount, ensure the two plastic lugs (arrowed) align

5.2a Undo the control arm balljoint nut . . .

5.2b . . . and separate the balljoint

5.5a Undo the three control arm bolts (arrowed) at the subframe . . .

5.5b . . . and remove the control arm

5 Front control arm and balljoint – removal, overhaul and refitting

Removal

1 Loosen the appropriate front wheel bolts. Chock the rear wheels and apply the handbrake, then jack up the front of the vehicle and support it on axle stands (see *Jacking and vehicle support*). Remove the roadwheel, then release the screws and remove the engine undershield.
2 Undo the nut securing the control arm balljoint to the hub carrier and separate the balljoint. Volvo use a special tool (999 7310) for this task and we were unable to separate the balljoint using a proprietary splitter (it was separated using an alternative method with the hub carrier removed from the vehicle)

7.2 Anti-roll bar connecting link upper bolt (arrowed)

(see illustrations). Refer to a Volvo dealer or specialist parts supplier.
3 Slacken and remove the bolt securing the driveshaft to the hub. Have an assistant depress the brake pedal to prevent the hub from rotating. Discard the bolt, a new one must be used.
4 Undo the brake caliper mounting bolts.
5 Undo the 3 bolts (1 at the front and 2 at the rear) securing the control arm to the subframe and remove the arm. Note that on the right-hand side, the lower control arm has a link bolted to it for the front ride height position sensor (see illustrations).

Overhaul

6 Thoroughly clean the control arm and the area around the control arm mountings. Inspect the arm for any signs of cracks, damage or distortion, and carefully check the inner pivot bushes for signs of swelling, cracks or deterioration of the rubber.

7.3 Anti-roll bar connecting link lower nut (arrowed)

7 If either bush requires renewal, the work should be entrusted to a Volvo dealer or specialist. A hydraulic press and suitable spacers are required to remove and refit the bushes and a setting gauge is needed for accurate positioning of the bushes in the arm.

Refitting

8 Locate the arm in its mountings on the subframe, and fit the new mounting bolts. Tighten the nuts to their specified torque.
9 Engage the balljoint shank in the hub carrier, then tighten the new nut to the specified torque.
10 The remainder of refitting is a reversal of removal.

6 Front anti-roll bar – removal and refitting

Note: *Volvo advise that this task can be undertaken by lowering the rear of the front subframe. In practice, this is likely to prove difficult unless the vehicle can be raised sufficiently using a ramp or lift. We therefore removed the subframe in order to undertake this task.*

Removal

1 Remove the front subframe as described in Section 8.
2 Note that the anti-roll bar clamps on each side of the subframe are secured by the rear 2 bolts for the lower control arm (see illustration 5.5a). With the subframe removed, the anti-roll bar can be withdrawn.
3 Examine the anti-roll bar for signs of damage or distortion, and the connecting links and mounting bushes for signs of deterioration of the rubber. The bushes are vulcanised to the anti-roll bar, and are not available separately.

Refitting

4 Manipulate the anti-roll bar into position on the subframe and refit the subframe as described in Section 8.

7 Front anti-roll bar connecting link – removal and refitting

Removal

1 Loosen the front wheel bolts. Chock the rear wheels, then jack up the front of the vehicle and support it on axle stands (see *Jacking and vehicle support*). Remove the relevant roadwheel.
2 Undo the bolt securing the link to the bottom of the suspension strut (see illustration).
3 Undo the retaining nut, and separate the anti-roll bar connecting link from the end of the anti-roll bar (see illustration). If necessary, use a Torx bit in the end of the balljoint shank to counterhold the nut. The connecting link can now be removed.

8.2 Remove both front wheel arch liners

8.4 Undo the lower control arm mounting bolts (arrowed) at the subframe

8.7 Undo the steering rack bolt on each side

Refitting

4 Refitting is a reversal of removal, using new nuts and ensuring they are tightened to the specified torque.

8 Front subframe – removal and refitting

Removal

1 Drive the car forwards and park it with the steering wheels in the straight-ahead position. Remove the remote unit to lock the steering in this position.

2 Loosen the front wheel bolts. Chock the rear wheels then jack up the front of the vehicle and support it on axle stands (see *Jacking and vehicle support*). You will need to ensure there is adequate clearance below the vehicle, so undertaking this task using a ramp or lift is recommended. Remove both front roadwheels and both front wheel arch liners (see illustration).

3 Undo the securing screws and remove the engine undershield.

4 Volvo advise the removal of the front lower control arm. However as we were unable to release the lower control arm balljoint at the hub carrier without the Volvo tool (999 7130), we removed the brake caliper, undid the driveshaft retaining bolt, undid the lower control arm bolts at the subframe, undid the

suspension strut lower mounting bolt, and removed the subframe complete with the hub and lower control arm. Note that on the right-hand side, the lower control arm has a link bolted to it for the front ride height position sensor (see illustration).

5 On both sides separate the track rod end balljoints at the hub carrier.

6 On both sides undo the retaining nut, and separate the anti-roll bar connecting links on each side from the ends of the anti-roll bar. If necessary, use a Torx bit in the end of the balljoint shank to counterhold the nut.

7 Undo the bolts securing the steering rack to the subframe, and tie the steering rack securely to a suitable point on the engine (see illustration).

8 Undo the rear lower torque rod bolt at the engine mounting (see illustration).

9 Undo the 2 bolts securing the exhaust hanger bracket to the rear of the subframe (see illustration). Take care not to forcibly bend the flexible section of the exhaust.

10 Make some alignment marks between the subframe and the vehicle body to aid refitting (see illustration), and support the subframe from beneath using a jack.

11 At the rear of the subframe undo the 2 bolts each side securing the crossmember to the floor and the subframe bolt on each side, and remove the rear crossmember (see illustrations).

12 Undo the front subframe bolts, lower the subframe, and pull from beneath the vehicle

8.8 Undo the lower torque rod bolt (arrowed) at the engine mounting

8.9 Exhaust bracket hanger bolts (arrowed)

8.10 Make alignment marks between the subframe and the vehicle body to aid refitting

8.11a Undo the two bolts each side securing the crossmember to the body . . .

8.11b . . . and the rear subframe bolt on each side

8.12 Front subframe bolt

8.13a Use new subframe bolts and washers

8.13b If possible, use a suitable alignment tool (arrowed)

(see illustration). As the assembly is being lowered, unclip any pipes or cables and ensure that pipes or other components do not become trapped between the subframe and the vehicle body.

Refitting

13 Refitting is a reversal of removal, noting the following points:

a) When raising the subframe into position, ensure that pipes and other components do not become trapped between the subframe and the vehicle body.

b) Refit the rear crossmember to the body, and tighten the bolts hand-tight only at this stage.

c) Secure the subframe to the rear crossmember using the new bolts, also hand-tight only.

d) Raise the front of the subframe using the jack and fit new washers and bolts, hand-tight only **(see illustration)**.

e) Ensure the alignment marks made previously are in the correct position before tightening all bolts to the specified torque. If possible, use suitable alignment tools inserted into the holes adjacent to the rear subframe mounts **(see**

illustration). These tools are available from parts specialists.

f) *Have the front wheel toe-in checked and adjusted by a Volvo dealer or suitably-equipped specialist.*

9 Rear hub bearings – renewal

1 Remove the brake disc as described in Chapter 9. Undo the bolts and remove the brake caliper bracket from the hub.

2 Disconnect the wiring plug for the ABS wheel speed sensor.

3 Undo the four bolts and withdraw the bearing assembly from the hub carrier **(see illustrations)**. Note that undoing the upper bolt on the anti-roll bar connecting link will allow the anti-roll bar to be twisted slightly, improving access to the bearing assembly bolts.

4 Fit the new assembly to the hub carrier then insert and tighten the new bolts (supplied in the bearing/hub kit) to the specified torque.

5 Refit the ABS wheel speed sensor and brake disc as described in Chapter 9.

10 Rear hub carrier – removal and refitting

Removal

1 Remove the coil spring as described in Section 12.

2 Remove the hub bearings as described in Section 9.

3 Disconnect the wiring plug from the ABS wheel sensor on the hub carrier.

4 Remove the brake backplate where fitted. If a gasket is fitted, obtain a new one if the original is in any way damaged.

5 Undo any clips that secure pipes or cables to the hub assembly.

6 Note their fitted positions then undo the bolts securing the anti-roll bar link, shock absorber, upper and lower control arms, and the tie-rod to the hub carrier. Undo the bolts securing the lateral links to the vehicle body with reference to the relevant Section in this chapter. Discard the bolts; new ones must be fitted. Withdraw the hub carrier from the vehicle.

7 If any of the various metal-elastic bushes on

9.3a Rear hub bearing bolts (arrowed)

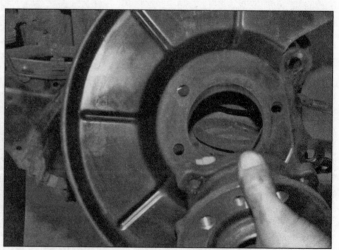

9.3b Remove the bearing from the hub

11.3a Lower shock absorber mounting bolt (arrowed)

11.3b Upper shock absorber mounting bolts (arrowed)

12.3 Compress the spring with a suitable spring compressor

the hub carrier appear damaged or worn, have them renewed by a Volvo dealer or specialist, as access to special tools and a hydraulic press is required.

Refitting

8 Position the hub carrier, connect the various link arms, and fit the new bolts. Only finger-tighten the bolts at this stage.
9 Check the hub carrier is in the 'normal' position as described in Section 16.
10 Now tighten the various mounting bolts to the specified torque where given.
11 The remainder of refitting is a reversal of removal.

11 Rear shock absorber – removal and refitting

Removal

1 Chock the front wheels then jack up the rear of the vehicle and support it on axle stands (see *Jacking and vehicle support*). Although not essential, access will be improved if the rear wheel is removed.
2 To make removal easier, position a jack under the outer end of the lower control arm, and raise the jack sufficiently to take the load off the shock absorber.
3 Undo the shock absorber lower mounting

bolt, and the 2 upper mounting bolts **(see illustrations)**.
4 Check the condition of the shock absorber and renew as necessary.

Refitting

5 Refitting is a reversal of removal, tightening all nuts and bolts to the specified torques.

12 Rear coil spring – removal and refitting

Removal

1 Loosen the rear wheel bolts. Chock the rear wheels, then jack up the front of the vehicle and support it on axle stands (see *Jacking and vehicle support*). Remove the relevant roadwheel.
2 Undo the upper bolt at the anti-roll bar connecting link as described in Section 15.
3 Attach the proprietary spring compressors and compress the spring **(see illustration)**.
4 Lift out the spring from its location.
5 Examine all the components for wear or damage, and renew as necessary.

Refitting

6 Refitting is a reversal of removal ensuring that the spring seats correctly in the lower arm.

13 Rear link arms – removal and refitting

Removal

1 Loosen the rear wheel bolts. Chock the front wheels, then jack up the rear of the vehicle and support it on axle stands (see *Jacking and vehicle support*). Remove the roadwheel(s).

Tie-rod

2 Remove the coil spring as described in Section 12.
3 Undo the bolts that secure the tie-rod to the subframe and to the longitudinal stay **(see illustration)**.
4 Disconnect the height sensor and remove the tie-rod from the vehicle.

Upper arm

5 Remove the coil spring as described in Section 12.
6 Undo the bolts securing the upper arm to the hub carrier and to the subframe, and remove it from the vehicle **(see illustrations)**.

Lower arm

7 Remove the coil spring as described in Section 12.
8 Undo the bolts securing the inner end of the lower control arm to the subframe, and the outer end to the hub carrier. Undo the anti-roll

13.3 Tie-rod inner mounting bolt (arrowed)

13.6a Upper arm inner bolt (arrowed)

13.6b Upper arm outer bolt (arrowed) at hub carrier

13.8a Lower arm inner bolts (arrowed)

13.8b Lower arm outer bolt (arrowed)

13.8c Disconnect the anti-roll bar connecting link (arrowed) before removing the lower arm

bar connecting link. Detach the lower arm **(see illustrations)**.

Refitting

9 Refitting any of the link arms is a reversal of removal, noting the following points:
  a) *Always renew the link arms' mounting bolts.*
  b) *Tighten all fasteners to their specified torque where given.*
  c) *Before tightening any links arm mounting bolts, ensure the suspension is in the 'normal' position as described in Section 16.*

14.3 Anti-roll bar clamp bolts (arrowed)

14 Rear anti-roll bar – removal and refitting

Removal

1 Chock the front wheels, then jack up the rear of the vehicle and support it on axle stands (see *Jacking and vehicle support*).
2 Undo the bolts on each side securing the anti-roll bar to the connecting link as described in Section 15.
3 Undo the bolts securing the anti-roll bar clamps to the subframe, manoeuvre the anti-roll bar past the subframe and withdraw it from the vehicle **(see illustration)**.

Refitting

4 Refitting is a reversal of removal.

15 Rear anti-roll bar connecting link – removal and refitting

1 Loosen the rear wheel bolts. Chock the front wheels, then jack up the front of the vehicle and support it on axle stands (see *Jacking*

and vehicle support). Remove the relevant roadwheel.
2 Undo the bolt securing the link to the lower arm **(see illustration)**.
3 Undo the bolt securing the link to the anti-roll bar **(see illustration)**. The connecting link can now be removed.
4 Refitting is a reversal of removal, using new nuts and ensuring they are tightened to the specified torque.

16 Rear subframe assembly – removal and refitting

Removal

1 To improve access, undo the anti-roll bar upper connecting link bolts and remove both rear coil springs as described in Section 12 (if refitting the old spring, make alignment marks between the spring and spring seat to aid refitting).
2 Undo the lower mounting bolts for the rear shock absorbers.
3 Undo the screws/bolts on each side and remove the underbody panels from the floorpan.

15.2 Connecting link lower mounting bolt (arrowed)

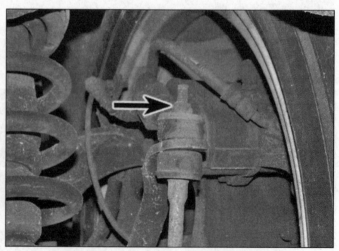

15.3 Connecting link upper mounting bolt (arrowed)

16.4a Lateral link brake pipe bracket bolts (arrowed)

16.4b Lateral link exhaust hanger bracket

16.4c Undo the lateral link-to-body bolts

4 On both sides undo the bolt securing the brake pipe bracket where the lateral link is bolted to the vehicle body **(see illustration)**. On the left-hand side at the same point, undo the 2 bolts securing the exhaust hanger. Undo the 2 bolts on each side securing the lateral link arm to the body **(see illustrations)**.

5 Undo the bolts on each side securing the suspension upper arm to the hub carrier. This is only required in order to remove the brake pipe bracket **(see illustration)**.

6 Activate the handbrake service mode (refer to Chapter 9, Section 5), disconnect the ABS sensor wiring plug, and the wiring plug for the handbrake actuator.

7 Undo the brake caliper guide pin bolts at the hub carrier and move the calipers to one side. Suspend the calipers from the vehicle bodywork to prevent any strain on the flexible brake hose. On the right-hand side, we found it easiest to remove the wheel arch liner **(see illustration)** and tie the caliper to the bracket for the fuel filler pipe. On the left-hand side,

the caliper can be tied to the top of the shock absorber **(see illustrations)**.

8 Release the exhaust mounting above the subframe **(see illustration)**. Unclip the wiring that is secured to the subframe adjacent to the fuel filter.

9 Position 2 trolley jacks under the subframe and make alignment marks between the subframe mountings and the vehicle body to aid refitment.

10 Undo the 4 bolts securing the subframe mountings and brackets to the vehicle body

16.5 Remove the brake pipe bracket from the hub carrier by undoing the upper arm bolt (arrowed)

16.7a Remove both wheel arch liners

16.7b Tie the right-hand side brake caliper to the fuel filler pipe bracket . . .

16.7c . . . and the left-hand side brake caliper to the top of the rear shock absorber

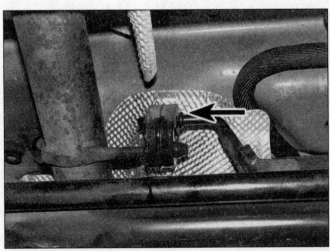

16.8 Release the exhaust hanger (arrowed) above the subframe

16.10a Subframe front bolt (arrowed)

16.10b Subframe rear bolt (arrowed)

16.10c Release the fuel filter from its bracket (arrowed)

(see illustrations). Gradually lower the subframe ensuring no pipes or cables become trapped between the subframe and other components. As the subframe is lowered, the fuel filter can be released from its bracket and tied to the fuel filler pipe using cable-ties or similar. When the assembly is clear of the underbody, withdraw it rearwards and out from under the car.

11 With the subframe removed, the bearings can be pressed from place (see illustrations)

Refitting

12 Refitting is a reversal of removal bearing in mind the following points:

a) Manoeuvre the subframe assembly into position using the jacks and secure with the four new mounting bolts each side, align the previously-made marks and tighten the bolts to the specified torque.
b) Use new bolts for suspension and brake components as described in the relevant Sections.
c) With the wiring plug for the handbrake actuator reconnected, deactivate the service mode.
d) Before finally tightening the bolts for the suspension components, the suspension needs to be in its 'normal' position. This

should be carried out before the rear springs are refitted. Position a trolley jack under the control arm at the point where it is attached to the hub carrier and raise the assembly until the distance from the wheel arch to the hub centre is 350 mm (see illustration). If necessary, place some ballast in the luggage compartment to increase the weight of the vehicle, so that the suspension can be compressed enough by the jack without lifting the vehicle from the axle stands. Tighten all mounting bolts to the specified torque.

17 Steering wheel – removal and refitting

 Warning: Handle the airbag unit with extreme care as a precaution against personal injury, and always hold it with the cover facing away from the body. If in doubt concerning any proposed work involving the airbag unit or its control circuitry, consult a Volvo dealer.

Removal

1 Drive the car forwards and park it with the front wheels in the straight-ahead position.

16.11a Press the subframe bearing from place

16.11b Subframe bearing located in the subframe

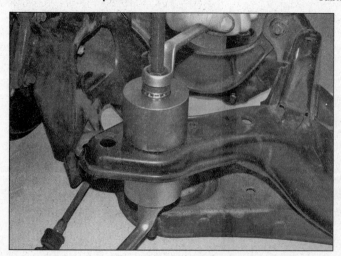

16.11c Press the new subframe bearing into place

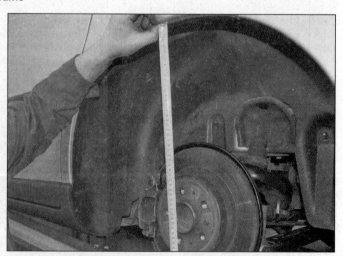

16.12 The distance from the top of the wheel arch to the hub centre should be 350 mm

2 Disconnect the battery negative lead, and wait for 10 minutes before proceeding.
3 Place a piece of masking tape on the top of the steering wheel hub, and another piece on the top of the steering column upper shroud. Draw a pencil line across both pieces of tape to act as an alignment mark to centralise the steering wheel when refitting.
4 Remove the airbag unit from the steering wheel as described in Chapter 12.
5 Loosen the steering wheel centre retaining bolt slightly. A degree of force is required to undo the bolt and this will prevent damage to the contact reel when it is locked in place.
6 Ensure the steering wheel is in the 'straight-ahead' position, then remove the lower screw from its storage position and insert it into the hole to lock the rotary contact reel.
7 Undo the steering wheel centre retaining bolt (see illustration).
8 Lift the steering wheel off the column shaft, and feed the wiring and plastic strip through the hole in the wheel.

Refitting

9 Ensure that the front wheels are still in the straight-ahead position.
10 Feed the wiring through the hole in the steering wheel, then engage the wheel with the steering column shaft. Ensure that the marks made on removal are aligned, and that the pegs on the contact reel engage with the recesses on the steering wheel hub. Note that the upper shroud is attached to the instrument

panel surround. Do not attempt to turn the steering wheel with the contact reel locked, otherwise the reel will be damaged.
11 Refit the steering wheel retaining bolt, and tighten it finger-tight only.
12 Referring to the information in Chapter 12, remove the airbag contact reel locking screw, and refit the screw to the location provided in the steering wheel.
13 Tighten the steering wheel retaining bolt to the specified torque.
14 Refit the airbag unit to the steering wheel as described in Chapter 12.

18 Steering column – removal and refitting

Removal

1 Disconnect the battery negative lead – see Chapter 5A.
2 Fully extend the steering column then remove the steering wheel (see Section 17).
3 Remove the steering column shrouds. Unclip the flexible section below the instrument panel from the rear of the top shroud and unclip the top shroud from the lower shroud. Undo the 3 screws from under the steering column lower shroud and remove (see illustrations).
4 Remove the steering wheel control module. Ensuring that the contact reel is locked in position, undo the 4 screws, disconnect the wiring plug, and remove the module. Note

17.7 Undo the steering wheel centre retaining bolt

that on refitting, the module may need to be reprogrammed using dedicated Volvo test equipment – entrust this task to a Volvo dealer or suitably-equipped specialist.
5 Remove the trim panel under the facia on the driver's side, which is secured by 2 screws, and is then pulled out of its locating slots at the top. Disconnect the wiring plug from the footwell light.
6 Undo the pinch-bolt at the universal joint on the intermediate steering column shaft, and pull the joint up from the lower shaft (see illustration). Discard the bolt, a new one must be fitted.
7 Detach the wiring loom guide from the underside of the column, and allow it to hang down.
8 Undo the four bolts securing the column to

18.3a Unclip the flexible section from the upper shroud

18.3b Unclip the upper shroud from the lower shroud . . .

18.3c . . . and remove the upper shroud

18.3d Undo the three screws (arrowed) . . .

18.3e . . . and remove the lower shroud

18.6 Undo the steering column universal joint pinch-bolt (arrowed)

18.8a Undo the two upper steering column mounting bolts . . .

18.8b . . . and the two lower mounting bolts

20.2a Lift the power steering fluid reservoir from its mounting bracket

the facia, and pull the assembly rearwards, disconnecting any wiring plugs as it is withdrawn (shown with the column removed for clarity) **(see illustrations)**.

Refitting

9 Refitting is a reversal of removal, bearing in mind the following points:
a) *Lubricate the intermediate shaft splines with grease before engaging the steering column.*
b) *When refitting the column retaining bolts, tighten the rearmost bolts first.*
c) *Use a new universal joint pinch-bolt.*

19 Steering lock – removal and refitting

The steering lock is electrically-operated and is located beneath the steering column. It is accessible with the lower column shroud removed. It should be noted that incorrect removal could result in the assembly becoming permanently locked, and a complete new steering column would be required. We therefore advise entrusting this task to a Volvo dealer or specialist.

20 Steering rack – removal and refitting

Note: *Volvo advise that this task can be undertaken by lowering the rear of the front*

20.2b Disconnect the pipe at the bottom of the reservoir and collect the fluid in a suitable container

subframe. *In practice, this is likely to prove difficult unless the vehicle can be raised sufficiently using a ramp or lift. We therefore removed the subframe in order to undertake this task.*

Removal

1 Undo the steering column pinch-bolt at the universal joint in the driver's footwell **(see illustration 18.6)**. Discard the pinch-bolt nut, a new one must be fitted.
2 Drain the power steering fluid reservoir by disconnecting the pipe at the bottom of the reservoir and collecting the fluid in a suitable container **(see illustrations)**.
3 Wipe clean the area around the fluid pipe unions on the steering rack pinion housing, unscrew the union nut and carefully pull the pipes clear **(see illustration)**. Be prepared for some fluid leakage.

20.3 Undo the pipe union nut (arrowed) at the steering rack

4 Follow the process for removing the front subframe (with the exception of Paragraph 7) as described in Section 8.
5 Undo the 2 bolts securing the steering rack to the subframe and withdraw the assembly.

Refitting

6 Refitting is a reversal of removal, using new bolts tightened to the specified torque.
7 Refill and bleed the steering rack as described in Section 22.
8 Have the front wheel toe-in checked and adjusted by a Volvo dealer or suitably-equipped repairer.

21 Steering rack gaiters – renewal

1 Count and record the number of exposed threads on the track rod from the end of the rod to the track rod end locknut.
2 Remove the track rod end on the side concerned as described in Section 25. Unscrew the locknut from the track rod.
3 Release the two clips and peel off the gaiter **(see illustrations)**.
4 Clean out any dirt and grit from the inner end of the track rod and (when accessible) the rack.
5 Wrap insulating tape around the track rod threads to protect the new gaiter whilst installing.
6 Refit the track rod end locknut, and position

21.3a Release the inner . . .

21.3b . . . and outer steering rack gaiter clips

it so that the same number of threads counted on removal are visible.

7 Refit the track rod end as described in Section 25.

22 Steering rack – bleeding

1 The power steering fluid reservoir is located on the right-hand side of the engine compartment, just in front of the coolant expansion tank.

2 The MAX and MIN marks are indicated on the reservoir. The fluid level must be kept within the marks at all times.

3 If topping-up is necessary, wipe clean the area around the reservoir filler neck, and unscrew the filler cap from the reservoir. Use clean fluid of the specified type (see *Lubricants and fluids*).

4 After component renewal, or if the fluid level has been allowed to fall so low that air has entered the hydraulic system, bleeding must be carried out as follows.

5 Fill the reservoir to the correct level as described above.

6 Chock the rear wheels, then jack up the front of the vehicle and support it on axle stands (see *Jacking and vehicle support*).

7 Turn the steering wheel repeatedly from full lock one way, to full lock the other way, and top-up the fluid level as necessary.

8 Lower the car to the ground then start the engine and allow it to idle.

9 Turn the steering wheel slowly to the full-right lock position, and hold it there for 2 seconds.

10 Now turn the steering wheel slowly to the full-left lock position, and hold it there for 2 seconds.

11 Top-up the fluid level again if necessary.

12 Repeat paragraphs 9 and 10 ten. Repeatedly check and if necessary top-up the fluid level during this operation.

13 On completion, stop the engine, recheck the fluid level then refit the reservoir filler cap.

23 Steering pump – removal and refitting

Removal

1 Pull up and remove the engine cover.

2 Remove the auxiliary drivebelt as described in Chapter 1.

3 Undo the pipe union on the side of the pump. Be prepared for fluid leakage and seal the openings of the pipes to prevent contamination.

4 Undo the bolt securing the pipe mounting bracket to the side of the pump.

5 Undo the union on the pump for the pipe

that carries fluid from the reservoir. Be prepared for leakage and seal the opening to prevent contamination.

6 Undo the 3 bolts and withdraw the pump from the engine bay.

Refitting

7 Refitting is a reversal of removal, bearing in mind the following points:
  a) Use new O-ring seals where fitted.
  b) Tighten the pump mounting bolts to the specified torque.
  c) Refit the auxiliary drivebelt as described in Chapter 1.
  d) Refill/top-up the fluid reservoir, and bleed the system as described in Section 22.

24 Steering oil cooler – removal and refitting

Removal

1 Remove the right-hand headlamp as described in Chapter 12.

2 Remove the front bumper as described in Chapter 11.

3 Drain the power steering fluid reservoir by disconnecting the pipe at the bottom of the reservoir and collecting the fluid in a suitable container.

4 Undo the screws and remove the triangular plastic upper radiator locating lugs **(see illustration)**. Gently tilt the radiator rearwards a little.

24.4 Remove the upper radiator locating lugs

24.8 Undo the screw (arrowed) securing the power steering oil cooler to the radiator

5 Working from the side of the right-hand side headlamp aperture, undo the steering fluid pipe bracket.

6 Disconnect the steering fluid pipe union adjacent to the fluid reservoir **(see illustration)**. Be prepared for fluid spillage.

7 Working from the front of the vehicle, remove the plastic panel on the right-hand side of the radiator.

8 Undo the screw securing the oil cooler to the radiator and remove the oil cooler and pipework from the front of the radiator **(see illustration)**.

Refitting

9 Refitting is a reversal of removal. Top-up and bleed the system as described in Section 22.

25 Track rod end – removal and refitting

Removal

1 Loosen the appropriate front wheel bolts. Chock the rear wheels, then jack up the front of the vehicle and support it on axle stands (see *Jacking and vehicle support*). Remove the roadwheel.

2 Counterhold the track rod, and slacken the track rod end locknut by half a turn **(see illustration)**. If the locknut is now left in this position, it will act as a guide for refitting.

24.6 Disconnect the fluid pipe union (arrowed) adjacent to the fluid reservoir

25.2 Slacken the track rod end locknut (arrowed)

25.3a Undo the track rod end balljoint nut (arrowed) . . .

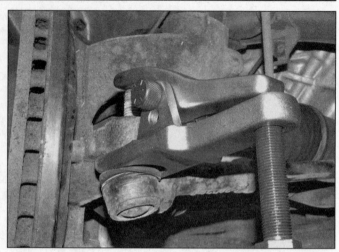

25.3b . . . and separate the balljoint using a balljoint separator

26.1 Front wheel geometry

3 Unscrew the track rod end balljoint nut. Separate the balljoint from the steering arm with a proprietary balljoint separator, then remove the nut and disengage the balljoint from the arm **(see illustrations)**.

4 Unscrew the track rod end from the track rod, counting the number of turns needed to remove it. Make a note of the number of turns, so that the tracking can be reset (or at least approximated) on refitting.

Refitting

5 Screw the track rod end onto the track rod by the same number of turns noted during removal.

6 Engage the balljoint in the steering arm. Fit a new nut and tighten it to the specified torque.

7 Counterhold the track rod and tighten the locknut.

8 Refit the front wheel, lower the car and tighten the wheel bolts in a diagonal sequence to the specified torque.

9 Have the front wheel toe-in (tracking) checked and adjusted by a Volvo dealer or suitably-equipped repairer.

26 Wheel alignment and steering angles – general information

1 A car's steering and suspension geometry is defined in four basic settings – all angles are expressed in degrees; the relevant settings are camber, castor, steering axis inclination, and toe setting **(see illustration)**. On the models covered by this manual, only the front camber, and the front and rear wheel toe settings are adjustable. All other suspension and steering angles are set during manufacture, and no adjustment is possible. It can be assumed, therefore, that unless the vehicle has suffered accident damage, all the preset angles will be correct.

Camber

2 Camber is the angle at which the front wheels are set from the vertical when viewed from the front or rear of the car. Negative camber is the amount (in degrees) that the wheels are tilted inward at the top from the vertical.

3 The front camber angle is adjusted by slackening the hub carrier-to-suspension strut mounting bolts and repositioning the hub carrier assemblies as necessary.

Castor

4 Castor is the angle between the steering axis and a vertical line when viewed from each side of the car. Positive castor is when the steering axis is inclined rearward at the top.

Steering axis inclination

5 Steering axis inclination is the angle (when viewed from the front of the vehicle) between the vertical and an imaginary line drawn through the front suspension strut upper mounting and the control arm balljoint.

Toe

6 Toe setting is the amount by which the distance between the front inside edges of the roadwheels (measured at hub height) differs from the diametrically opposite distance measured between the rear inside edges of the roadwheels. Toe-in is when the roadwheels point inwards, towards each other at the front, while toe-out is when they splay outwards from each other at the front.

7 The front wheel toe setting is adjusted by altering the length of the steering track rods on both sides. This adjustment is normally referred to as the tracking.

8 The rear wheel toe setting is adjusted by altering the position of the rear suspension transverse arm-to-trailing arm mountings.

27.3a Front height sensor retaining screws (arrowed)

27.3b Rear height sensor retaining screw (arrowed)

9 Special optical measuring equipment is necessary to accurately check and adjust the front and rear toe settings, and front camber angles, and this work should be carried out by a Volvo dealer or similar expert. Most tyre fitting centres have the expertise and equipment to carry out at least a front wheel toe setting (tracking) check for a nominal charge.

27 Suspension ride height sensor – removal and refitting

Removal

1 Jack up the front or rear of the vehicle and support it securely on axle stands (see *Jacking and vehicle support*).

2 Undo the nut and disconnect the link arm from the front or rear sensor.
3 Disconnect the sensor wiring plug, undo the retaining screws and remove the sensor **(see illustrations)**.

Refitting

4 Refitting is a reversal of removal.

Chapter 11
Bodywork and fittings

Contents

Degrees of difficulty

Easy, suitable for novice with little experience	Fairly easy, suitable for beginner with some experience	Fairly difficult, suitable for competent DIY mechanic	Difficult, suitable for experienced DIY mechanic	Very difficult, suitable for expert DIY or professional

Specifications

Torque wrench settings	Nm	lbf ft
Bonnet hinge bolts	24	18
Door hinge bolts	24	18
Facia crossmember:		
To A-pillar	50	37
To centre console brackets	24	18
Heater unit frame bolts	10	7
Front seat retaining bolts	40	30
Seat belts:		
Anchorage to front seat	45	33
All other bolts	40	30
Rear seat cushion retaining bolts	25	18
Tailgate hinge bolts	24	18

1 General information

The bodyshell is made of pressed-steel sections. Most components are welded together, but some use is made of structural adhesives. The doors and door pillars are reinforced against side impacts as part of the side impact protection system (SIPS).

A number of structural components and body panels are made of galvanised steel to provide a high level of protection against corrosion. Extensive use is also made of plastic materials, mainly in the interior, but also in exterior components. The front and rear bumpers are moulded from a synthetic material that is very strong and yet light. Plastic components such as wheel arch liners are fitted to the underside of the vehicle to further improve corrosion resistance.

2 Maintenance – bodywork and underframe

The general condition of a vehicle's bodywork is the one thing that significantly affects its value. Maintenance is easy but needs to be regular. Neglect, particularly after minor damage, can lead quickly to further deterioration and costly repair bills. It is important also to keep watch on those parts of the vehicle not immediately visible, for instance the underside, inside all the wheel arches and the lower part of the engine compartment.

The basic maintenance routine for the bodywork is washing preferably with a lot of water, from a hose. This will remove all the loose solids which may have stuck to the vehicle. It is important to flush these off in such a way as to prevent grit from scratching the finish. The wheel arches and underframe need washing in the same way to remove any accumulated mud which will retain moisture and tend to encourage rust. Oddly enough, the best time to clean the underframe and wheel arches is in wet weather when the mud is thoroughly wet and soft. In very wet weather the underframe is usually cleaned of large accumulations automatically and this is a good time for inspection.

Periodically, except on vehicles with a wax-based underbody protective coating, it is a good idea to have the whole of the underframe of the vehicle steam-cleaned, engine compartment included, so that a thorough inspection can be carried out to see what minor repairs and renovations are necessary. Steam-cleaning is available at many garages, and is necessary for removal of the accumulation of oily grime which sometimes is allowed to become thick in certain areas. If steam-cleaning facilities are not available, there are one or two excellent grease solvents available which can be brush applied; the dirt can then be simply hosed off. Note that these methods should not be used on vehicles with

wax-based underbody protective coating, or the coating will be removed. Such vehicles should be inspected annually, preferably just prior to winter, when the underbody should be washed down and any damage to the wax coating repaired using underseal. Ideally, a completely fresh coat should be applied. It would also be worth considering the use of such wax-based protection for injection into door panels, sills, box sections, etc, as an additional safeguard against rust damage where such protection is not provided by the vehicle manufacturer.

After washing paintwork, wipe off with a chamois leather to give an unspotted clear finish. A coat of clear protective wax polish will give added protection against chemical pollutants in the air. If the paintwork sheen has dulled or oxidised, use a cleaner/polisher combination to restore the brilliance of the shine. This requires a little effort, but such dulling is usually caused because regular washing has been neglected. Care needs to be taken with metallic paintwork, as special non-abrasive cleaner/polisher is required to avoid damage to the finish.

Always check that the door and ventilator opening drain holes and pipes are completely clear, so that water can be drained out. Brightwork should be treated in the same way as paintwork. Windscreens and windows can be kept clear of the smeary film which often appears by the use of a proprietary glass cleaner. Never use any form of wax or other body or chromium polish on glass, especially not on the windscreen or tailgate.

3 Maintenance – upholstery and carpets

Mats and carpets should be brushed or vacuum cleaned regularly to keep them free of grit. If they are badly stained, remove them from the vehicle for scrubbing or sponging, and make quite sure they are dry before refitting. Seats and interior trim panels can be kept clean by wiping with a damp cloth and a proprietary upholstery cleaner. If they do become stained (which can be more apparent on light-coloured upholstery) use a little liquid detergent and a soft nail brush to scour the grime out of the grain of the material. Do not forget to keep the headlining clean in the same way as the upholstery. When using liquid cleaners inside the vehicle, do not over-wet the surfaces being cleaned. Excessive damp could get into the seams and padded interior causing stains, offensive odours or even rot.

4 Minor body damage – repair

Minor scratches

If the scratch is very superficial, and does not penetrate to the metal of the bodywork, repair is

very simple. Lightly rub the area of the scratch with a paintwork renovator, or a very fine cutting paste, to remove loose paint from the scratch, and to clear the surrounding bodywork of wax polish. Rinse the area with clean water.

In the case of metallic paint, the most commonly-found 'scratches' are not in the paint, but in the lacquer top coat, and appear white. If care is taken , these can sometimes be rendered less obvious by very careful use of paintwork renovator (which would otherwise not be used on metallic paintwork); otherwise, repair of these scratches can be achieved by applying lacquer with a fine brush.

Apply touch-up paint to the scratch using a fine paint brush; continue to apply fine layers of paint until the surface of the paint in the scratch is level with the surrounding paintwork. Allow the new paint at least two weeks to harden: then blend it into the surrounding paintwork by rubbing the scratch area with a paintwork renovator or a very fine cutting paste. Finally, apply wax polish.

Where the scratch has penetrated right through to the metal of the bodywork, causing the metal to rust, a different repair technique is required. Remove any loose rust from the bottom of the scratch with a penknife, then apply rust-inhibiting paint, to prevent the formation of rust in the future. Using a rubber or nylon applicator fill the scratch with bodystopper paste. If required, this paste can be mixed with cellulose thinners, to provide a very thin paste which is ideal for filling narrow scratches. Before the stopper-paste in the scratch hardens, wrap a piece of smooth cotton rag around the top of a finger. Dip the finger in cellulose thinners, and then quickly sweep it across the surface of the stopper-paste in the scratch; this will ensure that the surface of the stopper-paste is slightly hollowed. The scratch can now be painted over as described earlier in this Section.

Dents

When deep denting of the vehicle's bodywork has taken place, the first task is to pull the dent out, until the affected bodywork almost attains its original shape. There is little point in trying to restore the original shape completely, as the metal in the damaged area will have stretched on impact, and cannot be reshaped fully to its original contour. It is better to bring the level of the dent up to a point which is about 3 mm below the level of the surrounding bodywork. In cases where the dent is very shallow anyway, it is not worth trying to pull it out at all. If the underside of the dent is accessible, it can be hammered out gently from behind, using a mallet with a wooden or plastic head. Whilst doing this, hold a suitable block of wood firmly against the outside of the panel to absorb the impact from the hammer blows and thus prevent a large area of the bodywork from being 'belled-out'.

Should the dent be in a section of the bodywork which has a double skin or some other factor making it inaccessible from behind, a different technique is called for. Drill several small holes through the metal inside the area – particularly in the deeper section. Then screw long self-tapping screws into the holes just sufficiently for them to gain a good purchase in the metal. Now the dent can be pulled out by pulling on the protruding heads of the screws with a pair of pliers.

The next stage of the repair is the removal of the paint from the damaged area, and from an inch or so of the surrounding 'sound' bodywork. This is accomplished most easily by using a wire brush or abrasive pad on a power drill, although it can be done just as effectively by hand using sheets of abrasive paper. To complete the preparation for filling, score the surface of the bare metal with a screwdriver or the tang of a file, or alternatively, drill small holes in the affected area. This will provide a really good 'key' for the filler paste.

To complete the repair, see the Section on filling and re-spraying.

Rust holes or gashes

Remove all paint from the affected area, and from an inch or so of the surrounding 'sound' bodywork, using an abrasive pad or a wire brush on a power drill. If these are not available, a few sheets of abrasive paper will do the job just as effectively. With the paint removed, you will be able to gauge the severity of the corrosion, and therefore decide whether to renew the whole panel (if this is possible) or to repair the affected area. New body panels are not as expensive as most people think, and it is often quicker and more satisfactory to fit a new panel than to attempt to repair large areas of corrosion.

Remove all fittings from the affected area, except those which will act as a guide to the original shape of the damaged bodywork. Then, using tin snips or a hacksaw blade, remove all loose metal and any other metal badly affected by corrosion. Hammer the edges of the hole inwards in order to create a slight depression for the filler paste.

Wire-brush the affected area to remove the powdery rust from the surface of the remaining metal. Paint the affected area with rust-inhibiting paint; if the back of the rusted area is accessible treat this also.

Before filling can take place, it will be necessary to block the hole in some way. This can be achieved by the use of aluminium or plastic mesh, or aluminium tape.

Aluminium or plastic mesh or glass fibre matting is probably the best material to use for a large hole. Cut a piece to the approximate size and shape of the hole to be filled, then position it in the hole so that its edges are below the level of the surrounding bodywork. It can be retained in position by several blobs of filler paste around its periphery.

Aluminium tape should be used for small or very narrow holes. Pull a piece off the roll and trim it to the approximate size and shape required, then pull off the backing paper (if used) and stick the tape over the hole; it can be overlapped if the thickness of one piece is insufficient. Burnish down the edges of the tape with the handle of a screwdriver or similar, to ensure that the tape is securely attached to the metal underneath.

Filling and re-spraying

Before using this Section, see the Sections on dent, deep scratch, rust holes and gash repairs.

Many types of bodyfiller are available, but generally speaking those proprietary kits which contain a tin of filler paste and a tube of resin hardener are best for this type of repair; some can be used directly from the tube. A wide, flexible plastic or nylon applicator will be found invaluable for imparting a smooth and well contoured finish to the surface of the filler.

Mix up a little filler on a clean piece of card or board – measure the hardener carefully (follow the maker's instructions on the pack) otherwise the filler will set too rapidly or too slowly. Using the applicator, apply the filler paste to the prepared area; draw the applicator across the surface of the filler to achieve the correct contour and to level the filler surface. As soon as a contour that approximates to the correct one is achieved, stop working the paste – if you carry on too long the paste will become sticky and begin to 'pick up' on the applicator. Continue to add thin layers of filler paste at twenty-minute intervals until the level of the filler is just proud of the surrounding bodywork.

Once the filler has hardened, excess can be removed using a metal plane or file. From then on, progressively finer grades of abrasive paper should be used, starting with a 40-grade production paper and finishing with a 400-grade wet-and-dry paper. Always wrap the abrasive paper around a flat rubber, cork, or wooden block – otherwise the surface of the filler will not be completely flat. During the smoothing of the filler surface the wet-and-dry paper should be periodically rinsed in water. This will ensure that a very smooth finish is imparted to the filler at the final stage.

At this stage the 'dent' should be surrounded by a ring of bare metal, which in turn should be encircled by the finely 'feathered' edge of the good paintwork. Rinse the repair area with clean water, until all of the dust produced by the rubbing-down operation has gone.

Spray the whole repair area with a light coat of primer – this will show up any imperfections in the surface of the filler. Repair these imperfections with fresh filler paste or bodystopper, and once more smooth the surface with abrasive paper. If bodystopper is used, it can be mixed with cellulose thinners to form a really thin paste which is ideal for filling small holes. Repeat this spray and repair procedure until you are satisfied that the surface of the filler, and the feathered edge of the paintwork are perfect. Clean the repair area with clean water and allow to dry fully.

The repair area is now ready for final spraying. Paint spraying must be carried out in a warm, dry, windless and dust free atmosphere. This condition can be created artificially if you have access to a large indoor working area, but if you are forced to work in the open, you will have to pick your day very carefully. If you are working indoors, dousing the floor in the work area with water will help to settle the dust which would otherwise be in the atmosphere. If the repair area is confined to one body panel, mask off the surrounding panels; this will help to minimise the effects of a slight mis-match in paint colours. Bodywork fittings (eg chrome strips, door handles etc) will also need to be masked off. Use genuine masking tape and several thicknesses of newspaper for the masking operations.

Before commencing to spray, agitate the aerosol can thoroughly, then spray a test area (an old tin, or similar) until the technique is mastered. Cover the repair area with a thick coat of primer; the thickness should be built up using several thin layers of paint rather than one thick one. Using 400 grade wet-and-dry paper, rub down the surface of the primer until it is really smooth. While doing this, the work area should be thoroughly doused with water, and the wet-and-dry paper periodically rinsed in water. Allow to dry before spraying on more paint.

Spray on the top coat, again building up the thickness by using several thin layers of paint. Start spraying in the centre of the repair area and then, with a single side-to-side motion, work outwards until the whole repair area and about 50 mm of the surrounding original paintwork is covered. Remove all masking material 10 to 15 minutes after spraying on the final coat of paint.

Allow the new paint at least two weeks to harden, then, using a paintwork renovator or a very fine cutting paste, blend the edges of the paint into the existing paintwork. Finally, apply wax polish.

Plastic components

With the use of more and more plastic body components by the vehicle manufacturers (eg bumpers, spoilers, and in some cases major body panels), rectification of more serious damage to such items has become a matter of either entrusting repair work to a specialist in this field, or renewing complete components. Repair of such damage by the DIY owner is not really feasible owing to the cost of the equipment and materials required for effecting such repairs. The basic technique involves making a groove along the line of the crack in the plastic using a rotary burr in a power drill. The damaged part is then welded back together by using a hot-air gun to heat up and fuse a plastic filler rod into the groove. Any excess plastic is then removed and the area rubbed down to a smooth finish. It is important that a filler rod of the correct plastic is used, as body components can be made of a variety of different types (eg polycarbonate, ABS, polypropylene).

Damage of a less serious nature (abrasions, minor cracks etc) can be repaired by the DIY owner using a two-part epoxy filler repair material. Once mixed in equal proportions, this is used in similar fashion to the bodywork filler used on metal panels. The filler is usually cured in twenty to thirty minutes, ready for sanding and painting.

If the owner is renewing a complete component himself, or if he has repaired it with epoxy filler, he will be left with the problem of finding a suitable paint for finishing which is compatible with the type of plastic used. At one time the use of a universal paint was not possible owing to the complex range of plastics encountered in body component applications. Standard paints, generally speaking, will not bond to plastic or rubber satisfactorily. However, it is now possible to obtain a plastic body parts finishing kit which consists of a pre-primer treatment, a primer and coloured top coat. Full instructions are normally supplied with a kit, but basically the method of use is to first apply the pre-primer to the component concerned and allow it to dry for up to 30 minutes. Then the primer is applied and left to dry for about an hour before finally applying the special coloured top coat. The result is a correctly-coloured component where the paint will flex with the plastic or rubber, a property that standard paint does not normally possess.

5 Major body damage – repair

Where serious damage has occurred or large areas need renewal due to neglect, completely new sections or panels will need welding in – this is best left to professionals. If the damage is due to impact, it will also be necessary to check completely the alignment of the body shell structure. Due to the principle of construction, the strength and shape of the whole can be affected by damage to a part. In such instances, the services of a Volvo agent with specialist checking jigs are essential. If a body is left misaligned, it is first of all dangerous as the car will not handle properly

and secondly uneven stresses will be imposed on the steering, engine and transmission, causing abnormal wear or complete failure. Tyre wear may also be excessive.

6 Bonnet – removal, refitting and adjustment

Removal

1 Open the bonnet, and disconnect the hoses from the washer jets, as described in Chapter 12.
2 Where applicable, disconnect the washer jet's wiring plugs and pull the loom from the bonnet.
3 Mark around the hinge bracket on the underside of the bonnet with a felt tip pen for reference when refitting. Prise out the clip and pull the support from place.
4 With the aid of an assistant, support the bonnet and remove the hinge bolts **(see illustration)**. Lift off the bonnet and store it in a safe place.

Refitting and adjustment

5 Before refitting, place pads of rags under the corners of the bonnet near the hinges to protect the paintwork from damage.
6 Fit the bonnet and insert the hinge bolts. Just nip the bolts up in their previously-marked positions.
7 Reconnect the washer tube and wiring plugs.
8 Shut the bonnet and check its fit. If necessary slacken the bolts and reposition the bonnet.
9 Tighten the hinge bolts securely when adjustment is correct and refit the support.

7 Bonnet release cable – removal, refitting and adjustment

Removal

1 Remove the grille as described in Section 21.
2 Remove the battery as described in Chapter 5A.

3 Undo the two screws, and remove the trim panel above the driver's pedals.
4 Undo the bolt in the handle cover, pull the handle forward slightly, and disconnect the cable **(see illustration)**.
5 With the cable ends disconnected from the lock levers and release catch, release the cable-ties and remove the cable.

Refitting and adjustment

6 Refit by reversing the removal operations.

8 Bonnet lock – removal and refitting

Removal

1 Volvo advise that the lock can be reached by removing the grille. However, given the difficulty in removing the grille with the bumper in place, we recommend removing the front bumper to prevent any damage occuring.
2 Undo the 2 bolts and remove the lock mechanism, disconnecting the cable as the assembly is withdrawn **(see illustration)**.

Refitting

3 Refitting is a reversal of removal. Only finger-tighten the lock retaining bolts, then shut the bonnet to centralise the catch. Tighten the retaining bolts securely.

9 Doors – removal, refitting and adjustment

Removal

1 Disconnect the battery negative lead (see Chapter 5A).
2 Open the door and support it with a jack or axle stand, using rags to protect the paintwork.
3 Disconnect the front door electrical wiring. Pull back the rubber boot, then use a small screwdriver to release the clip and unplug the connector. If removing a rear door, release the convoluted sleeve from the door pillar, pull the connector from the pillar, depress the clip and separate the two halves of the connector.

6.4 Unclip the support strut and undo the hinge bolts (arrowed)

7.4 Undo the bolt (arrowed) in the bonnet release handle cover

8.2 Bonnet lock bolts (arrowed)

9.4 Door check strap retaining bolt (arrowed)

9.5a Undo the upper . . .

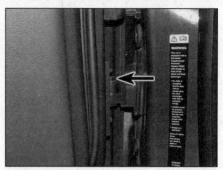

9.5b . . . and lower hinge bolts (arrowed)

4 Release the door check strap by undoing the bolt securing it to the pillar bracket **(see illustration)**.
5 Undo the upper and lower hinge bolts at the pillar **(see illustrations)**.
6 With the help of an assistant, remove the door.

Refitting and adjustment

7 Refit the door by reversing the removal operations.
8 Volvo technicians use a special tool to adjust the position of the door hinges. This task should be entrusted to a Volvo dealer or suitably-equipped specialist.

10 Door interior trim panel – removal and refitting

Removal

Front doors

1 Ensure the ignition is switched off, and remove the remote unit from the slot. This is to ensure the ignition is not accidentally switched on, and the airbag systems energised. Wait at least one minute for any stored electrical energy to dissipate before commencing work.
2 Carefully prise the speaker trim panel from the door mirror mounting **(see illustration)**.
3 Use a flat-bladed tool to prise out the trim piece beneath the door pull handle, then undo the two Torx bolts exposed **(see illustration)**.
4 The door trim panel is further secured by 8 clips around the edge of the panel **(see illustration)**.

5 With the clips released, pull the panel away from the door sufficiently to gain access to the speaker, electric window, and electric mirror wiring plugs and the handle release cable behind it **(see illustrations)**. Noting their locations, disconnect the plugs and lift the tab on the rear of the door handle to release the cable.

10.2 Prise the speaker trim from the door mirror mounting

10.4 Unclip the trim panel from the door

10.5b . . . and disconnect the wiring plugs

6 Lift the trim panel upwards and away from the door **(see illustration)**.

Rear doors

7 Use a flat-bladed tool to prise out the trim piece behind the door pull handle, then undo the Torx bolt exposed **(see illustration)**.

10.3 Undo the two bolts (arrowed)

10.5a Unclip the door handle cable . . .

10.6 Lift the trim panel from the door

10.7 Undo the bolt (arrowed)

8 The door trim panel is further secured by 7 clips around the edge of the panel.
9 With the clips released, pull the panel away from the door sufficiently to gain access to the speaker and electric window wiring plugs, and the handle release cable behind it. Noting their locations, disconnect the plugs and lift the tab on the rear of the door handle to release the cable.
10 Lift the trim panel upwards and away from the door.

Refitting

11 Refitting is a reversal of removal. Obtain and fit new fasteners for the base/edges of the panel if any were broken during removal. Check the operation of all switches before finally fitting the trim panel into place.

---

11 Door handle and lock components – removal and refitting

Outer handle

1 The operation is the same for both front and rear doors.
2 Prise out the cap at the top of the door's rear edge **(see illustration)**.
3 Insert a screwdriver through the hole and loosen the screw by no more than 5 turns **(see illustration)**. On the driver's door, the screw should be loosened by no more than 7 turns which will release the lock cylinder and its cover from the handle **(see illustration)**.
4 Remove the outer handle, disengaging the forward pivot from the location in the door. Recover the rubber seal between the handle and door when removing **(see illustrations)**.
5 Models fitted with a keyless entry system

11.2 Prise out the cap at the edge of the door

have wiring connected to the outer handle. As the handle is withdrawn, gently pull the wiring connector forwards to lock it in position before separating the connector.
6 Refitting is a reversal of removal.

Front door lock cylinder

7 Follow the process described above for handle removal.
8 Withdraw the lock cylinder and cover from the handle. Release the 2 clips to separate the lock cylinder from the cover **(see illustration)**.

11.3b Remove the lock trim from the handle

11.3a Loosen the screw

9 Refitting is a reversal of removal, noting the following points:
a) *Make sure the lock cylinder is inserted the correct way round.*
b) *Do not insert the key in the lock cylinder when it is being refitted, or the cylinder may be installed in the wrong position.*

Front door lock assembly

10 The door lock assembly is removed at the same time as the door carrier, and is attached to the carrier by 3 plastic bushes and a wiring

11.4a Disengage the handle from its pivot . . .

11.4b . . . and recover the rubber seal

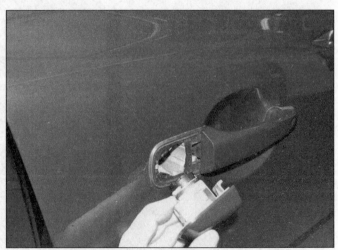

11.8 Withdraw the lock cylinder from the handle

11.10a The lock is attached to the door carrier by three plastic bushes (arrowed)

11.10b Disconnect the lock wiring plug

11.10c Unhook the release cable . . .

11.10d . . . and unclip the cable from the bracket

11.10e Release the clip at this section of the lock . . .

11.10f . . . and at this section, and separate the lock

plug **(see illustrations)**. Refer to Section 12 for door carrier removal. Lock parts can be separated **(see illustrations)**, but if in doubt refer to a Volvo dealer.

Rear door lock assembly

11 See the note above regarding removal of the front door lock assembly.

Door interior handles

12 Note that the process is the same for both front and rear doors.
13 Remove the door trim panel as described in Section 10. Disconnect any cables and wiring plugs as the panel is withdrawn.
14 Using a flat-bladed tool, carefully prise off the trim piece above the inner door handle.
15 At the rear of the door trim panel, use a 6 mm drill to drill out the rivets securing the handle to the trim panel, and remove the handle.

16 On refitting or renewal, the handle should be secured to the door trim panel using locking washers. The remainder is a reversal of removal.

---

12 Door carrier – removal and refitting

Removal

Front door

1 Remove the door inner trim panel as described in Section 10.
2 Remove the outer door handle (and the lock cylinder on the driver's door) as described in Section 11.
3 Remove the window glass as described in Section 13.

4 Release any clips securing cables to the panel and undo the 10 bolts securing the carrier to the door **(see illustration)**. Undo the 4 screws in the rear frame of the door securing the lock assembly, and the screw located at the pivot point of the outer door handle **(see illustrations)**.

12.4a Front door carrier bolts (arrowed)

12.4b Undo the three screws around the lock . . .

12.4c . . . the single screw beneath . . .

12.4d . . . and the screw located at the pivot point of the outer door handle

12.6 Unclip the lock button rod

12.7 Lift the front carrier from the door

12.11a Remove the rubber caps and loosen the bolts (arrowed) by no more than two turns

12.11b Secure the glass to the door using tape

12.13 Rear door carrier bolts (arrowed)

12.15 Lift the rear carrier from the door

5 Undo the clip and disconnect the wiring plug at the door pillar. Release the clip and push the wiring connector into the door as the wiring will be withdrawn as the carrier panel is removed. Disconnect the electric mirror wiring plug and unclip it from the door frame.

6 Manoeuvre the lock assembly until the lock button rod can be unclipped (see illustration).

7 Remove the carrier panel, together with the lock assembly, disconnecting any cables or wiring as it is withdrawn (see illustration).

Rear door

8 Lower the window until the top of the glass is 260 mm from the lower weatherseal.

9 Remove the door inner trim panel as described in Section 10.

10 Remove the outer door handle as described in Section 11.

11 Remove the 2 rubber caps and loosen the 2 bolts by no more than 2 turns (see illustration). Pull the window up by hand and secure to the door using tape (see illustration).

12 Undo the clip and disconnect the wiring plug at the B-pillar. Push the wiring connector into the door as the wiring will be withdrawn as the carrier panel is removed.

13 Undo the 8 bolts securing the carrier to the door (see illustration). Undo the 3 screws in the rear frame of the door securing the lock assembly. Undo the screw located at the pivot point of the outer door handle.

14 Manoeuvre the lock assembly until the lock button rod can be unclipped.

15 Remove the carrier panel, together with the lock assembly, disconnecting any cables or wiring as it is withdrawn (see illustration).

Refitting

16 For both doors, refitting is a reversal of the removal procedure. Before use, the window position must be initialised as described in Section 13.

13 Door window glass, motor and regulator – removal and refitting

Front door window glass

1 Lower the window until the top of the glass is 260 mm from the weather seal (measured at the rear, nearest the B-pillar).

13.4 Remove the rubber caps and loosen the bolts (arrowed)

2 Remove the door inner trim panel as described in Section 10.

3 Lever out the rubber cap at each end of the door carrier.

4 Loosen the bolt exposed in the aperture by no more than 2 turns (see illustration).

5 Lift the rear edge of the glass first, and manoeuvre it upwards and out of the door frame (see illustration).

6 Refitting is a reversal of removal.

Rear door window glass

7 Lower the window to the fully-down position.

8 Use a flat-bladed tool to prise the outer seal away from the rear of the window frame and use a 6 mm drill to drill out the 2 rivets exposed. A third rivet is located at the inside rear edge of door beneath a rubber grommet

13.5 Lift the rear edge of the glass and manoeuvre it from the door frame

13.8a Prise up the rubber seal at the rear edge of the door . . .

13.8b . . . and drill out the two rivets beneath the seal

13.8c Remove the rubber grommet and drill out the rivet in the aperture

– drilling this out also will allow the trim to be removed completely and make the job of removing the glass easier **(see illustrations)**.

9 Remove both the inner and outer weather seals at the base of the window, along with the inner rubber seal and trim section at the rear of the door frame **(see illustrations)**.

10 Raise the window until the top of the glass is 250 mm from the weather seal.

11 Remove the door trim panel as described in Section 10, and loosen the 2 bolts by no more than two turns.

12 Lift the glass from the frame **(see illustration)**.

13 Refitting is a reversal of removal, inserting new rivets at the rear of the frame **(see illustration)**.

Front and rear window motor

14 Disconnect the battery negative terminal as described in Chapter 5A, and remove the door trim panel as described in Section 10.

15 Undo the 3 screws securing the motor to the door carrier and disconnect the wiring plug as the motor is withdrawn **(see illustration)**.

16 Refitting is a reversal of the removal procedure. To synchronise the window mechanism, operate the switch to raise the window fully and hold the switch in this position for at least 5 seconds. Then lower the window fully and hold the switch in this position for at least 5 seconds. Repeat the process for raising the window. The window mechanism should now be synchronised.

13.8d Lift the trim from the door

13.9a Remove the inner . . .

13.9b . . . and outer window weather seals

13.9c Lift up the rubber seal at the rear edge of the door

13.12 Carefully lift the glass from the frame

13.13 Insert new rivets to secure the trim panel

13.15 Electric window motor bolts (arrowed)

13.17 Regulator retaining rivets (arrowed)

14.1a Prise out the plastic rivet . . .

14.1b . . . remove the lock cover . . .

14.1c . . . and undo the two screws (arrowed) for the inner handle

14.2a Undo the screw (arrowed) on each side

Front and rear window regulator

17 The regulator is integral with the carrier assembly and secured by 4 rivets (see illustration). Follow the instructions for removing the carrier assembly as described in Section 12, and for removing the window motor as described above. The regulator can then be removed.

14 Tailgate interior trim panel – removal and refitting

Removal

1 Open the tailgate, undo the plastic rivet and prise off the cover over the locking catch at the bottom of the tailgate (see illustrations). Undo the screws securing the inner handle (see illustration).
2 Undo the screw on each side securing the upper and lower trims and then, starting at the sides and working towards the top, release the clips and remove the upper trim panel. Then remove the lower trim panel, releasing the clips at the sides and then the bottom and prising out the switch for the power tailgate if fitted. Disconnect the wiring plug for the power tailgate switch (where fitted) as the panel is removed (see illustrations).

14.2b Unclip and remove the upper trim panel

14.2c Unclip and remove the lower trim panel

14.2d Where fitted, the switch for the power tailgate can be prised out

14.2e Disconnect the wiring plug for the power tailgate switch as the trim panel is removed

15.2 Disconnect the tailgate wiring plug

15.3a Carefully prise off the plastic hinge cover

15.3b Remove the cover . . .

Refitting

3 Refitting is a reversal of removal.

15 Tailgate – removal and refitting

Removal

1 Open the tailgate, and remove the upper trim panel as described in Section 14.
2 Disconnect the tailgate wiring plug and the washer jet hose (see illustration).
3 Have an assistant support the tailgate, then remove the plastic covers, undo the two hinge bolts each side, and detach the tailgate (see illustrations).

Refitting

4 Refitting is a reversal of removal.

16 Tailgate support struts – removal and refitting

Removing the support strut involves the partial removal of the headlining. As this requires considerable skill and experience if it is to be carried out without damage, this task is best entrusted to a dealer or automotive upholstery specialist.

17 Tailgate lock components – removal and refitting

Removal

Lock assembly

1 Remove the tailgate interior upper and lower trim panels as described in Section 14.
2 Undo the 3 screws and pull back the yellow tab to release the cable from the tailgate handle (see illustrations).
3 Disconnect the lock wiring plug and withdraw the lock from the tailgate (see illustration). Note that on models fitted with a power tailgate closing mechanism, the closing motor is connected to the lock assembly by a

15.3c . . . and undo the hinge bolts (arrowed)

17.2b Pull back the tab (arrowed) to release the cable from the tailgate handle

cable and it is easier to withdraw both units together (see below).

Power tailgate closing motor

4 Follow the steps above for removing the lock assembly. Undo the 3 screws,

17.4 Power tailgate closing motor screws (arrowed)

17.2a Undo the three screws (arrowed)

17.3 Disconnect the tailgate lock wiring plug

disconnect the wiring plug and withdraw the motor together with the lock assembly (see illustration).
5 With both units removed, the operating cable can be disconnected (see illustrations).

17.5a Release the cable from its bracket

17.5b Unhook the cable from the operating rod

17.5c Undo the three screws (arrowed) . . .

17.5d . . . and remove the lock cover plate

Tailgate oscillation damper

6 Remove the lock assembly as described previously.
7 Undo the 2 bolts, slide the damper to the right and remove **(see illustration)**.

Refitting

8 Refitting is a reversal of removal.

18 Windscreen and other fixed glass – removal and refitting

Special equipment and techniques are needed for successful removal and refitting of the windscreen, rear window and side windows. Have the work carried out by a Volvo dealer or a windscreen specialist.

19 Mirrors and associated components – removal and refitting

Warning: If the mirror glass is broken, wear gloves to protect your hands. This is good advice, in fact, even if the glass is not broken, due to the risk of glass breakage.

Door mirror glass

1 Pivot the mirror glass into the mirror housing as far as possible on the inside edge.
2 Insert a blunt, flat-bladed tool behind the outer edge of the glass and prise the glass from the mounting. Take care – excessive force will cause the glass to break. Disconnect the wiring plugs as the glass is withdrawn **(see illustrations)**.

3 Refitting is a reversal of removal.

Door mirror cover

4 Remove the mirror glass as described previously.
5 Insert a small screwdriver into the access hole in the mirror housing and release the clip **(see illustration)**.
6 Carefully prise the cover from the mirror **(see illustration)**.
7 Refitting is a reversal of removal, ensuring the lip of the cover fits correctly around the edge of the mirror housing.

Door mirror (complete unit)

8 Remove the door interior trim panel as described in Section 10 and disconnect the mirror wiring plug located on the door carrier **(see illustration)**.

17.7 Oscillation damper securing bolts (arrowed)

19.2a Use a blunt, flat-bladed tool to prise the mirror glass from its mountings

19.2b With the glass removed, disconnect any wiring plugs

19.5 Insert a small screwdriver into the access hole to release the clip

19.6 Remove the cover from the mirror assembly

19.8 Disconnect the mirror wiring plug

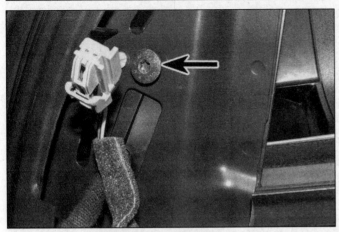

19.9a Undo the screw (arrowed)

19.9b A second screw (arrowed) is located beneath the rubber seal on the front edge of the door

19.10 Support the mirror housing and withdraw it from the door

9 Undo the screw located beneath the speaker cover, lift the rubber seal on the front edge of the door and undo the exposed screw **(see illustrations)**.

10 Support the mirror and withdraw the mirror from the door **(see illustration)**. Release the rubber grommet from the door as the mirror is withdrawn and feed the wiring through.

11 Refitting is a reversal of removal.

Interior mirror

Note: *Some models may be fitted with a proximity warning camera, in-vehicle humidity sensor, or electronic compass. Separate covers may need to be removed to gain access to the mirror mounting. Recalibration*

of these units may also be required on refitting and you should refer to a Volvo dealer.

12 Carefully prise off the cover below the mirror to allow access to the mounting.

13 Holding the mirror at the mounting point (and not the mirror itself) rotate clockwise and remove from the mounting. Disconnect any wiring plugs as it is withdrawn.

14 Refitting is a reversal of removal.

Blind spot information system

15 An optional blind spot information system (BLIS) may be fitted to warn the driver of a vehicle in the 'blind spot' area not visible in the door mirror on both sides of the car. The system uses digital camera technology to detect a vehicle in the 'blind spot' area on each side of the car and illuminate a warning light on the inside door panel next to the mirror. A switch on the facia panel allows the driver to enable the system when required. It should be noted that the system does not react to bicycles or mopeds, and at night-time will only react to vehicles with headlamps switched on.

16 The camera is located in the door mirror lower cowl and may be removed by first removing the door mirror cover as described earlier in this Section.

17 The warning light is located on the triangular trim panel over the door mirror mounting nut, and may be removed with

reference to the door interior trim panel removal procedure described in Section 10 of this Chapter.

Door mirror motor

18 We were unable to confirm the process for removing the mirror motor so this task should be entrusted to a Volvo dealer.

20 Bumpers –
removal and refitting

Note: *The bumpers consist of several sections, and once the bumper assembly has been removed as described below, further dismantling can take place. Refer to a Volvo dealer for advice on which sections are available separately.*

Front bumper

1 Open the bonnet and disconnect the battery negative terminal as described in Chapter 5A.

2 Undo the 7 plastic rivets on the top edge of the bumper **(see illustration)**.

3 Working in the wheel arch, undo the 5 screws that attach the wheel arch liner to the rear edge of the bumper **(see illustration)**.

4 From beneath the vehicle undo the 3 plastic screws in the centre of the bumper **(see illustration)**.

20.2 Undo the seven plastic rivets on top of the bumper (three are arrowed)

20.3 Undo the five screws in the wheel arch (two are arrowed)

20.4 Undo the three plastic screws beneath the bumper

20.5a Carefully unclip the bumper from below the front wing

20.5b Disconnect any wiring plugs as the bumper is withdrawn

20.9 Undo the Torx bolt on each side

20.10a Undo the wheel arch liner screws at the edge of the bumper . . .

20.10b . . . and the screw at the top of the bumper

20.11 Undo the two plastic bolts on the underside of the bumper (one is arrowed)

5 With the help of an assistant, pull the bumper sides outwards to release the clips below the headlamps and where the bumper meets the front wing, then pull it forward and remove it from the vehicle. Note their fitted positions and disconnect the various wiring plugs as the bumper is withdrawn. On models with headlight washers, disconnect the hose at the pump on the washer reservoir **(see illustrations)**.

6 Refitting is a reversal of removal, taking care to ensure that the bumper aligns correctly with surrounding body panels.

Rear bumper

7 Disconnect the battery negative terminal as described in Chapter 5A.

8 Open the tailgate.

9 Undo the Torx bolt at the lower corner of the opening on each side **(see illustration)**.

10 Working in the wheel arch, undo the 4 screws that attach the wheel arch liner to the rear edge of the bumper, and undo the fixing at the top of the bumper **(see illustrations)**.

11 Undo the 2 plastic bolts on the underside of the bumper in the centre **(see illustration)**.

12 With the help of an assistant, pull the bumper sides outwards to release the clips below the light units and where the bumper meets the rear wing, then pull it rearwards and remove it from the vehicle **(see illustration)**. Note their fitted positions and disconnect any wiring plugs as the bumper is withdrawn.

13 Refitting is a reversal of removal taking care to ensure that the bumper aligns correctly with surrounding body panels.

21 Front grille panel – removal and refitting

Removal

1 Volvo say the grille can be removed with the bumper in place. In practice this proved difficult and there is a risk of damage to the grille and surrounding paintwork, so we recommend removing the bumper first. Using a flat-bladed tool, release the retaining clips around the edge of the grille – there are 4 at the top, 4 at the bottom, and 1 each side towards the top. Remove the grille **(see illustration)**.

Refitting

2 Refit by reversing the removal operations.

22 Front seat – removal and refitting

Note: *All models are equipped with a SIPS airbag, fitted into the side of the front seat backrest, as part of the side impact protection system; refer to Chapter 12 for further information on the SRS and SIPS systems.*

Removal

1 Raise the seat base to its maximum height. Ensure that the ignition is switched off, then disconnect the battery negative lead as described in Chapter 5A. Wait at least

20.12 Carefully unclip the bumper from below the wing and light unit

21.1 Release the ten clips securing the grille (two are arrowed)

5 minutes for any residual electrical energy to dissipate before proceeding.

2 It's advisable to 'earth' the seat frame before removal to protect against static electricity discharge. Strip the insulation from both ends of a long length of electrical cable, and secure one end to the metal parts of the seat frame and the other end to a bare metal part of the vehicle body or similar.

3 Undo the 7 mm bolt under the front of the seat and disconnect the wiring plug **(see illustration)**.

4 On the driver's seat, use a small screwdriver to depress the quick-release catch through the hole in the cover, and pull the seat belt lower anchorage from the outside of the seat. On the passenger seat, pull back the rubber flap next to the anchorage and use a small screwdriver to depress the clip.

5 Remove the plastic covers and undo the 4 seat mounting bolts **(see illustrations)**.

6 Lift the seat and manoeuvre it from the vehicle. As the seats are very heavy, the help of an assistant would be a good idea. Note their fitted positions, and disconnect any wiring plugs as the seat is withdrawn. Take great care not to damage the connectors.

Refitting

7 Locate the seat over the guide pins, reconnect the wiring, and insert the retaining bolts. Tighten the bolts securely and refit the bolt covers.

8 Reconnect the seat belt lower anchorage, ensuring that the catch is fully engaged.

9 Make sure that no-one is inside the car, then reconnect the battery negative lead.

23 Rear seat – removal and refitting

Removal

Seat cushion

1 Pull the front edge of the seat upwards, slide the cushion towards the front of the car, and remove.

22.3 Undo the bolt (arrowed) and disconnect the wiring plug

22.5b Undo the front bolts . . .

22.5a Remove the plastic covers over the front seat bolts

22.5c . . . and the rear bolts

2 If the seat is heated, slide the cushion forwards slightly and disconnect the wiring plug located at the rear, nearest the side pad. Remove the cushion.

3 If the integrated child safety seat is fitted, pull the child seat into the fully-raised position and undo the screw/bolt each side at the front edge. The cushion can then be removed.

Outer backrest

4 Ensure that the ignition is switched off then disconnect the battery negative lead as described in Chapter 5A. Wait at least 5 minutes for any residual electrical energy to dissipate before proceeding.

5 Remove the seat cushion and side pad as described in this Section.

6 Undo the wiring plug and securing bolt and

remove the lower seat belt anchorages as appropriate.

7 Undo the bolt at the outer edge of the backrest, nearest to the door, withdraw the pivot from the base of the centre backrest and remove the backrest **(see illustrations)**.

Centre backrest/armrest

8 Remove the outer backrest as described above.

9 Pull out the plastic pivots on each side and remove the backrest/armrest **(see illustration)**.

Side pad

10 Tip the backrest forward and, using a screwdriver and a flat-bladed tool, one inserted on each side, release the clips

23.7a Rear seat backrest outer bolt (arrowed)

23.7b Withdraw the pivot from the base of the centre backrest

23.9 Pull out the plastic pivots on each side

23.10 Release the clip (arrowed) at the top of the side pad

24.11a Prise out the airbag label . . .

24.11b . . . undo the bolt (arrowed) . . .

located towards the top of the side pad **(see illustration)**.

11 Release the clip at the bottom and remove by pulling the side pad upwards and towards the centre of the car.

Refitting

12 Refit by reversing the removal operations.

24 Interior trim – removal and refitting

Note: *Refer to earlier Sections of this Chapter for specific procedures covering door and tailgate interior trim panels.*

General

1 The interior trim panels are secured using either screws or various types of trim fasteners, usually studs or clips.

2 Check that there are no other panels overlapping the one to be removed, or other components hindering removal; usually there is a sequence that has to be followed, and this will only become obvious on close inspection.

3 Some of the interior panels will additionally be retained by the screws which are used to secure other items, such as the grab handles.

4 Remove all visible retainers, such as screws, noting that these may be hidden under small plastic caps. If the panel will not come free, it is held by internal clips or fasteners. These are usually situated around the edges of the panel, and can be prised up to release them;

note, however, that they can break quite easily, so new ones should be available. The best way of releasing such clips is to use a large flat-bladed screwdriver or other wide-bladed tool. Note that in many cases, the adjacent sealing strip must be prised back to release a panel.

5 When removing a panel, **never** use excessive force or the panel may be damaged; always check carefully that all fasteners or other relevant components have been removed or released before attempting to withdraw a panel.

6 Refitting is a reversal of removal; secure the fasteners by pressing them firmly into place and ensure that all disturbed components are correctly secured to prevent rattles.

Carpets

7 The passenger compartment floor carpet is in three sections; front left, front right and rear, and is secured at the sides by the front and rear sill trim panels.

8 Carpet removal and refitting is reasonably straightforward, but is very time-consuming because all adjoining trim panels must be removed first, as must components such as the seats and seat belt lower anchorages.

Headlining

9 The headlining is clipped to the roof, and can be withdrawn only once all fittings such as grab handles, sunvisors, sunroof (if fitted), fixed window glass, and related trim panels have been removed and the relevant sealing strips have been prised clear.

10 Note that headlining removal and refitting requires considerable skill and experience if it is to be carried out without damage, and is therefore best entrusted to a dealer or automotive upholstery specialist.

A-pillar trims

11 Prise out the airbag label and undo the bolt in the label aperture **(see illustrations)**.

12 Pull the top of the A-pillar trim inwards towards the centre of the passenger cabin to release the clips, then pull the trim from the clips at the lower edge. The lower section of the A-pillar trim can also be unclipped **(see illustration)**.

13 Refitting is a reversal of removal. If any clips are damaged, new ones should be used when refitting, so as not to impair the inflatable safety curtain performance.

B-pillar trims

14 Pull the front door sill trim panel straight up to release it from the retaining clips. Repeat the procedure on the rear door sill trim panel **(see illustrations)**.

15 Remove the cover, depress the quick-release catch at the side and remove the seat belt lower anchorage from the outside of the seat.

16 Move the front seat as far forward as possible, then pull the rubber weatherstrips from the door apertures adjacent to the B-pillar.

17 Pull the lower edge of the B-pillar trim in towards the centre of the cabin to release the clips and disengage the air ducting (where

24.12 . . . and unclip the trim from the A-pillar

24.14a Carefully prise up the front door sill trim . . .

24.14b . . . and the rear door sill trim

24.17a Unclip the seat belt guide from the trim

24.17b Release the clips at the top of the trim and withdraw from the B-pillar

24.22a Prise out the airbag label on the C-pillar trim . . .

24.22b . . . and undo the bolt in the aperture

applicable), then pull it downwards at the same time as squeezing together the sides at the top of the trim to release the retaining clips located on the B-pillar below the weatherstrips. **(see illustrations).**

18 Feed the seat belt through the panel and remove it from the cabin.

19 To refit, reverse the removal process.

24.24 Unclip the cant rail trim panel

C-pillar trims

20 Remove the rear seat side pad as described in Section 23.

21 Release the clip and remove the cover for the rear seat belt inertia reel.

22 Prise out the airbag label and undo the bolt in the label aperture. Release the clips and remove the panel **(see illustrations).**

24.25 Release the clips and remove the D-pillar trim

Caution: Do not touch the inflatable safety curtain with bare hands, as this may cause a deformity in the cover.

23 Refitting is a reversal of removal.

D-pillar trims

24 Remove the cant rail trim panel located at the rear of the headlining. Using a flat-bladed tool carefully prise out the interior light unit and remove the exposed screw. Carefully release the retaining clips and remove the panel **(see illustration).**

25 Release the 3 clips securing the D-pillar trim and remove **(see illustration).**

26 Refitting is a reversal of removal.

Luggage area side panel

27 Remove the D-pillar trim as described above.

28 Remove the cover for the rear seat belt inertia reel. Undo the 2 screws at the top of the panel – 1 on each side – and pull the panel forwards to release the retaining clips. Lift the panel upwards and remove, disconnecting

24.28a Undo the screw (arrowed) . . .

24.28b . . . and remove the seat belt inertia reel cover

24.28c Undo the bolts at the top of the panel

24.28d Disconnect any wiring plugs . . .

24.28e . . . and lift the panel away

24.30a Undo the bolt (arrowed) on each side of the sill trim panel

24.30b Unclip the sill trim panel, noting that the clips are fixed very firmly. This operation needs care to avoid damage to the panel

any wiring plugs as the panel is withdrawn (see illustrations).

29 Refitting is a reversal of removal.

Luggage area sill trim panel

30 Pull up the floor panel/carpet from the luggage area and undo the bolt on both sides on the rear of the sill panel. Pull the trim panel upwards to release the clips, though note that the clips are secured very firmly so approach this task carefully to avoid damage to the trim (see illustrations).

31 Refitting is a reversal of removal.

Luggage area floor rails

32 Undo the bolt located at each end of the rail (see illustration).

33 Remove the luggage compartment side panel as described above, and undo the 2 bolts exposed in the centre of the rail when the trim panel is removed (see illustration).

34 Refitting is a reversal of removal.

Glovebox

35 Remove the facia lower trim panel above the passenger footwell. Undo the 2 screws, lower the panel slightly, disconnect the wiring plug for the footwell lamp, release the clip at the rear and remove.

36 Undo the 2 screws below the glovebox lid, exposed by the removal of the facia lower trim panel. Open the lid, remove the 2 bolts to the rear of the glovebox and the 4 screws around the upper edge of the opening. Push

24.32 Undo the bolt (arrowed) at each end of the luggage rail

24.33 With the side panel removed, undo the two bolts (arrowed) in the centre of the luggage rail

24.36a Undo the screws below the glovebox lid, exposed by removal of the lower trim panel

24.36b Undo the four screws around the upper edge of the opening (two are arrowed)

24.36c Undo the two bolts (arrowed) at the rear of the glovebox

24.36d The glovebox can now be withdrawn

24.38a Prise out the plastic covers . . .

24.38b . . . and undo the screw and bolt (arrowed)

the glovebox upwards and pull away from the facia, disconnecting any wiring plugs as it is withdrawn (see illustrations).

37 Refitting is a reversal of removal.

Sunvisor

38 Prise out the plastic covers and undo the bolt and screw exposed in the aperture (see illustrations).

39 Unclip the sunvisor from the inboard mounting and remove it. Disconnect the wiring plug as the sunvisor is withdrawn.

40 To remove the inboard mounting, prise down the retaining tab and remove the mounting from the headlining (see illustrations).

41 Refitting is a reversal of removal.

Grab handle

42 Hold down the grab handle, prise open

the plastic covers and undo the 2 retaining screws (see illustration).

43 Refitting is a reversal of removal.

25 Seat belts – general information, removal and refitting

1 All models are equipped with pyrotechnic front seat belt tensioners as part of the supplemental restraint system (SRS). The system is designed to instantaneously take up any slack in the seat belt in the case of a sudden frontal impact, therefore reducing the possibility of injury to the front seat occupants. Each front seat is fitted with the system, the tensioner being situated behind the upper B-pillar trim panel.

2 The seat belt tensioner is triggered along

with the driver's and passenger's airbag, by a frontal impact above a predetermined force. Lesser impacts, including impacts from behind, will not trigger the system.

3 When the system is triggered, the explosive gas in the tensioner mechanism retracts and locks the seat belt through a cable which acts on the inertia reel. This prevents the seat belt moving, and keeps the occupant firmly in position in the seat. Once the tensioner has been triggered, the seat belt will be permanently locked and the assembly must be renewed. If any abnormal rattling noises are heard when pulling out or retracting the belt, this also indicates that the tensioner has been triggered.

4 There is a risk of injury if the system is triggered inadvertently when working on the vehicle, and it is therefore strongly

24.40a Prise down the retaining tab

24.40b Remove the mounting from the headlining

24.42 Undo the two screws (arrowed)

25.7 Front seat belt tensioner wiring plug (arrowed)

25.8 Front inertia reel bolts (arrowed)

25.12 Rear seat belt tensioner wiring plug (arrowed)

recommended that any work involving the seat belt tensioner system is entrusted to a Volvo dealer. Note the following warnings before contemplating any work on the front seat belts.

⚠ *Warning: Switch off the ignition, disconnect the battery negative lead, and wait for at least 5 minutes for any residual electrical energy to dissipate before starting work involving the front seat belts.*
• *Do not expose the tensioner mechanism to temperatures in excess of 100°C.*
• *If the tensioner mechanism is dropped, it must be renewed, even it has suffered no apparent damage.*
• *Do not allow any solvents to come into contact with the tensioner mechanism.*

• *Do not attempt to open the tensioner mechanism, as it contains explosive gas.*
• *Tensioners from other vehicles, even from the same model and year, must not be fitted.*
• *Tensioners must be discharged before they are disposed of, but this task should be entrusted to a Volvo dealer or specialist.*

Removal

Front seat belts

5 Switch off the ignition then disconnect the battery negative lead as described in Chapter 5A. Wait for at least 5 minutes before proceeding.
6 To remove the inertia reel, remove the B-pillar trim as described in Section 24.

7 Confirm that the battery is disconnected, then unplug the wiring connector from the seat belt tensioner by squeezing together the two plug retaining clips (see illustration). This wiring plug should never be disconnected (or reconnected) while the battery negative lead is connected.
8 Unscrew and remove the 2 reel/tensioner retaining bolts, and remove the seat belt reel and tensioner from the car (see illustration).
9 To remove the belt buckle, remove the seat first, as described in Section 22. Cut the cable-ties securing the wiring to the seat and disconnect the wiring plug beneath the seat. The buckles are secured with a large Torx bolt.

Rear seat belts

10 Switch off the ignition then disconnect the battery negative lead as described in Chapter 5A. Wait for at least 5 minutes before proceeding.
11 To remove the inertia reel, remove the luggage compartment side panel as described In Section 24.
12 Confirm that the battery is disconnected, then unplug the wiring connector for the seat belt tensioner by squeezing together the two plug retaining clips (see illustration). This wiring plug should never be disconnected (or reconnected) while the battery negative lead is connected.
13 Undo the bolts securing the upper belt guide and the inertia reel, and remove the inertia reel (see illustrations).
14 To remove the lower belt anchorage, remove the rear seat cushion as described in Section 23 and the rear sill trims as described in Section 24. Pull up the sound deadening material and fold it back until the anchorage is accessible. Undo the bolt securing the anchorage to the floorpan. The rear seat buckles can also be removed if required (see illustrations).
15 To remove the centre rear seat belt and inertia reel requires the centre backrest to be dismantled. While the illustrations show part of this process, this is a potentially difficult task that could result in damage to the seat trim and was not undertaken in the workshop. We advise that you entrust this task to a Volvo

25.13a Rear inertia reel securing bolt (arrowed)

25.13b Rear seat belt guide bolt (arrowed)

25.14a Rear seat belt anchorage bolt (arrowed)

25.14b Rear seat belt buckle bolt (arrowed)

25.15a Undo the bolt and remove the centre seat belt inertia reel

25.15b Undo the bolt and remove the centre seat belt anchorage

25.15c Unclip the plastic trim section, undo the screws and remove the retaining plates (arrowed)

dealer or vehicle upholstery specialist **(see illustrations)**.

Refitting

16 In all cases, refit by reversing the removal operations. Tighten the seat belt mountings to the specified torque. When refitting the seat belts, note the following points:

a) *Reconnect the front seat belt lower anchorage, ensuring that the catch is fully engaged.*

b) *Make sure that no-one is inside the car. Switch on the ignition, then reconnect the battery negative lead. Switch the ignition off, then on again, and check that the airbag warning light comes on, then goes out within 15 seconds.*

25.15d Unclip the seat trim from the sides of the backrest

25.15e Release the fourteen clips and remove the seat trim from the front of the backrest

---

26 Centre console – removal and refitting

Removal

1 Fully apply the handbrake, then move the gear or selector lever to neutral – note that it may be necessary to move the gear or selector lever as the console is removed.

2 Ensure the front seats are in the fully lowered, rearmost position.

Upper console

3 Disconnect the battery negative terminal as described in Chapter 5A.

4 Using a flat-bladed tool, carefully prise off the trim panel around the audio unit **(see illustration)**.

5 Using the same tool, carefully prise up the trim panel surrounding the gear lever starting at the top just below the air conditioning controls **(see illustration)**.

6 Undo the 8 retaining screws. There are 2 at the top of the console, 2 in front of the gear lever, 2 behind the gear lever, and 2 at the rear of the console beneath the storage compartment lid (these last 2 are covered by rubber pads for the console lid – carefully prise off the pads first) **(see**

26.4 Carefully prise the trim from around the audio unit

26.5 Carefully prise the trim from around the gear lever

26.6a Undo the two screws (arrowed) at the top of the console . . .

26.6b . . . and the four screws (arrowed) around the gear lever

26.6c Lever out the rubber pads . . .

26.6d . . . and undo the two screws (arrowed)

26.7 Undo the screw on each side at the rear of the control panel

26.8a Disconnect the wiring plugs on the rear of the control panel

illustrations).

7 From the rear of the console, undo the 2 screws located just below where the console meets the bottom of the facia **(see illustration)**.

8 Pull the console upwards and remove, disconnecting any wiring plugs as the panel is withdrawn (note that wiring may also be clipped to the lower console) **(see illustrations)**. Note that the wiring may be of the fibre-optic variety and should not be bent excessively as this will cause damage.

Lower console

Note: *Although not strictly necessary, we found it easier when undertaking this task to remove the front section of the carpet on both the right- and left-hand side of the vehicle. However this does require removal of the front seats, the lower section of the A-pillar trim, the audio amplifier below the driver's seat, and the bonnet release handle. If you wish to undertake the task in this way,*

refer to the relevant Sections for component removal.

9 Disconnect the battery negative terminal as described in Chapter 5A.

10 Remove the upper console as described above.

11 Carefully prise off the front and rear

26.8b Unclip any wiring from the console

sections of the side panels on each side, pull the carpet to one side, and undo the exposed bolt (note that the bolt on the left-hand side points towards the rear of the vehicle, while the bolt on the right-hand side points outwards towards the door **(see illustrations)**.

12 Open the armrest, remove the storage

26.11a Unclip the front . . .

26.11b . . . and rear sections of the console side panels

26.11c Undo the bolt (arrowed) on the left-hand side . . .

26.11d . . . and the bolt (arrowed) on the right-hand side

26.12 Undo the two bolts (arrowed) in the base of the storage compartment

26.13 Undo the bolt (arrowed) in the base of the cup holder

26.14a Release the gear selector locking collar from its bracket

insert, and undo the 2 bolts at the bottom (not the 4 screws which secure the storage box to the console frame) **(see illustration)**.

13 Remove the base of the cup holder and undo the exposed bolt **(see illustration)**.

14 Detach the gear selector arm by pulling the locking collar forwards slightly to release it from the bracket and then using a small screwdriver to depress the locking tab. The arm can then be gently pulled from the selector housing **(see illustrations)**.

15 Pull the air vents to one side.

16 Disconnect any wiring plugs at the base of the console and unclip the wiring from the console frame. Carefully pull the console upwards and remove **(see illustrations)**.

17 Further dismantling of the lower console is required to access both the gear selector housing and the airbag control unit, and is carried out as follows. Undo the 4 screws in the bottom of the rear storage box and slide the box rearwards from the remainder of the console, disconnecting any wiring plugs as it is withdrawn. Undo the 2 screws ahead of the storage box position and the 4 screws around the gear selector housing, disconnect any wiring plugs, and lift the sections from the console frame **(see illustrations)**.

Centre armrest

26.14b Depress the release tab and remove the arm from the selector housing

26.16a Disconnect the wiring plugs (arrowed) at the base of the console

26.16b Carefully lift the console from position

26.17a Undo the four screws (arrowed) in the base of the storage compartment

26.17b Withdraw the rear section of the console

26.17c Undo the two screws (arrowed) . . .

26.17d . . . and the four screws around the gear selector housing (two are arrowed)

26.18a Prise the trim from the base of the console

26.18b Undo the two screws beneath the trim panel

26.19a Undo the screw on each side at the armrest hinge

26.19b Remove the upper section of trim

26.19c Undo the two screws (arrowed)

26.20 Disconnect any wiring plugs as the console section is removed

18 Using a flat-bladed tool, prise off the trim below the cigar lighter socket at the rear of the console. Prise off the lower trim panel where it meets the floor and undo the 2 screws/bolts exposed in the aperture **(see illustrations)**.

19 Undo the screw/bolt on each side located by the armrest hinge and remove the trim around the cigar lighter socket. Undo the 2 screws/bolts exposed by the removal of the trim **(see illustrations)**.

20 Carefully lift the armrest away, undoing any wiring plugs as it is withdrawn **(see illustration)**.

Refitting

21 Refitting is a reversal of removal.

27 Facia – removal and refitting

Removal

1 Ensure the front seats are in the rearmost positions, then disconnect the battery negative lead (see Chapter 5A), and wait at least 5 minutes before proceeding to allow any residual electrical energy to dissipate.

2 Remove the lower facia panels in the driver's and passenger's footwell. Each panel is retained by two screws and the wiring plugs for the footwell lamps must be disconnected as the panels are withdrawn **(see illustration)**.

3 Detach the diagnostic plug from its

mounting under the driver's side of the lower facia, above the pedals. On some models, simply release the retaining clip, on other models, the plug is fitted to a bracket retained by two screws **(see illustration)**.

4 Remove the steering wheel as described in Chapter 10.

5 Remove the glovebox and centre console as described in Sections 24 and 26, and the A-pillar trims as described in Section 24.

6 Remove the radio, headlight switch, handbrake switch, and hazard light switch as described in Chapter 12.

7 Remove the solar sensor as described in Chapter 3, and with the instrument panel removed, disconnect the wiring plug located above the steering column for the ignition/starter switch **(see illustration)**.

27.2 Undo the screws (arrowed) and remove the facia lower trim panels on both sides

27.3 Undo the screws (arrowed) for the diagnostic socket

27.7 Disconnect the starter wiring plug above the steering column

27.8 Prise the speaker grille from the top of the facia

27.9a Undo the two bolts (arrowed) on the passenger side . . .

27.9b . . . the two bolts (arrowed) on the driver's side . . .

27.9c . . . the two bolts (arrowed) below the glovebox . . .

27.9d . . . the two bolts (arrowed) below the passenger airbag . . .

27.9e . . . the two bolts (arrowed) in the audio unit aperture . . .

8 Using a blunt, flat-bladed tool carefully prise the grille from the top of the facia (this may contain a speaker). Undo the 6 screws in the aperture, remove the panel and disconnect the wiring plug **(see illustration)**.

9 Undo the facia retaining bolts. There are 2 at the A-pillar on each side, 2 below the glovebox, 2 below the passenger airbag, 2 in the radio aperture, 2 below the grille on top of the facia, 2 in the instrument panel aperture, 2 above the pedals in the driver's footwell, and 1 located at the top left in the instrument panel aperture **(see illustrations)**.

10 Unclip the wiring plug located behind the passenger side facia end panel and disconnect the passenger airbag wiring plug **(see illustration)**.

27.9f . . . the two bolts (arrowed) on the top of the facia below the speaker grille . . .

27.9g . . . the two bolts (arrowed) in the instrument panel aperture . . .

27.9h . . . the two bolts (arrowed) on the driver's side above the pedals . . .

27.9i . . . and the bolt at the rear of the instrument panel aperture

27.10 Unclip the wiring plug behind the passenger side facia end panel

27.11 Carefully withdraw the facia from the vehicle

11 Carefully withdraw the facia with the help of an assistant if possible, and remove from the vehicle **(see illustration)**.

⚠️ *Warning: Position the facia and airbag module in a safe place, with the mechanism facing downwards as a precaution against accidental operation. Do not attempt to open or repair the airbag module, or apply any electrical current to it. Do not re-use any airbag which is visibly damaged, or which has been tampered with.*

Refitting

12 Refitting is a reversal of removal.
13 On cars equipped with a passenger's airbag, make sure that no-one is inside the car. Switch on the ignition, then reconnect the battery negative lead. Switch the ignition off, then on again, and check that the SRS warning light comes on, then goes out within 15 seconds.

28 Sunroof – general information

An electrically-operated sunroof is available as standard or optional equipment, according to model.

The sunroof is maintenance-free, but any adjustment or removal and refitting of the component parts should be entrusted to a dealer or specialist, due to the complexity of the unit and the need to remove much of the interior trim and headlining to gain access. The latter operation is involved, and requires care and specialist knowledge to avoid damage.

If the sunroof action becomes sluggish, the slides and/or cables may need lubricating – consult a Volvo dealer or specialist for advice on a suitable product to use. Further checks in the event of non-operation are limited to checking the fuse and wiring, with reference to the wiring diagrams at the end of Chapter 12.

Drain tubes

It is advisable to check the sunroof water drain tubes on a periodic basis. If they become blocked, they may be cleared by probing them with a length of suitable cable (and old speedometer drive cable is ideal). The front drain tubes terminate at the front bulkhead at the rear of the engine bay. The rear drain tubes terminate ahead of the rear wheels inside the wheel arches.

Chapter 12
Body electrical system

Contents

Degrees of difficulty

Easy, suitable for novice with little experience	**Fairly easy,** suitable for beginner with some experience	**Fairly difficult,** suitable for competent DIY mechanic	**Difficult,** suitable for experienced DIY mechanic	**Very difficult,** suitable for expert DIY or professional

Specifications

General
System type . . . . 12 volt, negative earth
Fuses . . . . See wiring diagrams at end of Chapter and sticker on control box lid for specific vehicle details

Bulbs
	Wattage
Brake light	21 bayonet
Door mirror ground light	6 wedge
Foglight:	
Front	35 H8
Rear	21 bayonet
Footwell compartment illumination	5 wedge
Glovebox light	3 bayonet
Headlight:	
Halogen	55 H7
Bi-xenon	35 D2R
High-level brake light	LED type (non-renewable)
Indicator side repeater lights	5 wedge
Indicators (front and rear)	21 bayonet
Luggage compartment illumination	5 wedge
Number plate light	5 festoon
Reversing light	21 bayonet
Side marker lights:	
Front	5 wedge
Rear	10 bayonet
Sidelights	5 capless
Tail light	5 bayonet
Vanity mirror illumination	1.2 festoon

Torque wrench settings

	Nm	lbf ft
Airbag (passenger side):		
Retaining bolts	10	7
Bracket to airbag	10	7
Bracket to crossmember	6	4
Airbag control module	10	7
Airbag side crash sensors	6	4
Tailgate wiper motor bolts	10	7
Windscreen wiper linkage bolts/nuts	10	7
Windscreen wiper arm nuts	30	22

1 General information and precautions

The electrical system is of 12 volt negative earth type. Power for the lights and all electrical accessories is supplied by a lead-acid type battery, which is charged by the belt-driven alternator.

This Chapter covers repair and service procedures for the various electrical components not associated with the engine. Information on the battery, alternator and starter motor can be found in Chapter 5A.

⚠️ *Warning: Before carrying out any work on the electrical system, read through the precautions given in 'Safety first!' at the beginning of this manual.*

2 Electrical system fault finding – general information

Note: *Refer to the precautions given in this Chapter before starting work. The following tests relate to testing of the main electrical circuits, and should not be used to test delicate electronic circuits, particularly where an electronic control unit/module is used.*

General

1 A typical electrical circuit consists of an electrical component, any switches, relays, motors, fuses, fusible links or circuit breakers related to that component, and the wiring and connectors which link the component to both the battery and the chassis. To help to pinpoint a problem in an electrical circuit, wiring diagrams are included at the end of this Chapter.

2 Before attempting to diagnose an electrical fault, first study the appropriate wiring diagram, to obtain a complete understanding of the components included in the particular circuit concerned. The possible sources of a fault can be narrowed down by noting if other components related to the circuit are operating properly. If several components or circuits fail at one time, the problem is likely to be related to a shared fuse or earth connection.

3 Electrical problems usually stem from simple causes, such as loose or corroded connections, a faulty earth connection, a blown fuse, a melted fusible link, or a faulty relay. Visually inspect the condition of all fuses, wires and connections in a problem circuit before testing the components. Use the wiring diagrams to determine which terminal connections will need to be checked in order to pinpoint the trouble-spot.

4 The basic tools required for electrical fault finding include a circuit tester or voltmeter (a 12 volt bulb with a set of test leads can also be used for certain tests); an ohmmeter (to measure resistance and check for continuity); a battery and set of test leads; and a jumper wire, preferably with a circuit breaker or fuse incorporated, which can be used to bypass suspect wires or electrical components. Before attempting to locate a problem with test instruments, use the wiring diagram to determine where to make the connections.

⚠️ *Warning: Under no circumstances may live measuring instruments such as ohmmeters, voltmeters or a bulb and test leads be used to test any of the SRS airbag, SIPS bag, or pyrotechnical seat belt circuitry. Any testing of these components must be left to a Volvo dealer, as there is a danger of activating the system if the correct procedures are not followed.*
Caution: The Volvo V70 electrical system is extremely complex. Many of the ECMs are connected via a 'Databus' system, where they are able to share information from the various sensors, and communicate with each other. For instance, as the automatic gearbox approaches a gear ratio shift point, it signals the engine management ECM via the Databus. As the gearchange is made by the transmission ECM, the engine management ECM retards the ignition timing, momentarily reducing engine output to ensure a smoother transition from one gear ratio to the next. Due to the design of the Databus system, it is not advisable to backprobe the ECMs with a multimeter in the traditional manner. Instead, the electrical systems are equipped with a sophisticated self-diagnosis system, which can interrogate the various ECMs to reveal the stored fault codes, and help pinpoint faults. In order to access the self-diagnosis system, specialist test equipment (fault code reader/scanner) is required. Refer to your Volvo dealer or suitably-equipped specialist.

5 To find the source of an intermittent wiring fault (usually due to a poor or dirty connection, or damaged wiring insulation), a wiggle test can be performed on the wiring. This involves wiggling the wiring by hand to see if the fault occurs as the wiring is moved. It should be possible to narrow down the source of the fault to a particular section of wiring. This method of testing can be used in conjunction with any of the tests described in the following sub-Sections.

6 Apart from problems due to poor connections, two basic types of fault can occur in an electrical circuit – open-circuit, or short-circuit.

7 Open-circuit faults are caused by a break somewhere in the circuit, which prevents current from flowing. An open-circuit fault will prevent a component from working.

8 Short-circuit faults are caused by a short somewhere in the circuit, which allows the current flowing in the circuit to escape along an alternative route, usually to earth. Short-circuit faults are normally caused by a breakdown in wiring insulation, which allows a feed wire to touch either another wire, or an earthed component such as the bodyshell. A short-circuit fault will normally cause the relevant circuit fuse to blow.

Finding an open-circuit

9 To check for an open-circuit, connect one lead of a circuit tester or the negative lead of a voltmeter either to the battery negative terminal or to a known good earth.

10 Connect the other lead to a connector in the circuit being tested, preferably nearest to the battery or fuse. At this point, battery voltage should be present, unless the lead from the battery or the fuse itself is faulty (bearing in mind that some circuits are live only when the ignition switch is moved to a particular position).

11 Switch on the circuit, then connect the tester lead to the connector nearest the circuit switch on the component side.

12 If voltage is present (indicated either by the tester bulb lighting or a voltmeter reading, as applicable), this means that the section of the circuit between the relevant connector and the switch is problem-free.

13 Continue to check the remainder of the circuit in the same fashion.

14 When a point is reached at which no voltage is present, the problem must lie

2.20 Earth cable connections (arrowed) beneath the air cleaner housing

between that point and the previous test point with voltage. Most problems can be traced to a broken, corroded or loose connection.

Finding a short-circuit

15 To check for a short-circuit, first disconnect the load(s) from the circuit (loads are the components which draw current from a circuit, such as bulbs, motors, heating elements, etc).

16 Remove the relevant fuse from the circuit, and connect a circuit tester or voltmeter to the fuse connections.

17 Switch on the circuit, bearing in mind that some circuits are live only when the ignition switch is in a particular position.

18 If voltage is present (indicated either by the tester bulb lighting or a voltmeter reading, as applicable), this means that there is a short-circuit.

19 If no voltage is present during this test, but the fuse still blows with the load(s) reconnected, this indicates an internal fault in the load(s).

Finding an earth fault

20 The battery negative terminal is connected to earth – the metal of the engine/transmission and the vehicle body – and many systems are wired so that they only receive a positive feed, the current returning via the metal of the car body (see illustration). This means that the component mounting and the body form part of that circuit. Loose or corroded mountings can therefore cause a range of electrical faults, ranging from total failure of a circuit, to a puzzling partial failure. In particular, lights

may shine dimly (especially when another circuit sharing the same earth point is in operation), motors (eg, wiper motors or the radiator cooling fan motor) may run slowly, and the operation of one circuit may have an apparently-unrelated effect on another.

21 Note that on many vehicles, earth straps are used between certain components, such as the engine/transmission and the body, usually where there is no metal-to-metal contact between components, due to flexible rubber mountings, etc.

22 To check whether a component is properly earthed, disconnect the battery and connect one lead of an ohmmeter to a known good earth point. Connect the other lead to the wire or earth connection being tested. The resistance reading should be zero; if not, check the connection as follows.

23 If an earth connection is thought to be faulty, dismantle the connection, and clean both the bodyshell and the wire terminal (or the component earth connection mating surface) back to bare metal. Be careful to remove all traces of dirt and corrosion, then use a knife to trim away any paint, so that a clean metal-to-metal joint is made. On reassembly, tighten the joint fasteners securely; if a wire terminal is being refitted, use serrated washers between the terminal and the bodyshell, to ensure a clean and secure connection.

24 When the connection is remade, prevent the onset of corrosion in the future by applying a coat of petroleum jelly or silicone-based grease, or by spraying on (at regular intervals) a proprietary ignition sealer, or a water-dispersant lubricant.

3 Fuses and relays – general information

Fuses

1 The fuses are located in the central fusebox situated in the engine compartment on the left-hand side, just in front of the suspension turret, and in 3 modules behind the trim on the left-hand side of the luggage compartment (see illustrations).

2 If a fuse blows, the electrical circuit(s) protected by that fuse will cease to operate.

The fuse positions and the circuits protected depends on vehicle specification, model year and country. Refer to the wiring diagrams at the rear of this manual, and the sticker on the fusebox lid which gives details for the particular vehicle.

3 To remove a fuse, first switch off the ignition, then lift up the cover on the central fusebox. Using the plastic removal tool provided, pull the fuse out of its terminals (see illustration). The wire within the fuse should be visible; if the fuse is blown, the wire will be broken or melted.

4 Always renew a fuse with one of an identical rating; never use a fuse with a different rating from the original, or substitute anything else, as it may lead to a fire. Never renew a fuse more than once without tracing the source of the trouble. The fuse rating is stamped on top of the fuse; note that fuses are also colour-coded for easy recognition. Spare fuses are provided in the fusebox.

5 Persistent blowing of a particular fuse indicates a fault in the circuit(s) protected. Where more than one circuit is involved, switch on one item at a time until the fuse blows, so showing in which circuit the fault lies.

6 Besides a fault in the electrical component concerned, a blown fuse can also be caused by a short-circuit in the wiring to the component. Look for trapped or frayed wires allowing a live wire to touch vehicle metal, and for loose or damaged connectors.

7 Note that only the blade-type fuses should ever be renewed by the DIY mechanic. If one of the large fusible links in the main fusebox blows, this indicates a serious electrical fault, which should be diagnosed by a Volvo dealer or automotive electrical specialist.

Relays

8 A relay is an electrically-operated switch, which is used for the following reasons:
a) A relay can switch a heavy current remotely from the circuit in which the current is flowing, allowing the use of lighter-gauge wiring and switch contacts.
b) A relay can receive more than one control input, unlike a mechanical switch.
c) A relay can have a timer function – for example an intermittent wiper delay.

9 If a circuit which includes a relay develops a fault, remember that the relay itself could be

3.1a Central fusebox located on the left-hand side of the engine compartment

3.1b Fuse modules behind the left-hand side luggage area trim panel

3.3 Use the plastic tool to remove a fuse

4.3a Undo the two screws (arrowed)

4.3b Withdraw the switch from the steering column

4.3c Switch unit bolts (arrowed)

faulty. A basic test of relay operation is to have an assistant switch on the item concerned, while you listen for a click from the relay. This would at least determine whether the relay is switching or not, but is not conclusive proof that a relay is working.

10 Most relays have four or five terminals – two terminals supplying current to its solenoid winding to provide the switching, a main current input and either one or two outputs to either supply or isolate the component concerned (depending on its configuration). Using the wiring diagrams at the end of this Chapter, test to ensure that all connections deliver the expected voltage or good earth.

11 Ultimately, testing is by substitution of a known good relay, but be careful – relays which look similar are not necessarily identical for purposes of substitution.

12 The relays are found in the fusebox, on the passenger's side of the engine compartment, and in the luggage compartment fusebox.

13 To remove a relay, make sure that the ignition is switched off, then pull the relay from its socket. Push the new relay firmly in to refit.

4 Switches – removal and refitting

Steering column multi-function switches

1 Disconnect the battery negative lead.
2 Remove the steering column shrouds as described in Chapter 10, Section 18.

4.9 Release the clips and withdraw the light switch from the facia

3 Remove the switch in question. Each switch is secured by two screws **(see illustration)**. Remove the screws and pull the switch out to the side carefully. To remove the complete switch unit, undo the 2 bolts on the top of the steering column, disconnect the wiring plug, and slide the unit from the column **(see illustrations)**.
4 Refit the relevant switch using a reversal of removal.

Ignition/starter switch

5 Disconnect the battery as described in Chapter 5A.
6 Remove the instrument panel as described in Section 5.
7 Working through the instrument panel aperture, undo the 3 retaining bolts and disconnect the wiring plug. Pull the switch from the rear of the facia and withdraw through the instrument panel aperture **(see illustration in Chapter 5A, Section 10)**.
8 Refitting is a reversal of removal.

Headlight switch

9 Using a flat-bladed tool, carefully release the 2 clips at the top of the switch panel and the 2 clips at the bottom, and withdraw the switch from the facia. Disconnect the wiring connector as the switch is removed **(see illustration)**.
10 Refitting is a reversal of removal.

Hazard warning light switch

11 Using a flat-bladed tool, carefully prise the trim piece containing the switch from the facia panel (care is needed as the trim is fragile and

4.16a Unclip the central locking switch

easily broken). Withdraw from the facia and undo the wiring plug.
12 Squeeze together the retaining clips and press the switch from the facia trim piece.
13 Refitting is a reversal of removal.

Centre console switches

14 The switches are integral to the centre console panel. Refer to Chapter 11 for removal of the centre console.

Door panel switches

Front and rear doors

15 Remove the door trim panel as described in Chapter 11.
16 Disconnect the wiring plug, press in the retaining clips and push the assembly upwards and out of the door panel **(see illustrations)**. On the driver's door the central locking switch is secured by 2 clips, while electric window/mirror switch is secured by 6 clips – 3 above the switch and 3 below.
17 Refitting is a reversal of removal, but test the operation of the switch before refitting the door trim panel. To synchronise the window mechanism, operate the switch to raise the window fully and hold the switch in this position for at least 5 seconds. Then lower the window fully and hold the switch in this position for at least 5 seconds. Repeat the process for raising the window. The window mechanism should now be synchronised. **Note:** *If a new switch/module has been fitted, it may need to be programmed using dedicated Volvo test equipment – entrust this task to Volvo dealer or suitably-equipped specialist.*

4.16b Unclip the electric window switch panel

4.19 Drill out the rivets (arrowed) for the door panel switch module

4.23a Undo the handbrake switch screws (arrowed)

Door panel switch module

18 The operation is the same for both front and rear doors. Remove the door trim panel as described in Chapter 11.

19 Carefully drill out the 2 retaining rivets, disconnect the wiring plug, and remove the module **(see illustration)**.

20 Refitting, using new rivets, is a reversal of removal, but test the operation of the switch before refitting the door trim panel. To synchronise the window mechanism, operate the switch to raise the window fully and hold the switch in this position for at least 5 seconds. Then lower the window fully and hold the switch in this position for at least 5 seconds. Repeat the process for raising the window. The window mechanism should now be synchronised. **Note:** *If a new module has been fitted, it may need to be programmed using dedicated Volvo test equipment – entrust this task to Volvo dealer or suitably-equipped specialist.*

Courtesy light microswitches

21 The courtesy light microswitches are incorporated in the door/tailgate lock assembly, together with the central locking motor (refer to Chapter 11).

Brake light switch

22 Refer to Chapter 9.

Handbrake warning light switch

23 Undo the 2 screws beneath the switch, disconnect the wiring plug and withdraw the switch from the facia **(see illustrations)**.

24 Refitting is a reversal of removal.

Steering wheel switches

25 Remove the driver's airbag as described in Section 24.

26 Using a flat-bladed tool, carefully prise the switch panel from the wheel and disconnect the wiring plug as the switch is withdrawn **(see illustrations)**.

27 Refitting is a reversal of removal.

Sunroof switch

28 Remove the overhead courtesy light unit as described in Section 9.

4.23b Withdraw the switch from the facia

4.26b Disconnect the wiring plug (arrowed)

4.26a Prise the switch panel from the steering wheel

5.2 Unclip the trim between the upper column shroud and the instrument panel

29 Release the retaining clips, disconnect the wiring plug, and remove the switch.

30 Refitting is a reversal of removal.

---

5 Instrument panel – removal and refitting

Note: *If a new instrument panel is to be fitted, the vehicle data from the old panel must be retrieved before removal, then loaded into the new panel. This task must be entrusted to a Volvo dealer or suitably-equipped specialist.*

Removal

1 The instrument panel is linked into the Volvo on-board diagnosis system (OBD), which means that any faults occurring in the instrument panel will be logged, and can be read out using diagnostic equipment (typically, a fault code reader). It is advisable, therefore, to have any less-than-obvious faults investigated by a dealer or suitably-equipped garage in the first instance. The diagnostic test equipment will be able to locate the fault, and the dealer can advise on the best course of action. In this case, take the car to the dealer – do not remove the instrument panel for diagnosis.

2 Unclip the trim between the upper column shroud and the base of the instrument panel **(see illustration)**.

3 Undo the 2 upper and 2 lower screws,

5.3a Undo the two upper screws (arrowed) . . .

5.3b . . . and the two lower screws (arrowed)

5.3c Disconnect the wiring plug at the rear of the instrument panel

5.4 Withdraw the instrument panel from the facia

pull the instrument panel rearwards and disconnect the wiring connector (see illustrations).

4 Remove the instrument panel completely, and recover any soundproofing material above the panel (see illustration). No further dismantling is recommended.

Refitting

5 Refitting is a reversal of removal.

6 Electrical system sensors – removal and refitting

Note: Not all sensors are fitted to all models.

Vehicle speed sensor

1 Vehicle speed information for the speedometer is provided by the anti-lock braking system (ABS) wheel sensors. If the speedometer does not work, therefore, this indicates a possible problem with the signal from the ABS wheel sensors. Check the wiring connections to the wheel sensors, and to the ABS control unit – if no fault is revealed, refer to a Volvo dealer or suitably-equipped garage for diagnostic testing.

Brake fluid level sensor

2 The brake fluid level sensor is a float incorporated in the master cylinder reservoir. The sensor and reservoir are an assembly; renew the reservoir if the unit is faulty – see Chapter 9.

Coolant level sensor

3 Wait until the engine is cold before starting this procedure. The cooling system need not be drained.

4 Slowly unscrew the cooling system expansion tank filler cap to release any pressure remaining in the system. Refit the cap securely.

5 Undo the retaining screw and lift the expansion tank out of its mounting, and as far as possible, turn it upside-down without disconnecting any of the hoses.

6 Disconnect the wiring connector at the sensor located in the base of the tank (see illustration).

7 Taking care to avoid spilling any coolant, pull the sensor out of its sealing grommet.

8 Refitting is a reversal of removal. Top-up the expansion tank as described in Weekly checks if any coolant was lost.

Oil level sensor

9 The oil level sensor is located on the sump.

10 Wait until the engine is cold. Chock the rear wheels, then jack up the front of the car and support it on axle stands (see Jacking and vehicle support).

11 Release the screws and remove the engine undershield.

12 Drain the engine oil as described in Chapter 1.

13 Undo the 3 bolts and remove the sensor from the sump (see illustration). Expect some oil spillage as the sensor is withdrawn.

14 Refitting is a reversal of removal, refilling the engine with the specified quantity of oil.

15 Refitting is a reversal of removal, tightening the sensor securely.

Washer fluid level sensor

16 Gain access to the rear of the washer reservoir as described in Section 16.

17 The sensor and float are located at the base of the reservoir. Disconnect the wiring connector and pull the sensor from the reservoir. Expect some fluid spillage (see illustration).

18 Refitting is a reversal of removal.

Fuel level sender unit

19 Refer to Chapter 4A.

6.6 Coolant level sensor (arrowed)

6.13 Oil level sensor retaining bolts (arrowed)

6.17 Washer fluid level sensor

Coolant temperature sensor

20 Refer to Chapter 3.

Outside temperature sensor

21 Remove the passenger's door mirror glass and cover as described in Chapter 11.
22 Release the clips and push the sensor from the mirror housing. Disconnect the wiring plug as the sensor is withdrawn.
23 Refitting is a reversal of removal.

Air conditioning evaporator temperature sensor

24 Refer to Chapter 3, Section 10.

Clutch pedal position sensor

25 Refer to Chapter 6.

Brake master cylinder pressure sensor

26 The sensor is located on the underside of the master cylinder. Place rags or paper towels under the sensor to collect the spilt brake fluid.
27 Disconnect the sensor wiring plug, then using a deep 24 mm socket, unscrew the sensor. Immediately plug the port in the master cylinder to limit fluid loss.
28 Refitting is a reversal of removal, remembering to tighten the sensor securely, and bleed the brakes (if necessary) as described in Chapter 9.

Yaw rate/lateral acceleration sensor

29 Remove the driver's seat as described in Chapter 11.
30 Remove the audio module as described in Section 20.
31 Fold the carpet to one side then undo the bolts securing the sensor to the floor **(see illustration)**. Note the sensor fitted position, and disconnect the wiring plug as the sensor is withdrawn. Take care when handling the sensor as it is easily damaged – if it is dropped, a new one must be fitted.
32 Refitting is a reversal of removal. **Note:** *If a new sensor has been fitted, it must be calibrated using Volvo dedicated test equipment. Entrust this task to a Volvo dealer or suitably-equipped specialist.*

7 Central electronic module (CEM) – general information, removal and refitting

General information

The central electronic module (CEM) manages the functions of a number of items including the headlights, foglights, windscreen washers, tailgate washer (where applicable), brake lights, headlamp washers (where applicable), central locking, immobiliser, headlamp range adjustment, indicators,

6.31 Yaw rate/lateral acceleration sensor securing bolts (arrowed)

blindspot information system, courtesy lighting, rear electric windows, fuel pump, starter motor, speed-sensitive power steering, heated seats, and the horn, but also acts as a bridge between the high-speed and low-speed communication networks (Databuses). Consequently, it monitors the signals between most of the vehicle's sensors, actuators and control modules. As the CEM communicates with all other modules, it contains the vehicle's self-diagnosis system and stores any fault codes generated. The CEM also contains information specific to the vehicle: VIN, build details, and vehicle equipment options. Consequently, if the CEM needs renewing, the stored information must be retrieved prior to removal, and then programmed into the new unit.

Central electronic module

Note: *If the CEM is to be renewed, stored information must be retrieved and then programmed into the new CEM. As this task requires the use of dedicated Volvo test equipment, entrust it to a Volvo dealer or suitably-equipped specialist.*
1 Disconnect the battery negative lead as described in Chapter 5A.
2 Remove the glovebox as described in Chapter 11.
3 On early models, disconnect the wiring plugs and unclip the mounting at the top of the unit. Move the unit to the left and remove from the mounting.
4 On later models, remove the cover by

8.2 Release the wire clip and remove the cover at the rear of the headlight

7.4 Release the securing clips (arrowed) for the CEM

releasing the clip at the bottom. Disconnect the wiring plugs, and use a small screwdriver to release the top mountings. Move the unit forward and withdraw towards the right **(see illustration)**.
5 Refitting is a reversal of removal. **Note:** *If a new unit has been fitted, suitable software will need to be downloaded and installed.*

8 Bulbs (exterior lights) – renewal

General

1 Whenever a bulb is renewed, note the following points:
  a) *Remember that if the light has just been in use, the bulb may be extremely hot.*
  b) *Always check the bulb contacts and holder, ensuring that there is clean metal-to-metal contact between the bulb and its live(s) and earth. Clean off any corrosion or dirt before fitting a new bulb.*
  c) *Wherever bayonet-type bulbs are fitted, ensure that the live contact(s) bear firmly against the bulb contact.*
  d) *Always ensure that the new bulb is of the correct rating and that it is completely clean before fitting it; this applies particularly to headlight/foglight bulbs (see below).*
  e) *With quartz halogen bulbs (headlights and similar applications), use a tissue or clean cloth when handling the bulb; do not touch the bulb glass with the fingers. Even small quantities of grease from the fingers will cause blackening and premature failure. If a bulb is accidentally touched, clean it with methylated spirit and a clean rag.*

Headlight

Halogen dipped and main beam bulb

2 Remove the headlamp as described in Section 10, release the wire clip and unclip the cover from the rear of the unit **(see illustration)**.

8.3 Withdraw the bulb from the light unit

8.7a Use a pair of long-nose pliers to release the wire clip

8.7b Carefully withdraw the xenon bulb

3 Use the plastic prong on the bulb to depress the bulb in its holder, and withdraw the bulb from the holder along with the plastic prong (see illustration).
4 Refitting is a reversal of removal.

Bi-xenon bulb

Caution: Xenon bulbs are pressurised to approximately 10 bar. The bulbs must be handled delicately or there is a risk of explosion. Always wear gloves and safety goggles when handling xenon bulbs.
5 Due to the high voltages (22 000 volts approximately) required by xenon gas discharge bulbs, disconnect the battery negative lead (see Chapter 5A) then turn on the main and dipped beams alternately to dissipate any residual electrical energy – allow the bulb(s) to cool before commencing.
6 Remove the headlight as described in Section 10 and unclip the cover from the rear of the unit.

7 Use a pair of long-nose pliers to release the wire clip, disconnect the wiring plug at the base of the bulb unit, and carefully withdraw the bulb (see illustrations).
8 Refitting is a reversal of removal.

Daytime running lights

9 Remove the headlight and unclip the rear cover. To remove the inner running light bulb use a pair of long-nose pliers to pull the holder from the light unit. To remove the outer running light bulb, remove the circular plastic cover on the rear of the light unit and pull the bulb from its holder (see illustrations).
10 Refitting is a reversal of removal.

Front foglight

11 The foglight bulb is accessed from behind the light unit – if preferred, jack up the front of the car and remove the relevant wheel arch liner for better access.

12 The bulbholder has two tabs to make it easier to turn – twist the bulbholder anti-clockwise to release it from the back of the light unit (see illustration).
13 Remove the bulb from the bulbholder.
14 Refitting is a reversal of removal.

Front direction indicator

15 Remove the headlamp as described in Section 10.
16 Remove the circular plastic cover on the rear of the headlamp unit, and pull the bulb from its holder (see illustration).
17 Refitting is a reversal of removal.

Direction indicator side repeater

18 Remove door mirror glass as described in Chapter 11.
19 Pull the bulbholder from place, and pull the bulb from the holder (see illustration).
20 Refitting is a reversal of removal.

8.9a Use pliers to pull the inner running light bulb from its holder

8.9b Remove the circular plastic cover from the rear of the headlight

8.9c Pull the outer running light bulb from its holder

8.12 Twist the bulb holder anti-clockwise and withdraw it from the rear of the foglight

8.16 Use pliers to pull the indicator bulb from the headlight

8.19 Pull the bulbholder from the mirror and pull out the bulb

8.21 Remove the bulb from the upper rear light unit

8.22 Remove the access panel from the luggage area trim panel

8.24 Rotate the bulb holder anti-clockwise and withdraw it from the rear of the light unit

Rear light clusters

Upper light cluster

21 Some of the bulbs contained within the upper light cluster are of the LED variety. Refer to a Volvo dealer for advice on renewal. With the cluster removed (Section 10), the remaining bulbs can be renewed **(see illustration)**.

Lower light cluster

22 From within the luggage compartment, open the access panel on the side concerned **(see illustration)**.
23 Remove the sound insulation material covering the bulbholder.
24 Rotate the bulbholder anti-clockwise and pull it from the light unit withdraw the bulbholder. Push in and twist the bulb anti-clockwise to remove it from the bulbholder **(see illustration)**. Note that some bulbs may be of the LED variety and therefore cannot be renewed in this way. Refer to a Volvo dealer for advice on renewal.
25 Refitting is a reversal of removal.

High-level brake light

26 The high-level brake light does not contain conventional light bulbs, but rather a row of LEDs (light-emitting diodes). As a result, if the high-level brake light stops working, it may ultimately be necessary to renew the light unit complete – see Section 10. Before deciding that this is necessary, however, check the fuse and all wiring, using the information in

8.27 Undo the two retaining screws . . .

Section 2 and the wiring diagrams at the end of this Chapter.

Number plate light

27 Undo the 2 screws securing the light unit to the tailgate **(see illustration)**.
28 Carefully prise out the light unit.
29 Pull the bulb out of the holder **(see illustration)**.
30 Refitting is a reversal of removal.

Door mirror ground light bulb

31 Remove the door mirror glass as described in Chapter 11.
32 Remove the lens by inserting a small screwdriver into the slot and push in to release the clip. Withdraw the lens from beneath the mirror housing and pull out the bulb **(see illustrations)**.
33 Refitting is a reversal of removal.

8.29 . . . and withdraw the number plate light from the tailgate

9 Bulbs (interior lights) – renewal

General

1 Whenever a bulb is renewed, note the following points:
  a) *Remember that if the light has just been in use, the bulb may be extremely hot.*
  b) *Always check the bulb contacts and holder, ensuring that there is clean metal-to-metal contact between the bulb and its live(s) and earth. Clean off any corrosion or dirt before fitting a new bulb.*
  c) *Wherever bayonet-type bulbs are fitted, ensure that the live contact(s) bear firmly against the bulb contact.*
  d) *Always ensure that the new bulb is of the correct rating and that it is completely clean before fitting it.*
2 Some switch illumination/pilot bulbs are integral with their switches, and cannot be renewed separately.

Vanity mirror lights

3 Using a suitable flat-bladed tool or a small screwdriver, prise the mirror housing from the sunvisor, starting at the 2 slots in the centre and also below the rubber pads at each end. This should be undertaken carefully as the component is easily broken. With the mirror

8.32a Use a small screwdriver to release the lens cover from the mirror housing

8.32b Withdraw the lens from beneath the mirror housing and remove the bulb

9.3a Release the clips starting at the two slots in the centre

9.3b Release the clips at each side

9.3c Pull the bulbs from their holders

housing removed, the bulbs can be pulled from their holders **(see illustrations)**.

4 To refit the mirror housing, almost close the mirror cover and carefully push the housing back into place in the sunvisor, ensuring that the clips engage securely **(see illustration)**.

Courtesy/reading lights

Centre (incorporating alarm sensors)

5 Carefully prise the unit from the headlining, and disconnect the wiring plugs **(see illustration)**.

6 Remove the bulbholder (the bulb is integral with the holder and cannot be renewed separately) **(see illustration)**.

7 Refitting is a reversal of removal.

Front and rear

8 Carefully prise the lens/cover assembly from the headlining **(see illustration)**.

9 Rotate the bulbholders anti-clockwise by 90 degrees and remove from the unit **(see illustration)**.

10 Refitting is a reversal of removal. A multipin plug engages as the unit is refitted so ensure the lens/cover is pushed straight upwards to avoid damage to the pins.

Glovebox light

11 Carefully prise the light unit from the roof of the glovebox **(see illustration)**.

12 Pull the festoon bulb from the contacts.

13 Refitting is a reversal of removal.

Heater control/ switch panel illumination

14 The panel is illuminated by LEDs. If faulty the entire panel may need to be renewed – refer to a Volvo dealer.

Automatic transmission selector illumination

15 The selector panel is illuminated by LEDs. If faulty the entire panel must be renewed.

Instrument panel bulbs

16 The panel is illuminated by LEDs, which cannot be renewed independently of the instrument panel. In the event of a failure, refer to a Volvo dealer.

9.4 Push the cover back into place ensuring the clips engage securely

9.5 Prise the light unit from the headlining

9.6 Disconnect the wiring plugs as the unit is withdrawn

9.8 Carefully prise the light unit from the headlining

9.9 Rotate the bulb holder anti-clockwise by 90° and remove from the unit

9.11 Prise the light unit (arrowed) from the top of the glovebox

9.17 Carefully prise the lens from the headlining at the rear of the luggage compartment

10.1a Pull up the two levers on the lock panel

10.1b Carefully withdraw the headlight . . .

10.1c . . . and disconnect the wiring plug from the rear of the headlight

10.4a Release the clips securing the foglight grille surround

10.4b Undo the screw (arrowed) and withdraw the foglight

Luggage area illumination

17 Carefully prise the light unit from position (see illustration).
18 Remove the bulb from the holder.
19 Refitting is a reversal of removal.

Footwell lights

20 Taking care not to damage the facia trim, prise out the inner edge of the light unit, then disconnect its wiring plug and remove it.
21 Pull the festoon bulb from the contacts.
22 Refitting is a reversal of removal.

10 Exterior light units – removal and refitting

Caution: Ensure the ignition is turned off before proceeding

Headlight

1 Pull up the 2 sliding levers located on the lock panel above the headlights and disconnect the wiring plug as the unit is withdrawn from the front of the car (see illustrations).
2 Refitting is a reversal of removal. Have the headlight beam alignment checked on completion (see Section 11).

Front foglight

3 Apply the handbrake, chock the rear wheels, then jack up the front of the car and support it securely on axle stands.
4 From the rear of the bumper, undo the clips that secure the foglight grille surround. From the front, undo the retaining bolt, disconnect the wiring plug, then remove the foglight (see illustrations).
5 Refitting is a reversal of removal.

Rear light clusters

Lower light cluster

6 To remove the lower light unit, start by removing the access panel in the luggage compartment side panel and extracting the sound insulation material.
7 Disconnect the wiring plug and undo the 3 nuts on the rear of the light unit (fixings shown with the light unit removed for clarity) (see illustrations).
8 Remove the rear bumper as described in Chapter 11.
9 Undo the 3 bolts and remove the bracket below the light unit (see illustration). The light unit can now be withdrawn.

Upper light cluster

10 To remove the upper light unit, start by removing the upper and lower tailgate trim panels as described in Chapter 11.

10.7a Disconnect the wiring plug from the rear of the light unit

10.7b Undo the three retaining nuts on the rear of the light unit

10.9 Undo the three bolts (arrowed) and remove the bracket below the light unit

10.11a Undo the screw (arrowed) at the edge of the tailgate

10.11b Undo the two screws (arrowed) at the bottom of the light unit

10.11c Disconnect the wiring plug . . .

10.11d . . . and release the clips (one of the clips arrowed)

10.11e Carefully withdraw the light unit

11 Undo the screw at each side of the tailgate, and the 2 screws at the bottom of the unit visible when the lower trim panel is removed. Disconnect the wiring plug, release the clip at the top and bottom from the inner edge of the tailgate, and remove the light unit **(see illustrations)**.

12 Refitting is a reversal of removal.

High-level brake light

13 Remove the tailgate interior trim panels as described in Chapter 11.

14 Undo the central plastic rivet and the clip at each end, disconnect the wiring plug, and remove the light unit **(see illustrations)**.

15 Refitting is a reversal of removal.

Number plate light

16 Undo the screws securing the relevant light unit to the tailgate **(see illustration 8.27)**.

17 Carefully prise/slide out the light unit and disconnect the wiring plug as it is withdrawn.

18 Refitting is a reversal of removal.

Door mirror indicator lens

19 Remove the door mirror outer cover as described in Chapter 11. Use a small screwdriver to depress the plastic tab at the end of the lens and withdraw the lens from the mirror housing **(see illustrations)**.

20 Refitting is a reversal of removal.

10.14a Remove the central plastic rivet

10.14b Disconnect the wiring plug

10.14c Release the clip at each end and withdraw the light unit

10.19a Use a small screwdriver to depress the plastic tab at the end of the lens

10.19b Withdraw the lens from the mirror housing

11.2 Headlight adjustment access holes (arrowed)

12.2 Undo the two screws (arrowed) and remove the actuator from the rear of the headlight

13.1 Headlamp control module (arrowed)

11 Headlight beam alignment – checking and adjusting

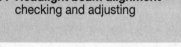

1 Beam alignment should be carried out by a Volvo dealer or other specialist heaving the necessary optical alignment equipment.
2 For reference, the headlights can be adjusted by means of the vertical and horizontal adjuster controls at the top of the headlight unit **(see illustration)**.
3 Some models are equipped with an electrically-operated headlight beam adjustment system which is controlled through the switch on the facia. On these models, ensure that the switch is set to the 'off' position before adjusting the headlight aim.

12 Adaptive headlight actuator – removal and refitting

Removal

1 Remove the headlamp as described in Section 10, and remove the plastic cover from the rear of the unit.
2 Disconnect the wiring connector at the actuator, undo the retaining screws, and withdraw the actuator from the headlamp unit **(see illustration)**.

Refitting

3 Refitting is a reversal of removal.

14.2 Horn securing screw (arrowed)

4 Have the beam adjustment checked, and if necessary adjusted, by a dealer or specialist.

13 Headlight control module – removal and refitting

Removal

1 The headlamp control module is located on the left-hand side of the engine bulkhead adjacent to the ABS hydraulic modulator **(see illustration)**.
2 Remove the plenum cover as described in Section 18, disconnect the wiring plug, undo the retaining screws, and remove the module.

Refitting

3 Refitting is a reversal of removal.

14 Horn – removal and refitting

Removal

1 Volvo advise that the horn units can be reached by removing the grille. However, given the difficulty in removing the grille with the bumper in place, we recommend removing the front bumper to prevent the risk of damage.
2 With the front bumper removed, unbolt the horn from its bracket and remove it **(see illustration)**. Disconnect the wiring plug as the horn is removed.

16.3 Washer pump wiring plug (arrowed)

Refitting

3 Refitting is a reversal of removal.

15 Sunroof motor – removal and refitting

Removal and refitting

1 Disconnect the battery as described in Chapter 5A.
2 Remove the front courtesy light unit as described in Section 9.
3 Undo the 3 bolts, disconnect the wiring plug, and remove the motor
4 Refitting is a reversal of removal.

Calibration

5 The motor may require calibration after refitting which should be carried out as follows.
6 With the sunroof closed, insert the remote unit and briefly pushing the 'start/stop' button.
7 Press the button to tilt the roof and release the button.
8 Move the button forwards and hold for approximately 30 seconds until the roof moves approximately 2 mm and the motor stops.
9 Release the button and then within half a second move the button forwards until the roof completes a full cycle of opening and closure. Calibration should then be complete.

16 Washer system components – removal and refitting

Washer pumps

1 The washer pumps can be accessed without removing the washer reservoir.
2 Undo the plastic rivets that secure the front of the left-hand side wheel arch liner to the front bumper, and carefully fold back the liner until the pump can be reached.
3 Note the fitted location, then pull the hose(s) from the pump, and disconnect the pump wiring plug **(see illustration)**.

16.8a Front reservoir securing screw (arrowed)

16.8b Rear reservoir securing screws (arrowed)

16.10a Disconnect the washer hose

4 Place a container under the reservoir, and be prepared for spillage.
5 Grip the washer pump and pull it out of the reservoir.
6 Refitting is a reversal of removal.

Washer reservoir

7 Remove the front bumper as described in Chapter 11.
8 Disconnect the wiring plugs from the level sensor and pump(s) on the reservoir, then undo the screw at the front of the reservoir and the 2 screws at the rear, and lower the reservoir from position **(see illustrations)**.

9 Refitting is a reversal of removal.

Washer jets

Windscreen

10 Open the bonnet, pull the plastic T-piece from the pipe, prise out the rubber grommet and remove the grommet from around the wiring. Unclip the wiring from the bonnet and disconnect the jet wiring plug **(see illustrations)**.
11 Insert a screwdriver in the aperture on the underside of the bonnet and push on the bottom of the jet to release it from the bonnet **(see illustrations)**.

16.10b Pull the plastic T-piece from the pipe

16.10c Remove the rubber grommet

16.10d Disconnect the wiring plug . . .

16.10e . . . and unclip the wiring from the bonnet

16.11a Use a screwdriver to push on the underside of the washer jet

16.11b Withdraw the washer jet from the bonnet

16.15a Undo the two washer jet securing bolts (arrowed)

16.15b Disconnect the wiring plug from the washer jet . . .

16.15c . . . and the washer hose

16.16a Unclip the body-coloured trim piece from the top of the bumper

16.16b Withdraw the washer jet from the rear of the bumper

17.1 Mark the position of the wipers prior to removal

12 Refitting is a reversal of removal.
13 It may be possible to adjust the jet nozzles using a pin, but if not the complete washer jet will need to be renewed.

Headlamp

14 Remove the front bumper as described in Chapter 11.
15 At the rear of the bumper undo the 2 screws securing the washer jet to its bracket and disconnect the wiring plug and washer hose **(see illustrations)**.
16 Working at the front of the bumper, unclip the body-coloured trim piece from the top of the washer jets. The unit can now be

withdrawn from the rear of the bumper **(see illustrations)**.
17 Refitting is a reversal of removal.

Washer fluid level sensor

18 Refer to Section 6.

17 Wiper arms –
removal and refitting

Removal

1 Place the wipers in the normal 'park' position. Mark the position of the wipers either

by using masking tape applied to the screen below the wiper, or by measuring the distance of the wiper from the bottom of the screen **(see illustration)**.
2 Lift up or prise off the cover (where applicable) then slacken the nut at the base of the wiper arm **(see illustration)**.
3 Press the front wiper arms down, and tap them gently to break the bond between the arm and spindle – use tape to protect the arm. Using a rocking motion, pull the arms off the splines. If necessary, use a puller to remove the arms **(see illustrations)**.
4 On the tailgate wiper, use a thin blade to prise off the cover (note that the cover is easily

17.2 Prise off the cap and undo the wiper arm nut

17.3a Use a suitable puller if necessary . . .

17.3b . . . and remove the wiper arm from the spindle

17.4a Carefully prise off the plastic cover, undo the nut . . .

17.4b . . . and remove the rear wiper arm from the spindle

damaged) and undo the nut securing the arm to the spindle. Pull the arm from the spindle using a rocking motion **(see illustrations)**.

Refitting

5 Refitting is a reversal of removal.

18 Windscreen wiper motor and linkage – removal and refitting

Removal

1 Switch the wipers on, then off again to ensure that the motor and linkage are parked.
2 Remove the windscreen wiper arms as described in Section 17.
3 Remove the plenum cover. Remove the battery cover which includes a section secured to the plenum cover with a plastic screw, pull up and remove the rubber seal on the front edge of the panel, then undo the 6 plastic clips. Release the catches at the rear of the panel on both sides and unhook the panel from the bottom edge of the screen **(see illustrations)**.
4 Undo the 3 bolts and remove the linkage/frame, disconnecting the wiring plug as the unit is withdrawn **(see illustrations)**.
5 Mark the position of the motor crank arm relative to the frame, undo the nut and remove the crank arm from the motor.

18.3a Remove the battery cover from the plenum cover

18.3b Pull up the rubber seal

18.3c Undo the six plastic clips (two are arrowed)

18.3d Unhook the panel from the bottom edge of the windscreen and withdraw it from the engine compartment

18.4a Undo the two bolts (arrowed) . . .

18.4b . . . and the third bolt (arrowed) at the end of the linkage

18.4c Carefully withdraw the linkage

18.4d Disconnect the wiring plug as it becomes accessible

6 Undo the three motor retaining bolts and remove the motor from the frame. The frame and linkage arms are an assembly, and cannot be individually renewed **(see illustration)**.

Refitting

7 Refit the motor to the frame, and secure with the 3 mounting bolts.
8 If a new motor is being fitted, temporarily reconnect the wiring connectors at the car, switch on the motor then switch it off again to ensure that it is parked.
9 Position the crank arm on the motor, with the marks made on removal aligned. Prevent the crank arm from turning by holding it with a spanner, then refit and tighten the nut.
10 Alternatively, if a new frame and linkage are being fitted, set the motor to the park position as described previously then, when connecting the crank arm to the motor, position it so that it is parallel with the linkage arm directly above.
11 The assembled components can now be refitted using a reversal of removal, noting that the grommet at the rear of the linkage locates on a bracket below the windscreen. Ensure that the plenum cover is refitted correctly at the bottom edge of the screen.

19 Tailgate wiper motor – removal and refitting

Removal

1 Switch the wiper on then off again to ensure that the motor and linkage are parked.
2 Remove the tailgate wiper arm as described in Section 17.
3 Remove the tailgate upper and lower interior trim panels as described in Chapter 11.
4 Disconnect the wiring plug, undo the three motor retaining bolts and withdraw it from the tailgate **(see illustration)**.

Refitting

5 Refit the motor to the tailgate and secure with the three mounting bolts.
6 If a new motor is being fitted, temporarily reconnect the wiring connector at the car, switch on the motor then switch it off again to ensure that it is parked.
7 Refitting is a reversal of removal.

20 Audio units – removal and refitting

Facia-mounted audio units

1 Remove the centre console as described in Chapter 11.
2 Undo the 2 retaining screws and pull the unit from the facia until the wiring plugs are accessible **(see illustration)**.
3 Disconnect the wiring plugs and remove the unit. Be aware that the wiring may be of

18.6 Wiper motor retaining bolts (arrowed)

19.4 Tailgate wiper motor bolts (arrowed)

the fibre optic variety and should not be bent excessively as this can cause damage. **Note:** *If a new Volvo audio unit has been fitted, suitable software will need to be downloaded and installed from Volvo. Entrust this task to a Volvo dealer or suitably-equipped specialist.*
4 Refitting is a reversal of removal.

Audio amplifier

5 Slide the driver's seat fully rearwards and undo the 2 retaining screws at the front of the unit **(see illustration)**.
6 Slide the seat fully forwards and undo the retaining screw at the rear of the unit on the right-hand side **(see illustration)**.
7 Disconnect the wiring plugs as the amplifier is withdrawn.
8 Refitting is the reversal of removal. **Note:** *If a new Volvo audio unit has been fitted,*

suitable software will need to be downloaded and installed from Volvo. Entrust this task to a Volvo dealer or suitably-equipped specialist.

21 Speakers – removal and refitting

Facia speaker

1 Carefully prise up the speaker/display unit grille on the top of the facia **(see illustration)**.
2 Undo the screws and lift the speaker/display unit up. Disconnect the wiring and remove the speaker.
3 Refitting is a reversal of removal, making sure the speaker is correctly located.

20.2 Audio unit retaining screws (arrowed)

20.5 Audio amplifier front securing screws (arrowed)

20.6 Audio amplifier side securing screw (arrowed)

21.1 Prise up the speaker grille on top of the facia

21.4a Unclip the panel containing the speaker ...

Door speakers

Front

4 A tweeter is located in the forward edge of the door ahead of the window. Carefully unclip the trim panel containing the speaker and disconnect the wiring plug as it is withdrawn. The speaker is integral with the trim panel so you should refer to a Volvo dealer regarding renewal **(see illustrations)**.
5 To remove the main speakers, remove the door trim panel as described in Chapter 11.
6 Drill out the rivets securing the speaker to the door carrier. Remove the speaker and disconnect the wiring plug **(see illustration)**.
7 Refitting is a reversal of removal.

Rear

8 Remove the door trim panel as described in Chapter 11.
9 Drill out the 3 rivets securing the speaker to the door carrier. Remove the speaker and disconnect the wiring plug **(see illustration)**.
10 Refitting is a reversal of removal.

Subwoofer

11 Lift up the panel in the floor of the luggage area and using a small screwdriver, release the clip at the bottom of the gas damper. Remove the storage tray.
12 Undo the 2 bolts/screws at the front of the unit, nearest the rear seat backs, and disconnect the wiring plugs.
13 Undo the 2 bolts/screws nearest to the bumper that secure the unit to the floor of the vehicle. and carefully lift the unit from place.
14 Refitting is a reversal of removal.

21.6 Front door speaker securing rivets (arrowed)

21.4b ... and disconnect the speaker wiring plug

22 Anti-theft alarm and immobiliser system – general information

Note: *This information is applicable only to the systems fitted by Volvo as original equipment.*

Immobiliser

The electronic immobiliser is automatically activated when the remote unit is removed from the starter panel on the facia. When activated, it cuts the ignition circuit, preventing the engine from being started.

The system is disarmed when the remote unit is inserted into the starter panel on the facia, as follows. The remote unit contains a transponder microchip, and the starter panel contains a reader. When the remote unit enters the starter panel, the reader recognises the signal from the microchip, and de-activates the immobiliser. It is essential that the tag showing the remote number is not lost (this will be supplied with the car when new). Any duplicate remotes will have to be obtained from a Volvo dealer, who will need the remote number to supply a duplicate.

Any problems or work involving the immobiliser system should be entrusted to a Volvo dealer or specialist, as dedicated electronic equipment is required to diagnose faults, or to 'match' the various components.

Alarm

An anti-theft alarm system is fitted as standard equipment. The alarm has switches

21.9 Rear door speaker securing rivets (arrowed)

on all the doors (including the tailgate), and the bonnet. If the tailgate, bonnet or any of the doors are opened or the ignition switch is switched on whilst the alarm is set, the alarm horn will sound and the hazard warning lights will flash. The alarm also has an immobiliser function which makes the ignition inoperable whilst the alarm is triggered.

Signals from the alarm system switches and contacts which are integral with the door, bonnet and tailgate locks are sent to a central control unit inside the car once the system is set. The control unit monitors the signals and activates the alarm if any of the signal loops are broken, or if an attempt is made to start the car (or to hot-wire the ignition).

The status of the system is displayed by means of a flashing LED.

Should the alarm system become faulty, bear in mind the following points:
a) *As with other electrical equipment, many faults are caused by poor connections or bad earths.*
b) *Check the operation of all the door, bonnet and tailgate switches, and the operation of all interior lights.*
c) *The alarm system may behave oddly if the vehicle battery is in poor condition, or if its terminals are loose.*
d) *If the system is operating correctly, but gives too many false alarms, a Volvo dealer or specialist may be able to reduce the sensitivity of some of the system sensors.*
e) *Ultimately, the vehicle may have to be taken to a Volvo dealer or a suitably-equipped garage for examination. They will have access to a special diagnostic tester which will quickly trace any fault present in the system.*

23 Airbag system – general information and precautions

A supplemental restraint system is fitted in various forms as standard or optional equipment depending on model and territory.

The main system component is a driver's airbag, which is designed to prevent serious chest and head injuries to the driver during an accident. Similar airbags for the front seat passenger, side airbags (built into the side of the front seats), and side curtain airbags are also standard fitment. Side impact crash sensors are located on the B- and C-pillars of the vehicle, with a frontal sensor incorporated into the SRS module located under the centre console. The module incorporates a deceleration sensor, and a microprocessor ECU, to monitor the severity of the impact and trigger the airbag where necessary. The airbag is inflated by a gas generator, which forces the bag out of the module cover in the centre of the steering wheel, or out of a cover on the passenger's side of the facia/seat cover/

headlining. A contact reel behind the steering wheel at the top of the steering column ensures that a good electrical connection is maintained with the airbag at all times as the steering wheel is turned in each direction.

In addition to the airbag units, the supplemental restraint system also incorporates pyrotechnical seat belt tensioners operated by gas cartridges in the belt inertia reel assembly. The pyrotechnical units are also triggered by the crash sensor, in conjunction with the airbags, to tighten the seat belts and provide additional collision protection.

All models also incorporate a side impact protection system (SIPS) as standard equipment. In its basic form, the SIPS system is essentially an integral part of the vehicle structure in which strengthening agents are used to distribute side impacts through the bodywork. This is done by reinforcing the lower areas of the doors and door pillars, and providing strengthening bars in the seats and centre console. In this way, side impacts are absorbed by the body structure as a whole, giving exceptional impact strength.

⚠ **Warning: The safe handling of the SRS components requires the use of Volvo special equipment. Any attempt to dismantle the airbag module, SIPS bag, crash sensors, contact reel, seat belt tensioners or any associated wiring or components without this equipment, and the specialist knowledge needed to use it correctly, could result in severe personal injury and/or malfunction of the system.**

• **Before carrying out any work on the SRS components, disconnect the battery and wait for at least 10 minutes for any residual electrical energy to dissipate before proceeding.**

• **Handle the airbag unit with extreme care as a precaution against personal injury, and always hold it with the cover facing away from the body. If in doubt concerning any proposed work involving the airbag unit or its control circuitry, consult a Volvo dealer.**

• **Note that the airbag(s) must not be subjected to temperatures in excess of 90°C. When the airbag is removed, ensure**

that it is stored with the pad up to prevent possible inflation.

• **Do not allow any solvents or cleaning agents to contact the airbag assemblies. They must be cleaned using only a damp cloth.**

• **The airbag(s) and control unit are both sensitive to impact. If either is dropped or damaged they should be renewed.**

• **Disconnect the airbag control unit wiring plug prior to using arc-welding equipment on the vehicle.**

24 Airbag system components – removal and refitting

Note: Before proceeding, refer to the warnings in Section 23.

Driver's airbag

1 Disconnect the battery negative lead (see Chapter 5A), and wait 10 minutes before proceeding.
2 Remove the upper and lower steering column shrouds as described In Chapter 10.
3 Insert a flat-bladed screwdriver in through the holes in the rear of the steering wheel, lift up the screwdriver handle and release the spring clip each side (see illustration). Turn the steering wheel 90° in each direction to gain access to the holes. Note that the clips can be tricky to reach and this task requires patience.
4 Return the wheel to the straight-ahead position.
5 Lift the airbag module off the steering wheel, disconnect the wiring connector(s) from the rear of the unit and remove it from the vehicle (see illustrations).

⚠ **Warning: Position the airbag unit in a safe place, with the pas facing upwards as a precaution against accidental operation. Do not attempt to open or repair the airbag unit, or apply any electrical current to it. Do not use any airbag which is visibly damaged or which has been tampered with.**

24.3 Release the spring clips at the rear of the steering wheel

6 Undo the contact unit locking screw from the steering wheel, then insert it into the contact unit plug to lock it in position (see illustration). Once it has been locked, no attempt should be made to turn the steering wheel, or the contact reel will be damaged.
7 Unlock the contact reel by removing the screw. Store the screw in the lower part of the steering wheel, returning it to its original location.
8 Rest the airbag unit on the bottom edge of the steering wheel hub and reconnect the wiring connector. Swing the airbag unit up into position, checking carefully that the wiring is not pinched.
9 Press the airbag into place, ensuring the clips fully engage.
10 Make sure that no-one is inside the car. Switch on the ignition, then reconnect the battery negative lead. Switch the ignition off, then on again, and check that the SRS warning light comes on, then goes out within 7 seconds.

Driver's airbag contact reel

11 Remove the airbag unit as described above, and the steering wheel as described in Chapter 10.
12 Taking care not to rotate the contact unit, undo the 3 retaining screws and remove it from the steering column switch

24.5a Lift the airbag module from the steering wheel . . .

24.5b . . . and disconnect the wiring plug as it's withdrawn

24.6 Insert the contact reel locking screw (arrowed)

24.12a Undo the three securing screws (arrowed)

24.12b Carefully lift the contact reel from the steering column . . .

24.12c . . . and disconnect the wiring plug

assembly. Disconnect the wiring plug **(see illustrations)**.

13 If a new contact unit is being fitted, cut the cable-tie which is fitted to prevent the unit accidentally rotating.

14 A new reel should be supplied in the centralised position – if not, or if there is a chance the unit is not centralised, proceed as follows. Turn the reel gently clockwise as far as it will go, then turn it back anti-clockwise two turns. Continue turning until a yellow mark is visible in the contact unit window. Lock the reel in this position by screwing in the locking screw located in the plastic retaining strip.

15 Fit the unit to the steering column switch

assembly and securely tighten its retaining screws.

16 Refit the steering wheel as described in Chapter 10, and the airbag unit as described above.

Passenger's airbag

17 Disconnect the battery negative lead (see Chapter 5A), and wait 10 minutes before proceeding.

18 Remove the glovebox as described in Chapter 11.

19 Undo the bolts securing the plate below the unit.

20 Disconnect the wiring plug, undo the 6

retaining nuts, and remove the airbag from its mounting **(see illustrations)**.

21 Refitting is a reversal of removal.

22 On completion, make sure that no-one is inside the car. Switch on the ignition, then reconnect the battery negative lead. Switch the ignition off, then on again, and check that the SRS warning light comes on, then goes out within 7 seconds.

Airbag control unit

23 Disconnect the battery negative lead as described in Chapter 5A. Wait at least 10 minutes before proceeding, to allow and residual electrical energy to dissipate.

24 Remove the centre console and dismantle the lower section as described in Chapter 11.

25 Release the locking catch and disconnect the sensor wiring plug.

26 Note its fitted location, undo the 4 screws and remove the module **(see illustration)**.

27 Refitting is a reversal of removal, ensuring the module is fitted with the arrow on its top surface facing forwards.

28 On completion, make sure that no-one is inside the car. Switch on the ignition, then reconnect the battery negative lead. Switch the ignition off, then on again, and check that the SRS warning light comes on, then goes out within 7 seconds. **Note:** *If a new control unit has been fitted, suitable software will need to be downloaded and installed from Volvo.*

24.20a Passenger airbag wiring plug (arrowed)

24.20b Undo the three nuts (arrowed) on one side of the airbag . . .

24.20c . . . and the 3 nuts (arrowed) on the other side

24.26 Airbag control unit securing screws (arrowed)

24.31 B-pillar crash sensor securing screw (arrowed)

24.32 C-pillar crash sensor securing screw (arrowed)

25.2 Parking assistance module clips (arrowed)

Entrust this task to a Volvo dealer or suitably-equipped specialist.

Side airbags

29 The side airbag units are built into the front seats, and their removal requires that the seat fabric be removed. This is not considered to be a DIY operation, and should be referred to a Volvo dealer or upholstery specialist.

Side crash sensors

30 The side crash sensors are fitted to the B-pillar (between the driver's and passenger's doors), and at the base of the C-pillar. The battery should be disconnected, as described in Chapter 5A, before any work is undertaken on the sensors.

31 To remove the sensor on the B-pillar, remove the pillar trim as described in Chapter 11. Release the clips and disconnect the wiring plug from the sensor (see illustration). Undo the retaining screw and remove the sensor.

32 To remove the sensor at the base of the C-pillar, remove the rear seat side pad as described in Chapter 11. Undo the retaining screw and remove the sensor (see illustration).

33 Refit the sensor(s) to the pillar(s) and tighten the retaining screws to the specified torque. Reconnect the wiring plug.

34 The remainder of refitting is a reversal of removal.

Front crash sensors

35 The front crash sensors are located behind each headlamp. Disconnect the battery, as described in Chapter 5A, before removing the sensors.

36 Remove the headlamp as described in Section 10. Disconnect the wiring plug from the sensor, undo the retaining screw and remove the sensor.

37 Refitting is a reversal of removal.

Side curtain airbag

38 In order to remove the side curtain airbag(s), the headlining must be removed. This is not considered a DIY operation, and should be entrusted to a Volvo dealer or upholstery specialist.

Airbag deactivation switch

39 Where fitted, the switch to deactivate the front passenger airbag is located in the trim panel at the end of the facia on the passenger side.

40 To remove the switch, first disconnect the battery negative terminal as described in Chapter 5A.

41 Carefully prise off the trim panel, pull forward slightly, and disconnect the wiring plug.

42 On the rear of the panel, release the securing clips and remove the switch.

43 Refitting is a reversal of removal.

25 Parking assistance system – removal and refitting

Control module

1 The parking assistance module (PAM) is located on the floorpan behind the luggage compartment right-hand side trim panel. Remove the panel as described in Chapter 11.

2 Release the retaining clips, remove the module and disconnect the wiring plugs (see illustration).

3 Refitting is a reversal of removal. A new unit may require recalibration and this should be entrusted to a Volvo dealer or suitably-equipped specialist.

Sensors

4 The sensors are set into the rear bumper. Remove the rear bumper as described in Chapter 11.

5 Disconnect the wiring plug from each sensor (see illustration).

6 Spread the retaining clips and pull the sensor from the inside of the bumper (see illustration).

7 Refitting is a reversal of removal.

25.5 Disconnect the wiring plug from the sensor

25.6 Spread the retaining clips and remove the sensor from the rear of the bumper

26.1a Undo the clips (arrowed) at the top of the trim panel

26.1b Undo the upper clip (arrowed) on the D-pillar . . .

26.1c . . . and the lower clip (arrowed)

26 Fuel filler flap locking motor
– removal and refitting

Removal

1 Remove the right-hand side luggage compartment side trim panel. Remove the further thin trim panel behind by undoing the 2 clips at the top and the 2 clips on the D-pillar (see illustrations).

2 Disconnect the wiring plug, pull on the emergency release tab to withdraw the plunger, and gently push the top of the motor towards the right-hand side to release it from the bracket. The motor can now be withdrawn (see illustrations).

Refitting

3 Refitting is a reversal of removal.

26.2a Disconnect the wiring plug from the motor

26.2b Push the top of the motor towards the right-hand side to release it from the bracket

26.2c Withdraw the motor from the bracket

VOLVO V70 wiring diagrams

Diagram 1

Key to symbols

Symbol		Symbol		Symbol	
Solenoid actuator		Bulb		Wire splice, soldered joint, or unspecified connector	
Earth point and location	E7	Switch		Connecting wires	
Wire colour (blue with red tracer)	BL/RT	Fuse/Fusible link	F26	Diode	
		Resistor		Light-emitting diode	
Dashed outline denotes part of a larger item, containing in this case an electronic or solid state device (pins 31 and 32 of a connector X14270).	X14270/31 X14270/32 K	Variable resistor		Item number	12
		Variable resistor		Motor/pump	M
				Heating element	

Earth locations

E1	Ground connection, PTC	E18	Engine ignition coils
E2	LH wheel housing	E19	Engine ignition coils
E3	Body, battery	E20	Engine ignition coils
E4	Engine	E21	LH wheel housing 2
E5	Engine compartment	E22	RH wheel housing 2
E6	Bottom rail, left	E23	LH wheel housing 3
E7	Bottom rail, left	E24	RH wheel housing 3
E8	Bottom rail, left	E25	Engine ignition coils
E9	Bottom rail, right	E26	Engine - Body
E10	Rear bumper abutment, left	E27	LH wheel housing
E11	Rear bumper abutment, right	E28	Ground connection, ECM
E12	Rear seat riser, LH side	E29	LH wheel housing 1
E13	Rear seat riser, LH side	E30	LH wheel housing 3 (ABS)
E14	Rear seat riser, right-hand side 1	E31	RH wheel housing
E15	Rear seat riser, RH side 2	E32	Rear bumper abutment, left
E16	Bottom rail, left	E33	Rear bumper abutment, right
E17	Bottom rail, right	E34	RH wheel housing

Typical passenger compartment distribution fusebox ⑤

(models from 2010)

Fuse	Rating	Circuit protected
F1	40 A	Subwoofer Module (SUB), Audio module (AUD), passenger compartment distribution fusebox
F2	-	Not used
F3	-	Not used
F4	-	Not used
F5	-	Not used
F6	-	Not used
F7	15A	12 V outlet cargo compartment, Refrigeration box
F8	25A	Driver Door Module (DDM)
F9	25A	Passenger Door Module (PDM)
F10	25A	Right rear door module (RDM)
F11	25A	Left rear door module (LDM)
F12	20A	Keyless Vehicle Module (KVM)
F13	20A	Switch unit, power driver's seat, Power Seat Module (PSM)
F14	20A	Switch unit, power passenger seat
F15	15A	Rear left head restraint solenoid, Rear right head restraint solenoid

Fuse	Rating	Circuit protected
F16	-	Not used
F17	10A	High Level Display Front (HLDF), Multimedia Module (MMM)
F18	15A	Integrated Audio Module (IAM), Infotainment Control Module (ICM), extra fuse holder (passenger compartment)
F19	5A	Phone Module (PHM)
F20	-	Not used
F21	5A	Sunroof Module (SRM), Damper Motor Module (DMM), Air Quality Sensor (AQS), Ceiling light
F22	15A	Outlet 12V front, Outlet 12V rear
F23	15A	S Control module, RH rear seat heater
F27	15A	Control module, rear left seat heater
F28	10A	Parking Assistance Module (PAM), Trailer Module (TRM)
F29	10A	Differential Electronic Module (DEM)
F30	5A	Suspensio n Module (SUM)

Passenger compartment extra fuse holder

(models from 2010)

Fuse	Rating	Circuit protected
F1	5A	Analog clock

Typical battery fuse box ㊶

Fuse	Rating	Circuit protected
PF1	150A	Engine fuse box
PF2	150A	Starter motor, alternator

H47433

VOLVO V70 wiring diagrams

Diagram 2

Typical engine compartment fusebox ⑥

(models up to 2010)

Fuse	Rating	Circuit protected
F1	50A	Passenger fuse box (CEM)
F2	50A	Passenger fuse box (CEM)
F3	60A	Luggage compartment fuse box
F4	60A	Luggage compartment fuse box
F5	60A	Luggage compartment fuse box
F6	-	Not used
F7	100A	Heater element (PTC)
F8	-	Not used
F9	30A	Wiper Motor Module (WMM)
F10	25A	Combustion Preheater Module (CPM)
F11	40A	Fan control module, passenger compartment fan
F12	-	Not used
F13	40A	Brake Control Module (BCM), pump
F14	20A	Brake Control Module (BCM), valves
F15	-	Not used
F16	10A	Headlamp Control Module (HCM), LH & RH front lamp housing
F17	20A	Passenger fuse box (CEM)
F18	5A	Forward Sensing Module (FSM), Forward-aimed radar (FLR)
F19	5A	Electronic power steering control module
F20	10A	Engine Control Module (ECM), Supplemental restraint system module (SRS), Transmission Control Module (TCM)
F21	10A	Heated windshield washer nozzle
F22	20A	Vacuum pump
F23	5A	Light Switch Module (LSM)

Fuse	Rating	Circuit protected
F24	15A	High pressure headlight washer motor
F25	15A	Front 12V outlet, Rear 12V outlet, Navigation system portable, DVD player/control module
F26	10A	Switch unit dome light, Sunroof module, Damper Motor Module (DMM), Air Quality Sensor (AQS), Control module, mobile phone handsfree
F27	5A	Relay (15-feed), Relay (comfort functions)
F28	20A	Relay (auxiliary lights), Auxiliary lights
F29	15A	Relay (horn), Horn
F30	10A	Main relay, engine management system
F31	15A	Transmission Control Module (TCM)
F32	15A	Electromagnetic clutch, climate control system
F33	5A	Relay (climate control system)
F34	30A	Starter motor
F35	10A	Glow plug
F36	15A	Throttle body motor, Control valve fuel pressure
F37	15A	Mass air flow sensor (MAF)
F38	-	Not used
F39	15A	Heated oxygen sensor
F40	20A	PTC resistor crankcase ventilation in hose
F41	-	Not used
F42	70A	Glow plug
F43	50A	Control module cooling fan
F44	60A	Trailer control unit

(models from 2010)

Fuse	Rating	Circuit protected
F1	50A	Passenger fuse box (CEM)
F2	50A	Passenger fuse box (CEM)
F3	60A	Luggage compartment fuse box
F4	60A	Luggage compartment fuse box
F5	60A	Luggage compartment fuse box
F6	-	Not used
F7	100A	Heater element (PTC)
F8	20A	Washer motor head light
F9	30A	Wiper Motor Module (WMM)
F10	25A	Combustion Preheater Module (CPM)
F11	40A	Fan control module, passenger compartment fan
F12	-	Not used
F13	40A	Brake Control Module (BCM), pump
F14	20A	Brake Control Module (BCM), valves
F15	-	Not used
F16	10A	Headlamp Control Module (HCM), LH &RH front lamp housing
F17	20A	Passenger fuse box (CEM)
F18	5A	Brake Control Module (BCM)
F19	5A	Electronic power steering control module
F20	10A	Engine Control Module (ECM), Supplemental restraint system module (SRS), Transmission Control Module (TCM)
F21	10A	Heated windshield washer nozzle
F22	5A	Vacuum pump, glow plug system
F23	5A	Light Switch Module (LSM)

Fuse	Rating	Circuit protected
F24	-	Not used
F25	-	Not used
F26	-	Not used
F27	5A	Relay (15-feed), Relay (comfort functions)
F28	20A	Relay (auxiliary lights), Auxiliary lights
F29	15A	Relay (horn), Horn
F30	10A	Main relay, engine management system
F31	15A	Transmission Control Module (TCM)
F32	15A	Electromagnetic clutch, climate control system
F33	5A	Relay (climate control system)
F34	30A	Starter motor
F35	10A	Glow plug
F36	15A	Throttle body motor, Control valve fuel pressure
F37	15A	Mass air flow sensor (MAF)
F38	-	Not used
F39	15A	Heated oxygen sensor
F40	20A	PTC resistor crankcase ventilation in hose
F41	5A	PTC-resistor crankcase ventilation
F42	70A	Glow plug
F43	80A	Control module cooling fan
F44	-	Not used

H47434

VOLVO V70 wiring diagrams

Diagram 3

Typical passenger compartment fusebox (CEM) ⑨

(models up to 2010)

Fuse	Rating	Circuit protected
F1	5A	Rain Sensor Module (RSM)
F2	10A	Supplemental restraint system module (SRS), Occupant Weight Sensor (OWS)
F3	5A	Brake Control Module (BCM)
F4	7.5A	Switch, heated rear seat, Accelerator pedal sensor, Automatic anti-dazzle rearview mirror, Heater element (PTC)
F5	-	Not used
F6	15A	Infotainment Control Module (ICM), Integrated Audio Module (IAM), DVD player/control module, Accessory USB unit (AUU)
F7	7.5A	Steering wheel switch left (SWSL), Steering wheel switch right (SWSR), RTI switch
F8	-	Not used
F9	15A	LH & RH front lamp housing
F10	20A	Sunroof Module (SRM)
F11	7.5A	LH & RH reversing light
F12	-	Not used
F13	15A	LH & RH fog light
F14	15A	Washer motor

Fuse	Rating	Circuit protected
F15	10A	Forward Sensing Module (FSM)
F16	-	Not used
F17	7.5A	Power passenger seat, power window driver, glove compartment lighting
F18	5A	Driver Information Module (DIM)
F19	5A	Power Seat Module (PSM)
F20	15A	Rear window wiper motor
F21	5A	Remote Keyless Entry (RKE), Remote Receiver Module (RRX), Ultrasonic sensor (IMS), Heartbeat sensor
F22	20A	Fuel pump
F23	20A	Steering Column Lock module (SCL)
F24	-	Not used
F25	10A	Lock unit tailgate, Lock motor fuel filler cover
F26	5A	Climate Control Module (CCM), Siren Control Module (SCM), Data link connector
F27	5A	Start Control Unit (SCU)
F28	5A	Keyless Vehicle Module (KVM), Auxiliary brake light, LH & RH brake lights

```
( F1 ) ( F2 ) ( F3 ) ( F4 ) ( F5 ) ( F6 ) ( F7 ) ( F8 ) ( F9 ) ( F10 ) ( F11 ) ( F12 ) ( F13 ) ( F14 )
( F15 ) ( F16 ) ( F17 ) ( F18 ) ( F19 ) ( F20 ) ( F21 ) ( F22 ) ( F23 ) ( F24 ) ( F25 ) ( F26 ) ( F27 ) ( F28 )
```

(models from 2010)

Fuse	Rating	Circuit protected
F1	15 A	Rear window wiper relay, Rear window wiper motor
F2	-	Not used
F3	7.5A	Power passenger seat, power window driver, glove compartment lighting, interior lighting
F4	5A	Driver Information Module (DIM)
F5	10A	Forward Sensing Module (FSM), Forward-aimed radar (FLR)
F6	7.5A	Rain Sensor Module (RSM)
F7	7.5A	Steering wheel switch
F8	10A	Lock motor, fuel filler cover
F9	15A	Washer motor
F10	15A	Washer motor
F11	10A	Central locking motor, trunk lid
F12	-	Not used
F13	20A	Fuel pump control module, Fuel pump

Fuse	Rating	Circuit protected
F14	5A	Climate Control Module (CCM), Ultrasonic sensor (IMS), Heart beat sensor (HBS)
F15	15A	Steering Column Lock Module (SCL)
F16	5A	Siren Control Module (SCM), Data link connector
F17	-	Not used
F18	10A	Supplemental Restraint System Module (SRS), Occupant Weight Sensor (OWS)
F19	5A	Forward Sensing Module (FSM), Forward-aimed radar (FLR)
F20	7.5A	Heated rear seat, accelerator pedal sensor, Auto-dimming rearview mirror, PTC-element (Heater)
F21	15A	Infotainment Control Module (ICM), Integrated Audio Module (IAM)
F22	5A	Contact brake light
F23	20A	Sunroof Module (SRM)
F24	5A	Start Control Module (SCU)

```
( F1 )  ( F9 )  ( F17 )
( F2 )  ( F10 ) ( F18 )
( F3 )  ( F11 ) ( F19 )
( F4 )  ( F12 ) ( F20 )
( F5 )  ( F13 ) ( F21 )
( F6 )  ( F14 ) ( F22 )
( F7 )  ( F15 ) ( F23 )
( F8 )  ( F16 ) ( F24 )
```

H47435

VOLVO V70 wiring diagrams

Diagram 4

Typical rear electrical center fusebox

(models up to 2010)

Fuse	Rating	Circuit protected
FA1	25A	Driver's Door Module (DDM)
FA2	25A	Passenger Door Module (PDM)
FA3	25A	Left rear Door Module (LDM)
FA4	25A	Right rear Door Module (RDM)
FA5	-	Not used
FA6	15A	Refrigeration box, 12V outlet(cargo compartment)
FA7	30A	Relay(rear window defroster), rear window defroster
FA8	-	Not used
FA9	15A	13-pin outlet, tow hitch cable harness
FA10	25A	Power Seat Module (PSM)
FA11	40A	Trailer Module (TRM), Accessory
FA12	30A	Power Operated Tailgate Module (POT)

(models from 2010)

Fuse	Rating	Circuit protected
FA1	30A	Park Brake Module (PBM)
FA2	30A	Park Brake Module (PBM)
FA3	30A	Relay, heated rear window
FA4	-	Not used
FA5	30A	Power Operated Tailgate Module (POT)
FA6	-	Not used
FA7	-	Not used
FA8	-	Not used
FA9	15A	13-pin outlet, tow hitch cable harness
FA10	-	Not used
FA11	40A	Trailer Module (TRM), Accessory
FA12	-	Not used

(models up to 2010)

Fuse	Rating	Circuit protected
FB1	-	Not used
FB2	15A	Suspension Module (SUM)
FB3	15A	Seat Heating Module (SHM), left
FB4	15A	Seat Heating Module (SHM), right
FB5	15A	Control module, rear right seat heater
FB6	15A	Differential Electronic Module (DEM)
FB7	15A	Control module, rear left seat heater
FB8	-	Not used
FB9	25A	Switch unit, power passenger seat
FB10	25A	Keyless Vehicle Module (KVM)
FB11	30A	Lock motor, rear left brake disc
FB12	30A	Lock motor, rear right brake disc

(models up to 2010)

Fuse	Rating	Circuit protected
FD1	10A	High Level Display Front module (HLDF), Multimedia Module (MMM)
FD2	-	Not used
FD3	25A	Subwoofer Module (SUB)
FD4	5A	Remote digital audio receiver (RDAR)
FD5	25A	Audio module (AUD)
FD6	15A	Infotainment Control Module (ICM), Integrated Audio Module (IAM), Accessory USB unit (AUU)
FD7	5A	Phone Module (PHM), Bluetooth Phone Module (BPM)
FD8	-	Not used
FD9	-	Not used
FD10	-	Not used
FD11	-	Not used
FD12	-	Not used

H47436

Colour codes

W	White	**R**	Red
BL	Blue	**GN**	Green
GR	Grey	**VO**	Violet
Y	Yellow	**SB**	Black
BN	Brown	**OR**	Orange
P	Pink		

Key to items

1 Battery
6 Engine fusebox
9 Central Electronic Module (CEM)
11 Steering wheel control unit
12 Steering wheel clock springs
41 Battery fusebox
142 Cruise control switch
143 Remote audio controls
144 Audio unit
146 LH rear door speaker

147 LH front door speaker
148 LH front tweeter
149 RH rear door speaker
150 RH front door speaker
151 RH front tweeter
180 Microphone
181 Auxiliary equipment input (AUX)
182 Infotainment Control Module (ICM)
183 Window antenna amplifier
184 Right-hand rear window antenna

Diagram 5

H47437

Typical audio system - models up to 2010

Typical audio system - models from 2010

Colour codes

W	White	**R**	Red
BL	Blue	**GN**	Green
GR	Grey	**VO**	Violet
Y	Yellow	**SB**	Black
BN	Brown	**OR**	Orange
P	Pink		

Key to items

1   Battery
6   Engine fusebox
9   Central electronic control unit
11   Steering wheel control unit
41   Battery fusebox
58   RH mirror assembly
     h = outside air temperature sensor
111 Climate control control unit
125 Engine management control unit

126 Auxiliary heater
     b = glow
     c = temperature
     e = overheat
     f = fuel preheat
127 Combustion preheater control unit
128 Coolant pump
130 Fuel tank unit
     a = fuel level sensor injector side
     b = fuel level sensor pump side

185 Fuel pump, auxiliary heater

Diagram 6

H47438

Typical auxiliary heater - models up to 2010

Typical auxiliary heater - models from 2010

Colour codes

W	White	R	Red
BL	Blue	GN	Green
GR	Grey	VO	Violet
Y	Yellow	SB	Black
BN	Brown	OR	Orange
P	Pink		

Key to items

1 Battery
6 Engine fusebox
9 Central Electronic Module (CEM)
41 Battery fuse box
42 Luggage compartment fusebox
55 LH door control unit
56 RH door control unit
57 LH mirror assembly
  b = up/down motor
  c = left/right motor
  d = mirror fold motor
  e = memory up/down
  f = memory left/right
  g = mirror heating

58 RH mirror assembly
  b = up/down motor
  c = left/right motor
  d = mirror fold motor
  e = memory up/down
  f = memory left/right
  g = mirror heating
111 Climate control control unit
116 Extended D1 feed relay
179 Switch, front door power window

Diagram 7

H47439

Typical electric mirrors - models up to 2010

Typical electric mirrors - models from 2010

12•30 Wiring diagrams

Colour codes

W	White	R	Red
BL	Blue	GN	Green
GR	Grey	VO	Violet
Y	Yellow	SB	Black
BN	Brown	OR	Orange
P	Pink		

Key to items

1	Battery	154	LH rear door switch
5	Passenger compartment distribution fusebox	155	RH rear door switch
		156	LH rear window motor
6	Engine fusebox	157	RH rear window motor
9	Central Electronic Module (CEM)	179	Switch, front door power window
41	Battery fusebox	201	Switch, passenger door power window
55	LH door control unit	202	Right rear Door Module (RDM)
56	RH door control unit	203	Left rear Door Module (LDM)
116	Extended D1 feed relay		
152	LH front window motor		
153	RH front window motor		

Diagram 8

H47440

Typical electric windows - models up to 2010

Typical electric windows - models from 2010

Colour codes

W	White	**R**	Red
BL	Blue	**GN**	Green
GR	Grey	**VO**	Violet
Y	Yellow	**SB**	Black
BN	Brown	**OR**	Orange
P	Pink		

Key to items

1	Battery
6	Engine fusebox
9	Central Electronic Module (CEM)
11	Steering wheel control unit
41	Battery fusebox
116	Extended D1 feed Relay
188	Rain Sensor Module (RSM)
189	Wiper Motor Module (WMM)
192	Washer relay 1
193	Washer relay 2
195	Washer motor

Diagram 9

H47441

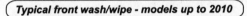

Typical front wash/wipe - models up to 2010

Typical front wash/wipe - model from 2010

Colour codes

W	White	R	Red
BL	Blue	GN	Green
GR	Grey	VO	Violet
Y	Yellow	SB	Black
BN	Brown	OR	Orange
P	Pink		

Key to items

1	Battery
6	Engine fusebox
9	Central Electronic Module (CEM)
11	Steering wheel control unit
41	Battery fusebox
167	LH rear door lock unit
176	Child lock switch
196	Telescopic nozzle, left
198	High pressure headlight washer motor
199	Relay, headlight washer motor

Diagram 10

H47442

Typical headlight washer - models up to 2010

Typical headlight washer - models from 2010 up to 2011

Typical headlight washer - models from 2011

Colour codes

W	White	**R**	Red
BL	Blue	**GN**	Green
GR	Grey	**VO**	Violet
Y	Yellow	**SB**	Black
BN	Brown	**OR**	Orange
P	Pink		

Key to items

1	Battery
5	Passenger compartment distribution fusebox
6	Engine fusebox
9	Central Electronic Module (CEM)
41	Battery fusebox
111	Climate control control unit
117	Blower control unit
118	Heater blower motor
119	LH temperature damper motor
120	RH temperature damper motor
121	Recirculation damper motor
176	Relay, comfort functions
186	Damper Motor Module (DMM), defroster
187	Damper Motor Module (DMM), floor/ventilation

Diagram 11

H47443

Typical heater blower - models up to 2010

Typical heater blower - models from 2010

Colour codes

W	White	R	Red
BL	Blue	GN	Green
GR	Grey	VO	Violet
Y	Yellow	SB	Black
BN	Brown	OR	Orange
P	Pink		

Key to items

1 Battery
6 Engine fusebox
9 Central Electronic Module (CEM)
41 Battery fusebox
55 LH front door control unit
56 RH front door control unit
77 Luggage compartment light (V70)
78 Rear reading light
80 LH vanity mirror illumination
81 RH vanity mirror illumination
82 Tailgate lock unit (V70)
85 LH front door lock

86 LH rear door lock unit
87 RH front door lock unit
88 RH rear door lock unit
91 Glove box light
92 LH front footwell light
94 RH front footwell light
116 Extended D1 feed relay
176 Relay, comfort functions
202 Right rear Door Module (RDM)
203 Left rear Door Module (LDM)
204 Ceiling light
205 Switch, parking brake

206 Front ashtray lighting
207 Rear headphone sockets
208 Trunk lid/tailgate closing switch, V70
210 Switch, central locking system, driver's door
211 Switch, central locking system, passenger door

Diagram 12

H47444

Typical interior lighting - models up to 2010

Colour codes

W	White	R	Red
BL	Blue	GN	Green
GR	Grey	VO	Violet
Y	Yellow	SB	Black
BN	Brown	OR	Orange
P	Pink		

Key to items

1	Battery	86	LH rear door lock unit
5	Passenger compartment	87	RH front door lock unit
	distribution fusebox	88	RH rear door lock unit
6	Engine fusebox	91	Glove box light
9	Central Electronic Module (CEM)	92	LH front footwell light
41	Battery fusebox	94	RH front footwell light
55	LH front door control unit	116	Extended D1 feed relay
56	RH front door control unit	176	Relay, comfort functions
77	Luggage compartment light (V70)	202	Right rear Door Module (RDM)
78	Rear reading light	203	Left rear Door Module (LDM)
80	LH vanity mirror illumination	204	Ceiling light
81	RH vanity mirror illumination	205	Switch, parking brake
82	Tailgate lock unit (V70)		
85	LH front door lock		

206	Front ashtray lighting
207	Rear headphone sockets
208	Trunk lid/tailgate closing switch, V70
210	Switch, central locking system, driver's door
211	Switch, central locking system, passenger door

Diagram 13

H47445

Typical interior lighting - models 2010

Colour codes

W	White	R	Red
BL	Blue	GN	Green
GR	Grey	VO	Violet
Y	Yellow	SB	Black
BN	Brown	OR	Orange
P	Pink		

Key to items

1 Battery
5 Passenger compartment
   distribution fusebox
6 Engine fusebox
9 Central Electronic Module (CEM)
41 Battery fusebox
55 LH front door control unit
56 RH front door control unit
77 Luggage compartment light (V70)
78 Rear reading light
80 LH vanity mirror illumination
81 RH vanity mirror illumination
82 Tailgate lock unit (V70)
85 LH front door lock

86 LH rear door lock unit
87 RH front door lock unit
88 RH rear door lock unit
91 Glove box light
92 LH front footwell light
94 RH front footwell light
116 Extended D1 feed relay
176 Relay, comfort functions
202 Right rear Door Module (RDM)
203 Left rear Door Module (LDM)
204 Ceiling light
205 Switch, parking brake

206 Front ashtray lighting
207 Rear headphone sockets
208 Trunk lid/tailgate closing switch, V70
210 Switch, central locking system, driver's door
211 Switch, central locking system, passenger door

Diagram 14

H47446

Typical interior lighting - models 2011

Colour codes

W	White	**R**	Red
BL	Blue	**GN**	Green
GR	Grey	**VO**	Violet
Y	Yellow	**SB**	Black
BN	Brown	**OR**	Orange
P	Pink		

Key to items

1 Battery
6 Engine fusebox
9 Central Electronic Module (CEM)
20 Light switch control unit
24 Left-hand front lamp housing
25 Right-hand front lamp housing

28 Number plate light
29 Driver Information Module (DIM)
38 LH rear upper light unit (V70)
39 RH rear upper light unit (V70)
41 Battery fusebox

Diagram 15

H47447

Typical side, tail &
number plate lights - models up to 2010

Typical side, tail &
number plate lights - models from 2010

Colour codes

W	White	R	Red
BL	Blue	GN	Green
GR	Grey	VO	Violet
Y	Yellow	SB	Black
BN	Brown	OR	Orange
P	Pink		

Key to items

1 Battery
6 Engine fusebox
9 Central Electronic Module (CEM)
11 Steering wheel control unit
20 Light switch control unit
24 LH front light unit
   b = dip beam
   c = main beam

25 RH front light unit
   b = dip beam
   c = main beam
29 Driver Information Module (DIM)
30 Main beam relay
41 Battery fusebox

Diagram 16

H47448

Typical headlights (Xenon) - models up to 2010

Typical headlights (Xenon) - models from 2010

Typical headlights (H4) - models up to 2010

Typical headlights (H4) - models from 2010

Colour codes

W	White	R	Red
BL	Blue	GN	Green
GR	Grey	VO	Violet
Y	Yellow	SB	Black
BN	Brown	OR	Orange
P	Pink		

Key to items

1 Battery
5 Passenger compartment
   distribution fusebox
6 Engine fusebox
9 Central Electronic Module (CEM)
11 Steering wheel control unit
24 LH front light unit
   b = direction indicator
25 RH front light unit
   b = direction indicator
29 Driver Information Module (DIM)
38 LH rear outer light unit
   b = direction indicator

39 RH rear outer light unit
   b = direction indicator
41 Battery fusebox
42 Luggage compartment fusebox
55 LH front door control unit
56 RH front door control unit
57 LH mirror assembly
   h = direction indicator
58 RH mirror assembly
   i= direction indicator
62 Hazard warning switch

Diagram 17

H47449

Typical direction indicators & hazard warning lights models upto 2010

Typical direction indicators & hazard warning lights models from 2010

Colour codes

W	White	**R**	Red
BL	Blue	**GN**	Green
GR	Grey	**VO**	Violet
Y	Yellow	**SB**	Black
BN	Brown	**OR**	Orange
P	Pink		

Key to items

1 Battery
6 Engine fusebox
9 Central Electronic Module (CEM)
20 Light switch control unit
41 Battery fusebox
67 LH headlight levelling motor
68 RH headlight levelling motor

223 Relay, 15-feed
224 Headlamp Control Module (HCM)
225 Height sensor, suspension, front right
226 Height sensor, suspension, rear right

Diagram 18

H47450

Typical headlight levelling models upto 2010

Typical headlight levelling models from 2010

Colour codes

W	White	**R**	Red
BL	Blue	**GN**	Green
GR	Grey	**VO**	Violet
Y	Yellow	**SB**	Black
BN	Brown	**OR**	Orange
P	Pink		

Key to items

1 Battery
6 Engine fusebox
9 Central Electronic Module (CEM)
26 LH rear inner light unit
27 RH rear inner light unit
38 LH rear outer light unit
39 RH rear outer light unit
41 Battery fusebox
43 High level brake light
44 Stop light switch

45 Reversing light switch
214 Keyless Vehicle Module (KVM)
222 Gear Selector Module (GSM)

Diagram 19

H47451

Typical stop lights - models up to 2010

Typical stop lights - models from 2010

Typical reversing lights models up to 2010

Typical reversing lights models from 2010

Colour codes

W	White	**R**	Red
BL	Blue	**GN**	Green
GR	Grey	**VO**	Violet
Y	Yellow	**SB**	Black
BN	Brown	**OR**	Orange
P	Pink		

Key to items

1 Battery
5 Passenger compartment distribution fusebox
6 Engine fusebox
9 Central Electronic Module (CEM)
11 Steering wheel control unit
20 Light switch control unit
26 LH rear inner light unit
   b= fog light
27 RH rear inner light unit
   b= fog light
29 Driver Information Module (DIM)

41 Battery fusebox
42 Luggage compartment fusebox
52 LH front foglight
53 RH front foglight
55 LH front door control unit
56 RH front door control unit
57 LH mirror assembly
58 RH mirror assembly

Diagram 20

H47452

Typical foglights - models up to 2010

Typical foglights - models from 2010

Typical exterior mirror courtesy lights - models up to 2010

Typical exterior mirror courtesy lights - models from 2010

Colour codes

W	White	R	Red
BL	Blue	GN	Green
GR	Grey	VO	Violet
Y	Yellow	SB	Black
BN	Brown	OR	Orange
P	Pink		

Key to items

1	Battery
5	Passenger compartment distribution fusebox
6	Engine fusebox
9	Central Electronic Module (CEM)
41	Battery fusebox
42	Luggage compartment fusebox
100	Trailer socket
178	Relay, 15-feed rear, V70
200	Trailer Module (TRM)

Diagram 21

Typical trailer wiring - models up to 2010

Typical trailer wiring - models from 2010

Colour codes

W	White	R	Red
BL	Blue	GN	Green
GR	Grey	VO	Violet
Y	Yellow	SB	Black
BN	Brown	OR	Orange
P	Pink		

Key to items

1	Battery
6	Engine fusebox
9	Central Electronic Module (CEM)
29	Driver Information Module (DIM)
41	Battery fusebox
42	Luggage compartment fusebox
55	LH front door control unit
56	RH front door control unit
82	Tailgate lock unit (V70)
85	LH front door lock unit
87	RH front door lock unit
167	LH rear door lock unit

168	RH rear door lock unit
173	Fuel filler flap unlocking relay
177	Fuel filler flap motor
201	Switch, passenger door power window
202	Right rear Door Module (RDM)
203	Left rear Door Module (LDM)
210	Switch, central locking system, driver's door
211	Switch, central locking system, passenger door
212	Remote Receiver Module (RRX)
215	Trunk handle switch, V70
216	Power Operated Tailgate Module (POT)

Diagram 22

H47454

Typical central locking - models up to 2010

Colour codes

W	White	**R**	Red
BL	Blue	**GN**	Green
GR	Grey	**VO**	Violet
Y	Yellow	**SB**	Black
BN	Brown	**OR**	Orange
P	Pink		

Key to items

1	Battery	168	RH rear door lock unit
5	Passenger compartment	173	Fuel filler flap unlocking relay
	distribution fusebox	177	Fuel filler flap motor
6	Engine fusebox	201	Switch, passenger door power window
9	Central Electronic Module (CEM)	202	Right rear Door Module (RDM)
29	Driver Information Module (DIM)	203	Left rear Door Module (LDM)
41	Battery fusebox	210	Switch, central locking system, driver's door
42	Luggage compartment fusebox	211	Switch, central locking system, passenger door
55	LH front door control unit	212	Remote Receiver Module (RRX)
56	RH front door control unit	215	Trunk handle switch, V70
82	Tailgate lock unit (V70)	216	Power Operated Tailgate Module (POT)
85	LH front door lock unit		
87	RH front door lock unit		
167	LH rear door lock unit		

Diagram 23

H47455

Typical central locking - models from 2010

Colour codes

W	White	**R**	Red
BL	Blue	**GN**	Green
GR	Grey	**VO**	Violet
Y	Yellow	**SB**	Black
BN	Brown	**OR**	Orange
P	Pink		

Key to items

1   Battery
3   Starter motor
4   Alternator
6   Engine fusebox
7   Engine cooling fan control unit
9   Central Electronic Module (CEM)
15 Power steering control unit
16 Power steering valve
41 Battery fusebox
177 Fuel filler flap motor
223 Relay, 15-feed

Diagram 24

H47456

Typical engine cooling fan

Typical starting and charging

Typical Power Steering - models up to 2010

Typical Power Steering - models from 2010

Colour codes

W	White	**R**	Red
BL	Blue	**GN**	Green
GR	Grey	**VO**	Violet
Y	Yellow	**SB**	Black
BN	Brown	**OR**	Orange
P	Pink		

Key to items

1 Battery
6 Engine fusebox
10 Horn
11 Steering wheel control unit
12 Steering wheel clock springs
13 Horn switch
41 Battery fusebox
42 Luggage compartment fusebox
71 Luggage compartment 12v outlet
72 Front 12v outlet
73 Rear 12v outlet
176 Relay, comfort functions

Diagram 25

H47457

Typical horn - models up to 2010

Typical horn - models from 2010

Typical 12V outlet - models up to 2010

Typical 12V outlet - models from 2010

Colour codes

W	White	**R**	Red
BL	Blue	**GN**	Green
GR	Grey	**VO**	Violet
Y	Yellow	**SB**	Black
BN	Brown	**OR**	Orange
P	Pink		

Key to items

1	Battery	109	Heated rear window
6	Engine fusebox	110	Heated rear window/mirror switch
9	Central Electronic Module (CEM)	111	Climate control control unit
11	Steering wheel control unit	116	Extended D1 feed relay
41	Battery fusebox		
42	Luggage compartment fusebox		
101	Washer pump unit		
106	Rear wiper motor		
108	Rear wiper relay		
109	Heated rear window		
110	Heated rear window/mirror switch		
111	Climate control control unit		
116	Extended D1 feed relay		

Diagram 26

H47458

Typical rear wash/wipe - models up to 2010

Typical rear wash/wipe - models from 2010

Typical rear window defroster - models up to 2010

Typical rear window defroster - models from 2010

Colour codes

W	White	R	Red
BL	Blue	GN	Green
GR	Grey	VO	Violet
Y	Yellow	SB	Black
BN	Brown	OR	Orange
P	Pink		

Key to items

1 Battery
5 Passenger compartment distribution fusebox
6 Engine fusebox
9 Central Electronic Module (CEM)
41 Battery fusebox
42 Luggage compartment fusebox
42 Footwell control unit
111 Climate control control unit
116 Extended D1 feed relay
131 LH heated seat
132 RH heated seat
135 Backrest angle control

136 Forward/backward control
137 Rear of seat up/down control
138 Front of seat up/down control
139 Driver's seat switch
178 Relay, 15-feed rear, V70

Diagram 27

H47459

Typical electric driver's seat - models up to 2010

Typical electric driver's seat - models from 2010

Typical heated seats - models up to 2010

Typical heated seats - models from 2010

Dimensions and weights

Note: *All figures are approximate, and may vary according to model. Refer to manufacturer's data for exact figures.*

Dimensions
Overall length . . . . 4710 mm
Overall width. . . . . 1804 mm
Overall height . . . . 1465 mm
Wheelbase . . . . 2755 mm

Weights
Kerb weight . . . . Refer to identification plate on the left-hand front inner wing
Maximum roof rack load . . . . 100 kg
Maximum trailer weight (braked) . . . . See vehicle identification plate

Fuel economy

Although depreciation is still the biggest part of the cost of motoring for most car owners, the cost of fuel is more immediately noticeable. These pages give some tips on how to get the best fuel economy.

Working it out

Manufacturer's figures

Car manufacturers are required by law to provide fuel consumption information on all new vehicles sold. These 'official' figures are obtained by simulating various driving conditions on a rolling road or a test track. Real life conditions are different, so the fuel consumption actually achieved may not bear much resemblance to the quoted figures.

How to calculate it

Many cars now have trip computers which will

display fuel consumption, both instantaneous and average. Refer to the owner's handbook for details of how to use these.

To calculate consumption yourself (and maybe to check that the trip computer is accurate), proceed as follows.

1. Fill up with fuel and note the mileage, or zero the trip recorder.
2. Drive as usual until you need to fill up again.
3. Note the amount of fuel required to refill the tank, and the mileage covered since the previous fill-up.
4. Divide the mileage by the amount of fuel used to obtain the consumption figure.

For example:

Mileage at first fill-up (a) = 27,903
Mileage at second fill-up (b) = 28,346
Mileage covered (b - a) = 443
Fuel required at second fill-up = 48.6 litres

The half-completed changeover to metric units in the UK means that we buy our fuel

in litres, measure distances in miles and talk about fuel consumption in miles per gallon. There are two ways round this: the first is to convert the litres to gallons before doing the calculation (by dividing by 4.546, or see Table 1). So in the example:

48.6 litres ÷ 4.546 = 10.69 gallons
443 miles ÷ 10.69 gallons = 41.4 mpg

The second way is to calculate the consumption in miles per litre, then multiply that figure by 4.546 (or see Table 2).

So in the example, fuel consumption is:

443 miles ÷ 48.6 litres = 9.1 mpl
9.1 mpl x 4.546 = 41.4 mpg

The rest of Europe expresses fuel consumption in litres of fuel required to travel 100 km (l/100 km). For interest, the conversions are given in Table 3. In practice it doesn't matter what units you use, provided you know what your normal consumption is and can spot if it's getting better or worse.

Table 1: conversion of litres to Imperial gallons

litres	1	2	3	4	5	10	20	30	40	50	60	70
gallons	0.22	0.44	0.66	0.88	1.10	2.24	4.49	6.73	8.98	11.22	13.47	15.71

Table 2: conversion of miles per litre to miles per gallon

miles per litre	5	6	7	8	9	10	11	12	13	14
miles per gallon	23	27	32	36	41	46	50	55	59	64

Table 3: conversion of litres per 100 km to miles per gallon

litres per 100 km	4	4.5	5	5.5	6	6.5	7	8	9	10
miles per gallon	71	63	56	51	47	43	40	35	31	28

Maintenance

A well-maintained car uses less fuel and creates less pollution. In particular:

Filters

Change air and fuel filters at the specified intervals.

Oil

Use a good quality oil of the lowest viscosity specified by the vehicle manufacturer (see Lubricants and fluids). Check the level often and be careful not to overfill.

Spark plugs

When applicable, renew at the specified intervals.

Tyres

Check tyre pressures regularly. Under-inflated tyres have an increased rolling resistance. It is generally safe to use the higher pressures specified for full load conditions even when not fully laden, but keep an eye on the centre band of tread for signs of wear due to over-inflation.

When buying new tyres, consider the 'fuel saving' models which most manufacturers include in their ranges.

Driving style

Acceleration

Acceleration uses more fuel than driving at a steady speed. The best technique with modern cars is to accelerate reasonably briskly to the desired speed, changing up through the gears as soon as possible without making the engine labour.

Air conditioning

Air conditioning absorbs quite a bit of energy from the engine – typically 3 kW (4 hp) or so. The effect on fuel consumption is at its worst in slow traffic. Switch it off when not required.

Anticipation

Drive smoothly and try to read the traffic flow so as to avoid unnecessary acceleration and braking.

Automatic transmission

When accelerating in an automatic, avoid depressing the throttle so far as to make the transmission hold onto lower gears at higher speeds. Don't use the 'Sport' setting, if applicable.

When stationary with the engine running, select 'N' or 'P'. When moving, keep your left foot away from the brake.

Braking

Braking converts the car's energy of motion into heat – essentially, it is wasted. Obviously some braking is always going to be necessary, but with good anticipation it is surprising how much can be avoided, especially on routes that you know well.

Carshare

Consider sharing lifts to work or to the shops. Even once a week will make a difference.

Electrical loads

Electricity is 'fuel' too; the alternator which charges the battery does so by converting some of the engine's energy of motion into electrical energy. The more electrical accessories are in use, the greater the load on the alternator. Switch off big consumers like the heated rear window when not required.

Freewheeling

Freewheeling (coasting) in neutral with the engine switched off is dangerous. The effort required to operate power-assisted brakes and steering increases when the engine is not running, with a potential lack of control in emergency situations.

In any case, modern fuel injection systems automatically cut off the engine's fuel supply on the overrun (moving and in gear, but with the accelerator pedal released).

Gadgets

Bolt-on devices claiming to save fuel have been around for nearly as long as the motor car itself. Those which worked were rapidly adopted as standard equipment by the vehicle manufacturers. Others worked only in certain situations, or saved fuel only at the expense of unacceptable effects on performance, driveability or the life of engine components.

The most effective fuel saving gadget is the driver's right foot.

Journey planning

Combine (eg) a trip to the supermarket with a visit to the recycling centre and the DIY store, rather than making separate journeys.

When possible choose a travelling time outside rush hours.

Load

The more heavily a car is laden, the greater the energy required to accelerate it to a given speed. Remove heavy items which you don't need to carry.

One load which is often overlooked is the contents of the fuel tank. A tankful of fuel (55 litres / 12 gallons) weighs 45 kg (100 lb) or so. Just half filling it may be worthwhile.

Lost?

At the risk of stating the obvious, if you're going somewhere new, have details of the route to hand. There's not much point in achieving record mpg if you also go miles out of your way.

Parking

If possible, carry out any reversing or turning manoeuvres when you arrive at a parking space so that you can drive straight out when you leave. Manoeuvering when the engine is cold uses a lot more fuel.

Driving around looking for free on-street parking may cost more in fuel than buying a car park ticket.

Premium fuel

Most major oil companies (and some supermarkets) have premium grades of fuel which are several pence a litre dearer than the standard grades. Reports vary, but the consensus seems to be that if these fuels improve economy at all, they do not do so by enough to justify their extra cost.

Roof rack

When loading a roof rack, try to produce a wedge shape with the narrow end at the front. Any cover should be securely fastened – if it flaps it's creating turbulence and absorbing energy.

Remove roof racks and boxes when not in use – they increase air resistance and can create a surprising amount of noise.

Short journeys

The engine is at its least efficient, and wear is highest, during the first few miles after a cold start. Consider walking, cycling or using public transport.

Speed

The engine is at its most efficient when running at a steady speed and load at the rpm where it develops maximum torque. (You can find this figure in the car's handbook.) For most cars this corresponds to between 55 and 65 mph in top gear.

Above the optimum cruising speed, fuel consumption starts to rise quite sharply. A car travelling at 80 mph will typically be using 30% more fuel than at 60 mph.

Supermarket fuel

It may be cheap but is it any good? In the UK all supermarket fuel must meet the relevant British Standard. The major oil companies will say that their branded fuels have better additive packages which may stop carbon and other deposits building up. A reasonable compromise might be to use one tank of branded fuel to three or four from the supermarket.

Switch off when stationary

Switch off the engine if you look like being stationary for more than 30 seconds or so. This is good for the environment as well as for your pocket. Be aware though that frequent restarts are hard on the battery and the starter motor.

Windows

Driving with the windows open increases air turbulence around the vehicle. Closing the windows promotes smooth airflow and

reduced resistance. The faster you go, the more significant this is.

And finally . . .

Driving techniques associated with good fuel economy tend to involve moderate acceleration and low top speeds. Be considerate to the needs of other road users who may need to make brisker progress; even if you do not agree with them this is not an excuse to be obstructive.

Safety must always take precedence over economy, whether it is a question of accelerating hard to complete an overtaking manoeuvre, killing your speed when confronted with a potential hazard or switching the lights on when it starts to get dark.

Conversion factors

Length (distance)

Inches (in)	x 25.4	= Millimetres (mm)	x 0.0394	= Inches (in)	
Feet (ft)	x 0.305	= Metres (m)	x 3.281	= Feet (ft)	
Miles	x 1.609	= Kilometres (km)	x 0.621	= Miles	

Volume (capacity)

Cubic inches (cu in; in³)	x 16.387	= Cubic centimetres (cc; cm³)	x 0.061	= Cubic inches (cu in; in³)	
Imperial pints (Imp pt)	x 0.568	= Litres (l)	x 1.76	= Imperial pints (Imp pt)	
Imperial quarts (Imp qt)	x 1.137	= Litres (l)	x 0.88	= Imperial quarts (Imp qt)	
Imperial quarts (Imp qt)	x 1.201	= US quarts (US qt)	x 0.833	= Imperial quarts (Imp qt)	
US quarts (US qt)	x 0.946	= Litres (l)	x 1.057	= US quarts (US qt)	
Imperial gallons (Imp gal)	x 4.546	= Litres (l)	x 0.22	= Imperial gallons (Imp gal)	
Imperial gallons (Imp gal)	x 1.201	= US gallons (US gal)	x 0.833	= Imperial gallons (Imp gal)	
US gallons (US gal)	x 3.785	= Litres (l)	x 0.264	= US gallons (US gal)	

Mass (weight)

Ounces (oz)	x 28.35	= Grams (g)	x 0.035	= Ounces (oz)	
Pounds (lb)	x 0.454	= Kilograms (kg)	x 2.205	= Pounds (lb)	

Force

Ounces-force (ozf; oz)	x 0.278	= Newtons (N)	x 3.6	= Ounces-force (ozf; oz)	
Pounds-force (lbf; lb)	x 4.448	= Newtons (N)	x 0.225	= Pounds-force (lbf; lb)	
Newtons (N)	x 0.1	= Kilograms-force (kgf; kg)	x 9.81	= Newtons (N)	

Pressure

Pounds-force per square inch (psi; lbf/in²; lb/in²)	x 0.070	= Kilograms-force per square centimetre (kgf/cm²; kg/cm²)	x 14.223	= Pounds-force per square inch (psi; lbf/in²; lb/in²)	
Pounds-force per square inch (psi; lbf/in²; lb/in²)	x 0.068	= Atmospheres (atm)	x 14.696	= Pounds-force per square inch (psi; lbf/in²; lb/in²)	
Pounds-force per square inch (psi; lbf/in²; lb/in²)	x 0.069	= Bars	x 14.5	= Pounds-force per square inch (psi; lbf/in²; lb/in²)	
Pounds-force per square inch (psi; lbf/in²; lb/in²)	x 6.895	= Kilopascals (kPa)	x 0.145	= Pounds-force per square inch (psi; lbf/in²; lb/in²)	
Kilopascals (kPa)	x 0.01	= Kilograms-force per square centimetre (kgf/cm²; kg/cm²)	x 98.1	= Kilopascals (kPa)	
Millibar (mbar)	x 100	= Pascals (Pa)	x 0.01	= Millibar (mbar)	
Millibar (mbar)	x 0.0145	= Pounds-force per square inch (psi; lbf/in²; lb/in²)	x 68.947	= Millibar (mbar)	
Millibar (mbar)	x 0.75	= Millimetres of mercury (mmHg)	x 1.333	= Millibar (mbar)	
Millibar (mbar)	x 0.401	= Inches of water (inH₂O)	x 2.491	= Millibar (mbar)	
Millimetres of mercury (mmHg)	x 0.535	= Inches of water (inH₂O)	x 1.868	= Millimetres of mercury (mmHg)	
Inches of water (inH₂O)	x 0.036	= Pounds-force per square inch (psi; lbf/in²; lb/in²)	x 27.68	= Inches of water (inH₂O)	

Torque (moment of force)

Pounds-force inches (lbf in; lb in)	x 1.152	= Kilograms-force centimetre (kgf cm; kg cm)	x 0.868	= Pounds-force inches (lbf in; lb in)	
Pounds-force inches (lbf in; lb in)	x 0.113	= Newton metres (Nm)	x 8.85	= Pounds-force inches (lbf in; lb in)	
Pounds-force inches (lbf in; lb in)	x 0.083	= Pounds-force feet (lbf ft; lb ft)	x 12	= Pounds-force inches (lbf in; lb in)	
Pounds-force feet (lbf ft; lb ft)	x 0.138	= Kilograms-force metres (kgf m; kg m)	x 7.233	= Pounds-force feet (lbf ft; lb ft)	
Pounds-force feet (lbf ft; lb ft)	x 1.356	= Newton metres (Nm)	x 0.738	= Pounds-force feet (lbf ft; lb ft)	
Newton metres (Nm)	x 0.102	= Kilograms-force metres (kgf m; kg m)	x 9.804	= Newton metres (Nm)	

Power

Horsepower (hp)	x 745.7	= Watts (W)	x 0.0013	= Horsepower (hp)	

Velocity (speed)

Miles per hour (miles/hr; mph)	x 1.609	= Kilometres per hour (km/hr; kph)	x 0.621	= Miles per hour (miles/hr; mph)	

Fuel consumption*

Miles per gallon, Imperial (mpg)	x 0.354	= Kilometres per litre (km/l)	x 2.825	= Miles per gallon, Imperial (mpg)	
Miles per gallon, US (mpg)	x 0.425	= Kilometres per litre (km/l)	x 2.352	= Miles per gallon, US (mpg)	

Temperature

Degrees Fahrenheit = (°C x 1.8) + 32   Degrees Celsius (Degrees Centigrade; °C) = (°F - 32) x 0.56

It is common practice to convert from miles per gallon (mpg) to litres/100 kilometres (l/100km), where mpg x l/100 km = 282

Spare parts are available from many sources, including maker's appointed garages, accessory shops, and motor factors. To be sure of obtaining the correct parts, it will sometimes be necessary to quote the vehicle identification number. If possible, it can also be useful to take the old parts along for positive identification. Items such as starter motors and alternators may be available under a service exchange scheme – any parts returned should be clean.

Our advice regarding spare parts is as follows.

Officially appointed garages

This is the best source of parts which are peculiar to your car, and which are not otherwise generally available (eg, badges, interior trim, certain body panels, etc). It is also the only place at which you should buy parts if the car is still under warranty.

Accessory shops

These are very good places to buy materials and components needed for the maintenance of your car (oil, air and fuel filters, light bulbs, drivebelts, greases, brake pads, touch-up paint, etc). Components of this nature sold by a reputable shop are usually of the same standard as those used by the car manufacturer.

Besides components, these shops also sell tools and general accessories, usually have convenient opening hours, charge lower prices, and can often be found close to home. Some accessory shops have parts counters where components needed for almost any repair job can be purchased or ordered.

Motor factors

Good factors will stock all the more important components which wear out comparatively quickly, and can sometimes supply individual components needed for the overhaul of a larger assembly (eg, brake seals and hydraulic parts, bearing shells, pistons, valves). They may also handle work such as cylinder block reboring, crankshaft regrinding, etc.

Engine reconditioners

These specialise in engine overhaul and can also supply components. It is recommended that the establishment is a member of the Federation of Engine Re-Manufacturers, or a similar society.

Tyre and exhaust specialists

These outlets may be independent, or members of a local or national chain. They frequently offer competitive prices when compared with a main dealer or local garage, but it will pay to obtain several quotes before making a decision. When researching prices, also ask what extras may be added – for instance fitting a new valve, balancing the wheel and tyre disposal all both commonly charged on top of the price of a new tyre.

Other sources

Beware of parts or materials obtained from market stalls, car boot sales, on-line auctions or similar outlets. Such items are not invariably sub-standard, but there is little chance of compensation if they do prove unsatisfactory. In the case of safety-critical components such as brake pads, there is the risk not only of financial loss, but also of an accident causing injury or death.

Second-hand components or assemblies obtained from a car breaker can be a good buy in some circumstances, but this sort of purchase is best made by the experienced DIY mechanic.

Vehicle identification numbers

Modifications are a continuing and unpublicised process in vehicle manufacture, quite apart from major model changes. Spare parts manuals and lists are compiled upon a numerical basis, the individual vehicle identification numbers being essential to correct identification of the component concerned.

When ordering spare parts always give as much information as possible. Quote the vehicle type and year, vehicle identification number (VIN), and engine number, as appropriate.

The vehicle identification number (VIN) appears in a number of locations, including on a plastic tag attached to the passenger side of the facia panel, visible through the windscreen, and in the driver's footwell (see illustrations).

The engine number is stamped on the right-hand end of the cylinder block.

The transmission identification numbers are located on a plate attached to the top of the transmission casing, or cast into the casing itself.

Chassis number at the base of the windscreen

Chassis number under the carpet in the driver's footwell

Whenever servicing, repair or overhaul work is carried out on the car or its components, observe the following procedures and instructions. This will assist in carrying out the operation efficiently and to a professional standard of workmanship.

Joint mating faces and gaskets

When separating components at their mating faces, never insert screwdrivers or similar implements into the joint between the faces in order to prise them apart. This can cause severe damage which results in oil leaks, coolant leaks, etc upon reassembly. Separation is usually achieved by tapping along the joint with a soft-faced hammer in order to break the seal. However, note that this method may not be suitable where dowels are used for component location.

Where a gasket is used between the mating faces of two components, a new one must be fitted on reassembly; fit it dry unless otherwise stated in the repair procedure. Make sure that the mating faces are clean and dry, with all traces of old gasket removed. When cleaning a joint face, use a tool which is unlikely to score or damage the face, and remove any burrs or nicks with an oilstone or fine file.

Make sure that tapped holes are cleaned with a pipe cleaner, and keep them free of jointing compound, if this is being used, unless specifically instructed otherwise.

Ensure that all orifices, channels or pipes are clear, and blow through them, preferably using compressed air.

Oil seals

Oil seals can be removed by levering them out with a wide flat-bladed screwdriver or similar implement. Alternatively, a number of self-tapping screws may be screwed into the seal, and these used as a purchase for pliers or some similar device in order to pull the seal free.

Whenever an oil seal is removed from its working location, either individually or as part of an assembly, it should be renewed.

The very fine sealing lip of the seal is easily damaged, and will not seal if the surface it contacts is not completely clean and free from scratches, nicks or grooves. If the original sealing surface of the component cannot be restored, and the manufacturer has not made provision for slight relocation of the seal relative to the sealing surface, the component should be renewed.

Protect the lips of the seal from any surface which may damage them in the course of fitting. Use tape or a conical sleeve where possible. Where indicated, lubricate the seal lips with oil before fitting and, on dual-lipped seals, fill the space between the lips with grease.

Unless otherwise stated, oil seals must be fitted with their sealing lips toward the lubricant to be sealed.

Use a tubular drift or block of wood of the appropriate size to install the seal and, if the seal housing is shouldered, drive the seal down to the shoulder. If the seal housing is unshouldered, the seal should be fitted with its face flush with the housing top face (unless otherwise instructed).

Screw threads and fastenings

Seized nuts, bolts and screws are quite a common occurrence where corrosion has set in, and the use of penetrating oil or releasing fluid will often overcome this problem if the offending item is soaked for a while before attempting to release it. The use of an impact driver may also provide a means of releasing such stubborn fastening devices, when used in conjunction with the appropriate screwdriver bit or socket. If none of these methods works, it may be necessary to resort to the careful application of heat, or the use of a hacksaw or nut splitter device. Before resorting to extreme methods, check that you are not dealing with a left-hand thread!

Studs are usually removed by locking two nuts together on the threaded part, and then using a spanner on the lower nut to unscrew the stud. Studs or bolts which have broken off below the surface of the component in which they are mounted can sometimes be removed using a stud extractor.

Always ensure that a blind tapped hole is completely free from oil, grease, water or other fluid before installing the bolt or stud. Failure to do this could cause the housing to crack due to the hydraulic action of the bolt or stud as it is screwed in.

For some screw fastenings, notably cylinder head bolts or nuts, torque wrench settings are no longer specified for the latter stages of tightening, "angle-tightening" being called up instead. Typically, a fairly low torque wrench setting will be applied to the bolts/nuts in the correct sequence, followed by one or more stages of tightening through specified angles.

When checking or retightening a nut or bolt to a specified torque setting, slacken the nut or bolt by a quarter of a turn, and then retighten to the specified setting. However, this should not be attempted where angular tightening has been used.

Locknuts, locktabs and washers

Any fastening which will rotate against a component or housing during tightening should always have a washer between it and the relevant component or housing.

Spring or split washers should always be renewed when they are used to lock a critical component such as a big-end bearing retaining bolt or nut. Locktabs which are folded over to retain a nut or bolt should always be renewed.

Self-locking nuts can be re-used in non-critical areas, providing resistance can be felt when the locking portion passes over the bolt or stud thread. However, it should be noted that self-locking stiffnuts tend to lose their effectiveness after long periods of use, and should then be renewed as a matter of course.

Split pins must always be replaced with new ones of the correct size for the hole.

When thread-locking compound is found on the threads of a fastener which is to be re-used, it should be cleaned off with a wire brush and solvent, and fresh compound applied on reassembly.

Special tools

Some repair procedures in this manual entail the use of special tools such as a press, two or three-legged pullers, spring compressors, etc. Wherever possible, suitable readily-available alternatives to the manufacturer's special tools are described, and are shown in use. In some instances, where no alternative is possible, it has been necessary to resort to the use of a manufacturer's tool, and this has been done for reasons of safety as well as the efficient completion of the repair operation. Unless you are highly-skilled and have a thorough understanding of the procedures described, never attempt to bypass the use of any special tool when the procedure described specifies its use. Not only is there a very great risk of personal injury, but expensive damage could be caused to the components involved.

Environmental considerations

When disposing of used engine oil, brake fluid, antifreeze, etc, give due consideration to any detrimental environmental effects. Do not, for instance, pour any of the above liquids down drains into the general sewage system, or onto the ground to soak away. Many local council refuse tips provide a facility for waste oil disposal, as do some garages. You can find your nearest disposal point by calling the Environment Agency on 08708 506 506 or by visiting www.oilbankline.org.uk.

Note: It is illegal and anti-social to dump oil down the drain. To find the location of your local oil recycling bank, call 08708 506 506 or visit www.oilbankline.org.uk.

The jack supplied with the vehicle tool kit should **only** be used for changing the roadwheels in an emergency – see *Wheel changing* at the front of this book. When carrying out any other kind of work, raise the vehicle using a heavy-duty hydraulic (or 'trolley') jack, and always supplement the jack with axle stands positioned under the vehicle jacking points. If the roadwheels do not have to be removed, consider using wheel ramps – if wished, these can be placed under the wheels once the vehicle has been raised using a hydraulic jack, and the vehicle lowered onto the ramps so that it is resting on its wheels.

Only ever jack the vehicle up on a solid, level surface. If there is even a slight slope, take great care that the vehicle cannot move as the wheels are lifted off the ground. Jacking up on an uneven or gravelled surface is not recommended, as the weight of the vehicle will not be evenly distributed, and the jack may slip as the vehicle is raised.

As far as possible, do not leave the vehicle unattended once it has been raised, particularly if children are playing nearby.

Before jacking up the front of the car, ensure that the handbrake is firmly applied. When jacking up the rear of the car, place wooden chocks in front of the front wheels, and engage first gear (or P).

The jack supplied with the vehicle locates in the sill flanges, at the points marked on each side of the car **(see illustration)**. Ensure that the jack head is correctly engaged before attempting to raise the vehicle.

When using a hydraulic jack or axle stands,

Front and rear jacking points

the jack head or axle stand head may be placed under one of the four jacking points inboard of the door sills. When jacking or supporting the vehicle at these points, always use a block of wood between the jack head or axle stand, and the vehicle body. It is also considered good practice to use a large block of wood when supporting under other areas, to spread the load over a wider area, and reduce the risk of damage to the underside of the car (it also helps to prevent the underbody

coating from being damaged by the jack or axle stand). **Do not** jack the vehicle under any other part of the sill, engine sump, floor pan, subframe, or directly under any of the steering or suspension components.

Never work under, around, or near a raised vehicle, unless it is adequately supported on stands. Do not rely on a jack alone, as even a hydraulic jack could fail under load. Makeshift methods should not be used to lift and support the car during servicing work.

Introduction

A selection of good tools is a fundamental requirement for anyone contemplating the maintenance and repair of a motor vehicle. For the owner who does not possess any, their purchase will prove a considerable expense, offsetting some of the savings made by doing-it-yourself. However, provided that the tools purchased meet the relevant national safety standards and are of good quality, they will last for many years and prove an extremely worthwhile investment.

To help the average owner to decide which tools are needed to carry out the various tasks detailed in this manual, we have compiled three lists of tools under the following headings: *Maintenance and minor repair, Repair and overhaul,* and *Special.* Newcomers to practical mechanics should start off with the *Maintenance and minor repair* tool kit, and confine themselves to the simpler jobs around the vehicle. Then, as confidence and experience grow, more difficult tasks can be undertaken, with extra tools being purchased as, and when, they are needed. In this way, a *Maintenance and minor repair* tool kit can be built up into a *Repair and overhaul* tool kit over a considerable period of time, without any major cash outlays. The experienced do-it-yourselfer will have a tool kit good enough for most repair and overhaul procedures, and will add tools from the *Special* category when it is felt that the expense is justified by the amount of use to which these tools will be put.

Maintenance and minor repair tool kit

The tools given in this list should be considered as a minimum requirement if routine maintenance, servicing and minor repair operations are to be undertaken. We recommend the purchase of combination spanners (ring one end, open-ended the other); although more expensive than open-ended ones, they do give the advantages of both types of spanner.

☐ *Combination spanners:*
   Metric - 8 to 19 mm inclusive
☐ *Adjustable spanner - 35 mm jaw (approx.)*
☐ *Spark plug spanner (with rubber insert) - petrol models*
☐ *Spark plug gap adjustment tool - petrol models*
☐ *Set of feeler gauges*
☐ *Brake bleed nipple spanner*
☐ *Screwdrivers:*
   Flat blade - 100 mm long x 6 mm dia
   Cross blade - 100 mm long x 6 mm dia
   Torx - various sizes (not all vehicles)
☐ *Combination pliers*
☐ *Hacksaw (junior)*
☐ *Tyre pump*
☐ *Tyre pressure gauge*
☐ *Oil can*
☐ *Oil filter removal tool (if applicable)*
☐ *Fine emery cloth*
☐ *Wire brush (small)*
☐ *Funnel (medium size)*
☐ *Sump drain plug key (not all vehicles)*

Repair and overhaul tool kit

These tools are virtually essential for anyone undertaking any major repairs to a motor vehicle, and are additional to those given in the *Maintenance and minor repair* list. Included in this list is a comprehensive set of sockets. Although these are expensive, they will be found invaluable as they are so versatile - particularly if various drives are included in the set. We recommend the half-inch square-drive type, as this can be used with most proprietary torque wrenches.

The tools in this list will sometimes need to be supplemented by tools from the *Special* list:

☐ *Sockets to cover range in previous list (including Torx sockets)*
☐ *Reversible ratchet drive (for use with sockets)*
☐ *Extension piece, 250 mm (for use with sockets)*
☐ *Universal joint (for use with sockets)*
☐ *Flexible handle or sliding T "breaker bar" (for use with sockets)*
☐ *Torque wrench (for use with sockets)*
☐ *Self-locking grips*
☐ *Ball pein hammer*
☐ *Soft-faced mallet (plastic or rubber)*
☐ *Screwdrivers:*
   Flat blade - long & sturdy, short (chubby), and narrow (electrician's) types
   Cross blade – long & sturdy, and short (chubby) types
☐ *Pliers:*
   Long-nosed
   Side cutters (electrician's)
   Circlip (internal and external)
☐ *Cold chisel - 25 mm*
☐ *Scriber*
☐ *Scraper*
☐ *Centre-punch*
☐ *Pin punch*
☐ *Hacksaw*
☐ *Brake hose clamp*
☐ *Brake/clutch bleeding kit*
☐ *Selection of twist drills*
☐ *Steel rule/straight-edge*
☐ *Allen keys (inc. splined/Torx type)*
☐ *Selection of files*
☐ *Wire brush*
☐ *Axle stands*
☐ *Jack (strong trolley or hydraulic type)*
☐ *Light with extension lead*
☐ *Universal electrical multi-meter*

Sockets and reversible ratchet drive

Brake bleeding kit

Hose clamp

Angular-tightening gauge

Torx key, socket and bit

Special tools

The tools in this list are those which are not used regularly, are expensive to buy, or which need to be used in accordance with their manufacturers' instructions. Unless relatively difficult mechanical jobs are undertaken frequently, it will not be economic to buy many of these tools. Where this is the case, you could consider clubbing together with friends (or joining a motorists' club) to make a joint purchase, or borrowing the tools against a deposit from a local garage or tool hire specialist.

The following list contains only those tools and instruments freely available to the public, and not those special tools produced by the vehicle manufacturer specifically for its dealer network. You will find occasional references to these manufacturers' special tools in the text of this manual. Generally, an alternative method of doing the job without the vehicle manufacturers' special tool is given. However, sometimes there is no alternative to using them. Where this is the case and the relevant tool cannot be bought or borrowed, you will have to entrust the work to a dealer.

- ☐ *Angular-tightening gauge*
- ☐ *Valve spring compressor*
- ☐ *Valve grinding tool*
- ☐ *Piston ring compressor*
- ☐ *Piston ring removal/installation tool*
- ☐ *Cylinder bore hone*
- ☐ *Balljoint separator*
- ☐ *Coil spring compressors (where applicable)*
- ☐ *Two/three-legged hub and bearing puller*
- ☐ *Impact screwdriver*
- ☐ *Micrometer and/or vernier calipers*
- ☐ *Dial gauge*
- ☐ *Tachometer*
- ☐ *Fault code reader*
- ☐ *Cylinder compression gauge*
- ☐ *Hand-operated vacuum pump and gauge*
- ☐ *Clutch plate alignment set*
- ☐ *Brake shoe steady spring cup removal tool*
- ☐ *Bush and bearing removal/installation set*
- ☐ *Stud extractors*
- ☐ *Tap and die set*
- ☐ *Lifting tackle*

Buying tools

Reputable motor accessory shops and superstores often offer excellent quality tools at discount prices, so it pays to shop around.

Remember, you don't have to buy the most expensive items on the shelf, but it is always advisable to steer clear of the very cheap tools. Beware of 'bargains' offered on market stalls, on-line or at car boot sales. There are plenty of good tools around at reasonable prices, but always aim to purchase items which meet the relevant national safety standards. If in doubt, ask the proprietor or manager of the shop for advice before making a purchase.

Care and maintenance of tools

Having purchased a reasonable tool kit, it is necessary to keep the tools in a clean and serviceable condition. After use, always wipe off any dirt, grease and metal particles using a clean, dry cloth, before putting the tools away. Never leave them lying around after they have been used. A simple tool rack on the garage or workshop wall for items such as screwdrivers and pliers is a good idea. Store all normal spanners and sockets in a metal box. Any measuring instruments, gauges, meters, etc, must be carefully stored where they cannot be damaged or become rusty.

Take a little care when tools are used. Hammer heads inevitably become marked, and screwdrivers lose the keen edge on their blades from time to time. A little timely attention with emery cloth or a file will soon restore items like this to a good finish.

Working facilities

Not to be forgotten when discussing tools is the workshop itself. If anything more than routine maintenance is to be carried out, a suitable working area becomes essential.

It is appreciated that many an owner-mechanic is forced by circumstances to remove an engine or similar item without the benefit of a garage or workshop. Having done this, any repairs should always be done under the cover of a roof.

Wherever possible, any dismantling should be done on a clean, flat workbench or table at a suitable working height.

Any workbench needs a vice; one with a jaw opening of 100 mm is suitable for most jobs. As mentioned previously, some clean dry storage space is also required for tools, as well as for any lubricants, cleaning fluids, touch-up paints etc, which become necessary.

Another item which may be required, and which has a much more general usage, is an electric drill with a chuck capacity of at least 8 mm. This, together with a good range of twist drills, is virtually essential for fitting accessories.

Last, but not least, always keep a supply of old newspapers and clean, lint-free rags available, and try to keep any working area as clean as possible.

Micrometers

Dial test indicator ("dial gauge")

Oil filter removal tool (strap wrench type)

Compression tester

Bearing puller

This is a guide to getting your vehicle through the MOT test. Obviously it will not be possible to examine the vehicle to the same standard as the professional MOT tester. However, working through the following checks will enable you to identify any problem areas before submitting the vehicle for the test.

It has only been possible to summarise the test requirements here, based on the regulations in force at the time of printing. Test standards are becoming increasingly stringent, although there are some exemptions for older vehicles.

An assistant will be needed to help carry out some of these checks.

The checks have been sub-divided into four categories, as follows:

1 Checks carried out **FROM THE DRIVER'S SEAT**

2 Checks carried out **WITH THE VEHICLE ON THE GROUND**

3 Checks carried out **WITH THE VEHICLE RAISED AND THE WHEELS FREE TO TURN**

4 Checks carried out on **YOUR VEHICLE'S EXHAUST EMISSION SYSTEM**

---

1 Checks carried out **FROM THE DRIVER'S SEAT**

Handbrake (parking brake)

☐ Test the operation of the handbrake. Excessive travel (too many clicks) indicates incorrect brake or cable adjustment.
☐ Check that the handbrake cannot be released by tapping the lever sideways. Check the security of the lever mountings.

☐ If the parking brake is foot-operated, check that the pedal is secure and without excessive travel, and that the release mechanism operates correctly.
☐ Where applicable, test the operation of the electronic handbrake. The brake should engage and disengage without excessive delay. If the warning light does not extinguish when the brake is disengaged, this could indicate a fault which will need further investigation.

Footbrake

☐ Depress the brake pedal and check that it does not creep down to the floor, indicating a master cylinder fault. Release the pedal, wait a few seconds, then depress it again. If the pedal travels nearly to the floor before firm resistance is felt, brake adjustment or repair is necessary. If the pedal feels spongy, there is air in the hydraulic system which must be removed by bleeding.

☐ Check that the brake pedal is secure and in good condition. Check also for signs of fluid leaks on the pedal, floor or carpets, which would indicate failed seals in the brake master cylinder.
☐ Check the servo unit (when applicable) by operating the brake pedal several times, then keeping the pedal depressed and starting the engine. As the engine starts, the pedal will move down slightly. If not, the vacuum hose or the servo itself may be faulty.

Steering wheel and column

☐ Examine the steering wheel for fractures or looseness of the hub, spokes or rim.
☐ Move the steering wheel from side to side and then up and down. Check that the steering wheel is not loose on the column, indicating wear or a loose retaining nut. Continue moving the steering wheel as before, but also turn it slightly from left to right.

☐ Check that the steering wheel is not loose on the column, and that there is no abnormal movement of the steering wheel, indicating wear in the column support bearings or couplings.
☐ Check that the ignition lock (where fitted) engages and disengages correctly.
☐ Steering column adjustment mechanisms (where fitted) must be able to lock the column securely in place with no play evident.

Windscreen, mirrors and sunvisor

☐ The windscreen must be free of cracks or other significant damage within the driver's field of view. (Small stone chips are acceptable.) Rear view mirrors must be secure, intact, and capable of being adjusted.

☐ The driver's sunvisor must be capable of being stored in the "up" position.

Seat belts and seats

Note: *The following checks are applicable to all seat belts, front and rear.*

☐ Examine the webbing of all the belts (including rear belts if fitted) for cuts, serious fraying or deterioration. Fasten and unfasten each belt to check the buckles. If applicable, check the retracting mechanism. Check the security of all seat belt mountings accessible from inside the vehicle, ensuring any height adjustable mountings lock securely in place.

☐ Seat belts with pre-tensioners, once activated, have a "flag" or similar showing on the seat belt stalk. This, in itself, is not a reason for test failure.

☐ The front seats themselves must be securely attached and the backrests must lock in the upright position.

Doors

☐ Both front doors must be able to be opened and closed from outside and inside, and must latch securely when closed.

Bonnet and boot/tailgate

☐ The bonnet and boot/tailgate must latch securely when closed.

2 Checks carried out WITH THE VEHICLE ON THE GROUND

Vehicle identification

☐ Number plates must be in good condition, secure and legible, with letters and numbers correctly spaced – spacing at (A) should be 33 mm and at (B) 11 mm. At the front, digits must be black on a white background and at the rear black on a yellow background. Other background designs (such as honeycomb) are not permitted.

☐ The VIN plate and/or homologation plate must be permanently displayed and legible.

Electrical equipment

☐ Switch on the ignition and check the operation of the horn.

☐ Check the windscreen washers and wipers, examining the wiper blades; renew damaged or perished blades. Also check the operation of the stop-lights.

☐ Check the operation of the sidelights and number plate lights. The lenses and reflectors must be secure, clean and undamaged.

☐ Check the operation and alignment of the headlights. The headlight reflectors must not be tarnished and the lenses must be undamaged.

☐ Switch on the ignition and check the operation of the direction indicators (including the instrument panel tell-tale) and the hazard warning lights. Operation of the sidelights and stop-lights must not affect the indicators - if it does, the cause is usually a bad earth at the rear light cluster. Indicators should flash at a rate of between 60 and 120 times per minute – faster or slower than this could indicate a fault with the flasher unit or a bad earth at one of the light units.

☐ Check the operation of the rear foglight(s), including the warning light on the instrument panel or in the switch.

☐ The warning lights must illuminate in accordance with the manufacturer's design. For most vehicles, the ABS and other warning lights should illuminate when the ignition is switched on, and (if the system is operating properly) extinguish after a few seconds. Refer to the owner's handbook.

Footbrake

☐ Examine the master cylinder, brake pipes and servo unit for leaks, loose mountings, corrosion or other damage. If ABS is fitted, this unit should also be examined for signs of leaks or corrosion.

☐ The fluid reservoir must be secure and the fluid level must be between the upper (**A**) and lower (**B**) markings.

☐ Inspect both front brake flexible hoses for cracks or deterioration of the rubber. Turn the steering from lock to lock, and ensure that the hoses do not contact the wheel, tyre, or any part of the steering or suspension mechanism. With the brake pedal firmly depressed, check the hoses for bulges or leaks under pressure.

Steering and suspension

☐ Have your assistant turn the steering wheel from side to side slightly, up to the point where the steering gear just begins to transmit this movement to the roadwheels. Check for excessive free play between the steering wheel and the steering gear, indicating wear or insecurity of the steering column joints, the column-to-steering gear coupling, or the steering gear itself.

☐ Have your assistant turn the steering wheel more vigorously in each direction, so that the roadwheels just begin to turn. As this is done, examine all the steering joints, linkages, fittings and attachments. Renew any component that shows signs of wear or damage. On vehicles with power steering, check the security and condition of the steering pump, drivebelt and hoses.

☐ Check that the vehicle is standing level, and at approximately the correct ride height.

Shock absorbers

☐ Depress each corner of the vehicle in turn, then release it. The vehicle should rise and then settle in its normal position. If the vehicle continues to rise and fall, the shock absorber is defective. A shock absorber which has seized will also cause the vehicle to fail.

Exhaust system

☐ Start the engine. With your assistant holding a rag over the tailpipe, check the entire system for leaks. Repair or renew leaking sections.

3 Checks carried out **WITH THE VEHICLE RAISED AND THE WHEELS FREE TO TURN**

Jack up the front and rear of the vehicle, and securely support it on axle stands. Position the stands clear of the suspension assemblies. Ensure that the wheels are clear of the ground and that the steering can be turned from lock to lock.

Steering mechanism

☐ Have your assistant turn the steering from lock to lock. Check that the steering turns smoothly, and that no part of the steering mechanism, including a wheel or tyre, fouls any brake hose or pipe or any part of the body structure.

☐ Examine the steering rack rubber gaiters for damage or insecurity of the retaining clips. If power steering is fitted, check for signs of damage or leakage of the fluid hoses, pipes or connections. Also check for excessive stiffness or binding of the steering, a missing split pin or locking device, or severe corrosion of the body structure within 30 cm of any steering component attachment point.

Front and rear suspension and wheel bearings

☐ Starting at the front right-hand side, grasp the roadwheel at the 3 o'clock and 9 o'clock positions and rock gently but firmly. Check for free play or insecurity at the wheel bearings, suspension balljoints, or suspension mount-ings, pivots and attachments.

☐ Now grasp the wheel at the 12 o'clock and 6 o'clock positions and repeat the previous inspection. Spin the wheel, and check for roughness or tightness of the front wheel bearing.

☐ If excess free play is suspected at a component pivot point, this can be confirmed by using a large screwdriver or similar tool and levering between the mounting and the component attachment. This will confirm whether the wear is in the pivot bush, its retaining bolt, or in the mounting itself (the bolt holes can often become elongated).

☐ Carry out all the above checks at the other front wheel, and then at both rear wheels.

Springs and shock absorbers

☐ Examine the suspension struts (when applicable) for serious fluid leakage, corrosion, or damage to the casing. Also check the security of the mounting points.

☐ If coil springs are fitted, check that the spring ends locate in their seats, and that the spring is not corroded, cracked or broken.

☐ If leaf springs are fitted, check that all leaves are intact, that the axle is securely attached to each spring, and that there is no deterioration of the spring eye mountings, bushes, and shackles.

☐ The same general checks apply to vehicles fitted with other suspension types, such as torsion bars, hydraulic displacer units, etc. Ensure that all mountings and attachments are secure, that there are no signs of excessive wear, corrosion or damage, and (on hydraulic types) that there are no fluid leaks or damaged pipes.

☐ Inspect the shock absorbers for signs of serious fluid leakage. Check for wear of the mounting bushes or attachments, or damage to the body of the unit.

Driveshafts (fwd vehicles only)

☐ Rotate each front wheel in turn and inspect the constant velocity joint gaiters for splits or damage. Also check that each driveshaft is straight and undamaged.

Braking system

☐ If possible without dismantling, check brake pad wear and disc condition. Ensure that the friction lining material has not worn excessively, (A) and that the discs are not fractured, pitted, scored or badly worn (B).

☐ Examine all the rigid brake pipes underneath the vehicle, and the flexible hose(s) at the rear. Look for corrosion, chafing or insecurity of the pipes, and for signs of bulging under pressure, chafing, splits or deterioration of the flexible hoses.

☐ Look for signs of fluid leaks at the brake calipers or on the brake backplates. Repair or renew leaking components.

☐ Slowly spin each wheel, while your assistant depresses and releases the footbrake. Ensure that each brake is operating and does not bind when the pedal is released.

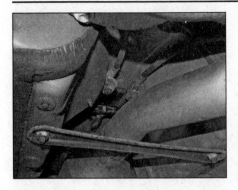

☐ Examine the handbrake mechanism, checking for frayed or broken cables, excessive corrosion, or wear or insecurity of the linkage. Check that the mechanism works on each relevant wheel, and releases fully, without binding.

☐ It is not possible to test brake efficiency without special equipment, but a road test can be carried out later to check that the vehicle pulls up in a straight line.

Fuel and exhaust systems

☐ Inspect the fuel tank (including the filler cap), fuel pipes, hoses and unions. All components must be secure and free from leaks. Locking fuel caps must lock securely and the key must be provided for the MOT test.

☐ Examine the exhaust system over its entire length, checking for any damaged, broken or missing mountings, security of the retaining clamps and rust or corrosion.

Wheels and tyres

☐ Examine the sidewalls and tread area of each tyre in turn. Check for cuts, tears, lumps, bulges, separation of the tread, and exposure of the ply or cord due to wear or damage. Check that the tyre bead is correctly seated on the wheel rim, that the valve is sound and properly seated, and that the wheel is not distorted or damaged.

☐ Check that the tyres are of the correct size for the vehicle, that they are of the same size and type on each axle, and that the pressures are correct.

☐ Check the tyre tread depth. The legal minimum at the time of writing is 1.6 mm over the central three-quarters of the tread width. Abnormal tread wear may indicate incorrect front wheel alignment or wear in steering or suspension components.

☐ If the spare wheel is fitted externally or in a separate carrier beneath the vehicle, check that mountings are secure and free of excessive corrosion.

Body corrosion

☐ Check the condition of the entire vehicle structure for signs of corrosion in load-bearing areas. (These include chassis box sections, side sills, cross-members, pillars, and all suspension, steering, braking system and seat belt mountings and anchorages.) Any corrosion which has seriously reduced the thickness of a load-bearing area (or is within 30 cm of safety-related components such as steering or suspension) is likely to cause the vehicle to fail. In this case professional repairs are likely to be needed.

☐ Damage or corrosion which causes sharp or otherwise dangerous edges to be exposed will also cause the vehicle to fail.

Towbars

☐ Check the condition of mounting points (both beneath the vehicle and within boot/hatchback areas) for signs of corrosion, ensuring that all fixings are secure and not worn or damaged. There must be no excessive play in detachable tow ball arms or quick-release mechanisms.

4 Checks carried out on **YOUR VEHICLE'S EXHAUST EMISSION SYSTEM**

Petrol models

☐ The engine should be warmed up, and running well (ignition system in good order, air filter element clean, etc).

☐ Before testing, run the engine at around 2500 rpm for 20 seconds. Let the engine drop to idle, and watch for smoke from the exhaust. If the idle speed is too high, or if dense blue or black smoke emerges for more than 5 seconds, the vehicle will fail. Typically, blue smoke signifies oil burning (engine wear); black smoke means unburnt fuel (dirty air cleaner element, or other fuel system fault).

☐ An exhaust gas analyser for measuring carbon monoxide (CO) and hydrocarbons (HC) is now needed. If one cannot be hired or borrowed, have a local garage perform the check.

CO emissions (mixture)

☐ The MOT tester has access to the CO limits for all vehicles. The CO level is measured at idle speed, and at 'fast idle' (2500 to 3000 rpm). The following limits are given as a general guide:

At idle speed – Less than 0.5% CO
At 'fast idle' – Less than 0.3% CO
Lambda reading – 0.97 to 1.03

☐ If the CO level is too high, this may point to poor maintenance, a fuel injection system problem, faulty lambda (oxygen) sensor or catalytic converter. Try an injector cleaning treatment, and check the vehicle's ECU for fault codes.

HC emissions

☐ The MOT tester has access to HC limits for all vehicles. The HC level is measured at 'fast idle' (2500 to 3000 rpm). The following limits are given as a general guide:

At 'fast idle' – Less then 200 ppm

☐ Excessive HC emissions are typically caused by oil being burnt (worn engine), or by a blocked crankcase ventilation system ('breather'). If the engine oil is old and thin, an oil change may help. If the engine is running badly, check the vehicle's ECU for fault codes.

Diesel models

☐ The only emission test for diesel engines is measuring exhaust smoke density, using a calibrated smoke meter. The test involves accelerating the engine at least 3 times to its maximum unloaded speed.

Note: *On engines with a timing belt, it is VITAL that the belt is in good condition before the test is carried out.*

☐ With the engine warmed up, it is first purged by running at around 2500 rpm for 20 seconds. A governor check is then carried out, by slowly accelerating the engine to its maximum speed. After this, the smoke meter is connected, and the engine is accelerated quickly to maximum speed three times. If the smoke density is less than the limits given below, the vehicle will pass:

Non-turbo vehicles: 2.5m-1
Turbocharged vehicles: 3.0m-1

☐ If excess smoke is produced, try fitting a new air cleaner element, or using an injector cleaning treatment. If the engine is running badly, where applicable, check the vehicle's ECU for fault codes. Also check the vehicle's EGR system, where applicable. At high mileages, the injectors may require professional attention.

Engine

- [ ] Engine fails to rotate when attempting to start
- [ ] Engine rotates, but will not start
- [ ] Engine difficult to start when cold
- [ ] Engine difficult to start when hot
- [ ] Starter motor noisy or excessively-rough in engagement
- [ ] Engine starts, but stops immediately
- [ ] Engine idles erratically
- [ ] Engine misfires at idle speed
- [ ] Engine misfires throughout the driving speed range
- [ ] Engine hesitates on acceleration
- [ ] Engine stalls
- [ ] Engine lacks power
- [ ] Engine backfires
- [ ] Oil pressure warning light illuminated with engine running
- [ ] Engine runs-on after switching off
- [ ] Engine noises

Cooling system

- [ ] Overheating
- [ ] Overcooling
- [ ] External coolant leakage
- [ ] Internal coolant leakage
- [ ] Corrosion

Fuel and exhaust systems

- [ ] Excessive fuel consumption
- [ ] Fuel leakage and/or fuel odour
- [ ] Excessive noise or fumes from exhaust system

Clutch

- [ ] Pedal travels to floor – no pressure or very little resistance
- [ ] Clutch fails to disengage (unable to select gears)
- [ ] Clutch slips (engine speed increases, with no increase in vehicle speed)
- [ ] Judder as clutch is engaged
- [ ] Noise when depressing or releasing clutch pedal

Manual transmission

- [ ] Noisy in neutral with engine running
- [ ] Noisy in one particular gear
- [ ] Difficulty engaging gears
- [ ] Jumps out of gear
- [ ] Vibration
- [ ] Lubricant leaks

Automatic transmission

- [ ] Fluid leakage
- [ ] Transmission fluid brown, or has burned smell
- [ ] General gear selection problems
- [ ] Transmission will not downshift (kickdown) with accelerator pedal fully depressed
- [ ] Engine will not start in any gear, or starts in gears other than Park or Neutral
- [ ] Transmission slips, shifts roughly, is noisy, or has no drive in forward or reverse gears

Driveshafts

- [ ] Vibration when accelerating or decelerating
- [ ] Clicking or knocking noise on turns (at slow speed on full-lock)

Braking system

- [ ] Vehicle pulls to one side under braking
- [ ] Noise (grinding or high-pitched squeal) when brakes applied
- [ ] Excessive brake pedal travel
- [ ] Brake pedal feels spongy when depressed
- [ ] Excessive brake pedal effort required to stop vehicle
- [ ] Judder felt through brake pedal or steering wheel when braking
- [ ] Brakes binding
- [ ] Rear wheels locking under normal braking

Suspension and steering

- [ ] Vehicle pulls to one side
- [ ] Wheel wobble and vibration
- [ ] Excessive pitching and/or rolling around corners, or during braking
- [ ] Wandering or general instability
- [ ] Excessively-stiff steering
- [ ] Excessive play in steering
- [ ] Lack of power assistance
- [ ] Tyre wear excessive

Electrical system

- [ ] Battery will not hold a charge for more than a few days
- [ ] Ignition/no-charge warning light remains illuminated with engine running
- [ ] Ignition/no-charge warning light fails to come on
- [ ] Lights inoperative
- [ ] Instrument readings inaccurate or erratic
- [ ] Horn inoperative, or unsatisfactory in operation
- [ ] Windscreen wipers inoperative, or unsatisfactory in operation
- [ ] Windscreen washers inoperative, or unsatisfactory in operation
- [ ] Electric windows inoperative, or unsatisfactory in operation
- [ ] Central locking system inoperative, or unsatisfactory in operation

Introduction

The vehicle owner who does his or her own maintenance according to the recommended service schedules should not have to use this section of the manual very often. Modern component reliability is such that, provided those items subject to wear or deterioration are inspected or renewed at the specified intervals, sudden failure is comparatively rare. Faults do not usually just happen as a result of sudden failure, but develop over a period of time. Major mechanical failures in particular are usually preceded by characteristic symptoms over hundreds or even thousands of miles. Those components which do occasionally fail without warning are often small and easily carried in the vehicle.

With any fault finding, the first step is to decide where to begin investigations. Sometimes this is obvious, but on other occasions, a little detective work will be necessary. The owner who makes half a dozen haphazard adjustments or replacements may be successful in curing a fault (or its symptoms), but will be none the wiser if the fault recurs, and ultimately may have spent more time and money than was necessary. A calm and logical approach will be found to be more satisfactory in the long run. Always take into account any warning signs or abnormalities that may have been noticed in the period preceding the fault – power loss, high or low gauge readings, unusual smells, etc – and remember that failure of components such as fuses or spark plugs may only be pointers to some underlying fault.

The pages which follow provide an easy-reference guide to the more common problems which may occur during the operation of the vehicle. These problems and their possible causes are grouped under headings denoting various components or systems, such as Engine, Cooling system, etc. The general Chapter which deals with the problem is also shown in brackets; refer to the relevant part of that Chapter for system-specific information. Whatever the fault, certain basic principles apply. These are as follows:

Verify the fault. This is simply a matter of being sure that you know what the symptoms are before starting work. This is particularly important if you are investigating a fault for someone else, who may not have described it very accurately.

Don't overlook the obvious. For example, if the vehicle won't start, is there fuel in the tank? (Don't take anyone else's word on this particular point, and don't trust the fuel gauge either). If an electrical fault is indicated, look for loose or broken wires before digging out the test gear.

Cure the disease, not the symptom. Substituting a flat battery with a fully-charged one will get you off the hard shoulder, but if the underlying cause is not attended to, the new battery will go the same way. Similarly, changing oil-fouled spark plugs for a new set will get you moving again, but remember that the reason for the fouling (if it wasn't simply an incorrect grade of plug) will have to be established and corrected.

Don't take anything for granted. Particularly, don't forget that a 'new' component may itself be defective (especially if it's been rattling around in the boot for months), and don't leave components out of a fault diagnosis sequence just because they are new or recently-fitted. When you do finally diagnose a difficult fault, you'll probably realise that all the evidence was there from the start.

Consider what work, if any, has recently been carried out. Many faults arise through careless or hurried work. For instance, if any work has been performed under the bonnet, could some of the wiring have been dislodged or incorrectly routed, or a hose trapped? Have all the fasteners been properly tightened? Were new, genuine parts and new gaskets used? There is often a certain amount of detective work to be done in this case, as an apparently-unrelated task can have far-reaching consequences.

Diesel engine fault diagnosis

The majority of starting problems on small diesel engines are electrical in origin. The mechanic who is familiar with petrol engines but less so with diesel may be inclined to view the diesel's injectors and pump in the same light as the spark plugs and distributor, but this is generally a mistake.

When investigating complaints of difficult starting for someone else, make sure that the correct starting procedure is understood and is being followed. Some drivers are unaware of the significance of the preheating warning light – many modern engines are sufficiently forgiving for this not to matter in mild weather, but with the onset of winter, problems begin. Glow plugs in particular are often neglected – just one faulty plug will make cold-weather starting very difficult.

As a rule of thumb, if the engine is difficult to start but runs well when it has finally got going, the problem is electrical (battery, starter motor or preheating system). If poor performance is combined with difficult starting, the problem is likely to be in the fuel system. The low-pressure (supply) side of the fuel system should be checked before suspecting the injectors and high-pressure pump. The most common fuel supply problem is air getting into the system, and any pipe from the fuel tank forwards must be scrutinised if air leakage is suspected.

Engine

Engine fails to rotate when attempting to start

☐ Battery terminal connections loose or corroded (see *Weekly checks*)
☐ Battery discharged or faulty (Chapter 5A)
☐ Broken, loose or disconnected wiring in the starting circuit (Chapter 5A)
☐ Defective starter solenoid or ignition switch (Chapter 5A or 12)
☐ Defective starter motor (Chapter 5A)
☐ Starter pinion or flywheel ring gear teeth loose or broken (Chapter 2A, 2B, 2C or 5A)
☐ Engine earth strap broken or disconnected (Chapter 5A)
☐ Engine suffering 'hydraulic lock' (eg, from water ingested after traversing flooded roads, or from a serious internal coolant leak) – consult a Volvo dealer or specialist for advice
☐ Automatic transmission not in position P or N (Chapter 7B)

Engine rotates, but will not start

☐ Fuel tank empty
☐ Battery discharged (engine rotates slowly) (Chapter 5A)
☐ Battery terminal connections loose or corroded (see *Weekly checks*)
☐ Immobiliser fault, or 'uncoded' remote unit being used (Chapter 12 or *Roadside repairs*)
☐ Crankshaft sensor fault (Chapter 4A)
☐ Preheating system faulty (Chapter 5B)
☐ Fuel injection system fault (Chapter 4A)
☐ Air in fuel system (Chapter 4B)
☐ Major mechanical failure (eg, timing belt snapped) (Chapter 2A, 2B or 2C)

Engine difficult to start when cold

☐ Battery discharged (Chapter 5A)
☐ Battery terminal connections loose or corroded (see *Weekly checks*)
☐ Preheating system faulty (Chapter 5B)
☐ Fuel injection system fault (Chapter 4A)
☐ Wrong grade of engine oil used (*Weekly checks*, Chapter 1)
☐ Low cylinder compression (Chapter 2A, 2B or 2C)

Engine difficult to start when hot

☐ Air filter element dirty or clogged (Chapter 1)
☐ Fuel injection system fault (Chapter 4A)
☐ Low cylinder compression (Chapter 2A, 2B or 2C)

Starter motor noisy or excessively-rough in engagement

☐ Starter pinion or flywheel ring gear teeth loose or broken (Chapter 2A, 2B, 2C or 5A)
☐ Starter motor mounting bolts loose or missing (Chapter 5A)
☐ Starter motor internal components worn or damaged (Chapter 5A)

Engine starts, but stops immediately

☐ Vacuum leak at the throttle body or inlet manifold (Chapter 4A)
☐ Blocked injectors/fuel injection system fault (Chapter 4A)
☐ Air in fuel, possibly due to loose fuel line connection (Chapter 4A)

Engine idles erratically

☐ Air filter element clogged (Chapter 1)
☐ Vacuum leak at the throttle body, inlet manifold or associated hoses (Chapter 4A)
☐ Uneven or low cylinder compression (Chapter 2A, 2B or 2C)
☐ Camshaft lobes worn (Chapter 2A, 2B or 2C)
☐ Timing belt incorrectly fitted (Chapter 2A, 2B or 2C)
☐ Blocked injectors/fuel injection system fault (Chapter 4A)
☐ Air in fuel, possibly due to loose fuel line connection (Chapter 4A)

Engine misfires at idle speed

☐ Vacuum leak at the throttle body, inlet manifold or associated hoses (Chapter 4A)
☐ Blocked injectors/fuel injection system fault (Chapter 4A)
☐ Faulty injector(s) (Chapter 4A)
☐ Uneven or low cylinder compression (Chapter 2A, 2B or 2C)
☐ Disconnected, leaking, or perished crankcase ventilation hoses (Chapter 4B)

Engine (continued)

Engine misfires throughout the driving speed range

- ☐ Fuel filter choked (Chapter 1)
- ☐ Fuel pump faulty, or delivery pressure low (Chapter 4A)
- ☐ Fuel tank vent blocked, or fuel pipes restricted (Chapter 4A)
- ☐ Vacuum leak at the throttle body, inlet manifold or associated hoses (Chapter 4A)
- ☐ Faulty injector(s) (Chapter 4A)
- ☐ Uneven or low cylinder compression (Chapter 2A, 2B or 2C)
- ☐ Blocked injector/fuel injection system fault (Chapter 4A)
- ☐ Blocked catalytic converter (Chapter 4B)
- ☐ Engine overheating (Chapter 3)
- ☐ Fuel tank level low (Chapter 4A)

Engine hesitates on acceleration

- ☐ Vacuum leak at the throttle body, inlet manifold or associated hoses (Chapter 4A)
- ☐ Blocked injectors/fuel injection system fault (Chapter 4A)
- ☐ Faulty injector(s) (Chapter 4A)
- ☐ Faulty clutch pedal switch (Chapter 6)

Engine stalls

- ☐ Vacuum leak at the throttle body, inlet manifold or associated hoses (Chapter 4A)
- ☐ Fuel filter choked (Chapter 1)
- ☐ Fuel pump faulty, or delivery pressure low (Chapter 4A)
- ☐ Fuel tank vent blocked, or fuel pipes restricted (Chapter 4A)
- ☐ Blocked injectors/fuel injection system fault (Chapter 4A)
- ☐ Faulty injector(s) (Chapter 4A)

Engine lacks power

- ☐ Air filter element blocked (Chapter 1)
- ☐ Fuel filter choked (Chapter 1)
- ☐ Fuel pipes blocked or restricted (Chapter 4A)
- ☐ Engine overheating (Chapter 3)
- ☐ Fuel tank level low (Chapter 4A)
- ☐ Accelerator position sensor faulty (Chapter 4A)
- ☐ Vacuum leak at the throttle body, inlet manifold or associated hoses (Chapter 4A)
- ☐ Blocked injectors/fuel injection system fault (Chapter 4A)
- ☐ Faulty injector(s) (Chapter 4A)
- ☐ Timing belt incorrectly fitted (Chapter 2A, 2B or 2C)
- ☐ Fuel pump faulty, or delivery pressure low (Chapter 4A)
- ☐ Uneven or low cylinder compression (Chapter 2A, 2B or 2C)
- ☐ Blocked catalytic converter (Chapter 4B)
- ☐ Brakes binding (Chapter 9)
- ☐ Clutch slipping (Chapter 6)

Engine backfires

- ☐ Timing belt incorrectly fitted (Chapter 2A, 2B or 2C)
- ☐ Vacuum leak at the throttle body, inlet manifold or associated hoses (Chapter 4A)

- ☐ Blocked injectors/fuel injection system fault (Chapter 4A)
- ☐ Blocked catalytic converter (Chapter 4B)

Oil pressure warning light illuminated with engine running

- ☐ Low oil level, or incorrect oil grade (see *Weekly checks*)
- ☐ Faulty oil pressure sensor, or wiring damaged (Chapter 12)
- ☐ Worn engine bearings and/or oil pump (Chapter 2A, 2B or 2C)
- ☐ High engine operating temperature (Chapter 3)
- ☐ Oil pump pressure relief valve defective (Chapter 2A, 2B or 2C)
- ☐ Oil pump pick-up strainer clogged (Chapter 2A, 2B or 2C)

Engine runs-on after switching off

- ☐ Excessive carbon build-up in engine (Chapter 2A, 2B or 2C)
- ☐ High engine operating temperature (Chapter 3)
- ☐ Fuel injection system fault (Chapter 4A)

Engine noises

Pre-ignition (pinking) or knocking during acceleration or under load

- ☐ Vacuum leak at the throttle body, inlet manifold or associated hoses (Chapter 4A)
- ☐ Excessive carbon build-up in engine (Chapter 2A, 2B or 2C)
- ☐ Blocked injector/fuel injection system fault (Chapter 4A)
- ☐ Faulty injector(s) (Chapter 4B)

Whistling or wheezing noises

- ☐ Leaking inlet manifold or throttle body gasket (Chapter 4A)
- ☐ Leaking exhaust manifold gasket or pipe-to-manifold joint (Chapter 4A or 4B)
- ☐ Leaking vacuum hose (Chapter 4A or 9)
- ☐ Blowing cylinder head gasket (Chapter 2A, 2B or 2C)
- ☐ Partially blocked or leaking crankcase ventilation system (Chapter 4B)

Tapping or rattling noises

- ☐ Worn valve gear or camshaft (Chapter 2A, 2B or 2C)
- ☐ Ancillary component fault (coolant pump, alternator, etc) (Chapter 3, 5A, etc)

Knocking or thumping noises

- ☐ Worn big-end bearings (regular heavy knocking, perhaps less under load) (Chapter 2D)
- ☐ Worn main bearings (rumbling and knocking, perhaps worsening under load) (Chapter 2D)
- ☐ Piston slap – most noticeable when cold, caused by piston/bore wear (Chapter 2D)
- ☐ Ancillary component fault (coolant pump, alternator, etc) (Chapter 3, 5A, etc)
- ☐ Engine mountings worn or defective (Chapter 2C)
- ☐ Front suspension or steering components worn (Chapter 10)

Cooling system

Overheating

- ☐ Insufficient coolant in system (see *Weekly checks*)
- ☐ Thermostat faulty (Chapter 3)
- ☐ Radiator core blocked, or grille restricted (Chapter 3)
- ☐ Cooling fan faulty, or control module fault (Chapter 3)
- ☐ Inaccurate coolant temperature sender (Chapter 3)
- ☐ Airlock in cooling system (Chapter 3)
- ☐ Expansion tank pressure cap faulty (Chapter 3)
- ☐ Engine management system fault (Chapter 4A)

Overcooling

- ☐ Thermostat faulty (Chapter 3)
- ☐ Inaccurate coolant temperature sender (Chapter 3)
- ☐ Cooling fan faulty (Chapter 3)
- ☐ Engine management system fault (Chapter 4A)

External coolant leakage

- ☐ Deteriorated or damaged hoses or hose clips (Chapter 1)
- ☐ Radiator core or heater matrix leaking (Chapter 3)
- ☐ Expansion tank pressure cap faulty (Chapter 1)
- ☐ Coolant pump internal seal leaking (Chapter 3)
- ☐ Coolant pump gasket leaking (Chapter 3)
- ☐ Boiling due to overheating (Chapter 3)
- ☐ Cylinder block core plug leaking (Chapter 2D)

Internal coolant leakage

- ☐ Leaking cylinder head gasket (Chapter 2A, 2B or 2C)
- ☐ Cracked cylinder head or cylinder block (Chapter 2)

Corrosion

- ☐ Infrequent draining and flushing (Chapter 1)
- ☐ Incorrect coolant mixture or inappropriate coolant type (see *Weekly checks*)

Fuel and exhaust systems

Excessive fuel consumption

- ☐ Air filter element dirty or clogged (Chapter 1)
- ☐ Fuel injection system fault (Chapter 4A)
- ☐ Engine management system fault (Chapter 4A)
- ☐ Crankcase ventilation system blocked (Chapter 4B)
- ☐ Tyres under-inflated (see *Weekly checks*)
- ☐ Brakes binding (Chapter 9)
- ☐ Fuel leak, causing apparent high consumption (Chapter 1 or 4A)

Fuel leakage and/or fuel odour

- ☐ Damaged or corroded fuel tank, pipes or connections (Chapter 4A)

Excessive noise or fumes from exhaust system

- ☐ Leaking exhaust system or manifold joints (Chapter 4A or 4B)
- ☐ Leaking, corroded or damaged silencers or pipe (Chapter 4A or 4B)
- ☐ Broken mountings causing body or suspension contact (Chapter 1, 4A or 4B)

Clutch

Pedal travels to floor – no pressure or very little resistance

- ☐ Air in hydraulic system/faulty master or slave cylinder (Chapter 6)
- ☐ Faulty hydraulic release system (Chapter 6)
- ☐ Clutch pedal return spring detached or broken (Chapter 6)
- ☐ Broken clutch release bearing or fork (Chapter 6)
- ☐ Broken diaphragm spring in clutch pressure plate (Chapter 6)

Clutch fails to disengage (unable to select gears)

- ☐ Air in hydraulic system/faulty master or slave cylinder (Chapter 6)
- ☐ Faulty hydraulic release system (Chapter 6)
- ☐ Clutch disc sticking on transmission input shaft splines (Chapter 6)
- ☐ Clutch disc sticking to flywheel or pressure plate (Chapter 6)
- ☐ Faulty pressure plate assembly (Chapter 6)
- ☐ Clutch release mechanism worn or incorrectly assembled (Chapter 6)

Clutch slips (engine speed increases, with no increase in vehicle speed)

- ☐ Faulty hydraulic release system (Chapter 6)
- ☐ Clutch disc linings excessively worn (Chapter 6)
- ☐ Clutch disc linings contaminated with oil or grease (Chapter 6)
- ☐ Faulty pressure plate or weak diaphragm spring (Chapter 6)

Judder as clutch is engaged

- ☐ Clutch disc linings contaminated with oil or grease (Chapter 6)
- ☐ Clutch disc linings excessively worn (Chapter 6)
- ☐ Faulty or distorted pressure plate or diaphragm spring (Chapter 6).
- ☐ Worn or loose engine or transmission mountings (Chapter 2C)
- ☐ Clutch disc hub or transmission input shaft splines worn (Chapter 6)

Noise when depressing or releasing clutch pedal

- ☐ Worn clutch release bearing (Chapter 6)
- ☐ Worn or dry clutch pedal bushes (Chapter 6)
- ☐ Worn or dry clutch master cylinder piston (Chapter 6)
- ☐ Faulty pressure plate assembly (Chapter 6)
- ☐ Pressure plate diaphragm spring broken (Chapter 6)
- ☐ Broken clutch disc cushioning springs (Chapter 6)

Manual transmission

Noisy in neutral with engine running
- [ ] Lack of oil (Chapter 1)
- [ ] Input shaft bearings worn (noise apparent with clutch pedal released, but not when depressed) (Chapter 7A)*
- [ ] Clutch release bearing worn (noise apparent with clutch pedal depressed, possibly less when released) (Chapter 6)

Noisy in one particular gear
- [ ] Worn, damaged or chipped gear teeth (Chapter 7A)*

Difficulty engaging gears
- [ ] Clutch fault (Chapter 6)
- [ ] Worn or damaged gearchange cables (Chapter 7A)
- [ ] Lack of oil (Chapter 7A)
- [ ] Worn synchroniser units (Chapter 7A)*

Jumps out of gear
- [ ] Worn or damaged gearchange cables (Chapter 7A)
- [ ] Worn synchroniser units (Chapter 7A)*
- [ ] Worn selector forks (Chapter 7A)*

Vibration
- [ ] Lack of oil (Chapter 7A)
- [ ] Worn bearings (Chapter 7A)*

Lubricant leaks
- [ ] Leaking driveshaft or selector shaft oil seal (Chapter 7A)
- [ ] Leaking housing joint (Chapter 7A)*
- [ ] Leaking input shaft oil seal (Chapter 7A)*

* Although the corrective action necessary to remedy the symptoms described is beyond the scope of the home mechanic, the above information should be helpful in isolating the cause of the condition, so that the owner can communicate clearly with a professional mechanic.

Automatic transmission

Note: Due to the complexity of the automatic transmission, it is difficult for the home mechanic to properly diagnose and service this unit. For problems other than the following, the vehicle should be taken to a dealer service department or automatic transmission specialist. Do not be too hasty in removing the transmission if a fault is suspected, as most of the testing is carried out with the unit still fitted. Remember that, besides the sensors specific to the transmission, many of the engine management system sensors described in Chapter 4A are essential to the correct operation of the transmission.

Fluid leakage
- [ ] Automatic transmission fluid is usually dark red in colour. Fluid leaks should not be confused with engine oil, which can easily be blown onto the transmission by airflow.
- [ ] To determine the source of a leak, first remove all built-up dirt and grime from the transmission housing and surrounding areas using a degreasing agent, or by steam-cleaning. Drive the vehicle at low speed, so airflow will not blow the leak far from its source. Raise and support the vehicle, and determine where the leak is coming from. The following are common areas of leakage:
  - a) Fluid pan
  - b) Dipstick tube
  - c) Transmission-to-fluid cooler unions (Chapter 7B)

Transmission fluid brown, or has burned smell
- [ ] Transmission fluid level low (Chapter 1)

General gear selection problems
- [ ] Chapter 7B deals with checking the selector cable on automatic

transmissions. The following are common problems which may be caused by a faulty cable or sensor:
- a) Engine starting in gears other than Park or Neutral.
- b) Indicator panel indicating a gear other than the one actually being used.
- c) Vehicle moves when in Park or Neutral.
- d) Poor gear shift quality or erratic gear changes.

Transmission will not downshift (kickdown) with accelerator pedal fully depressed
- [ ] Low transmission fluid level (Chapter 1)
- [ ] Engine management system fault (Chapter 4A)
- [ ] Faulty transmission sensor or wiring (Chapter 7B)
- [ ] Faulty selector cable (Chapter 7B)

Engine will not start in any gear, or starts in gears other than Park or Neutral
- [ ] Faulty transmission sensor or wiring (Chapter 7B)
- [ ] Engine management system fault (Chapter 4A)
- [ ] Faulty selector cable (Chapter 7B)

Transmission slips, shifts roughly, is noisy, or has no drive in forward or reverse gears
- [ ] Transmission fluid level low (Chapter 1)
- [ ] Faulty transmission sensor or wiring (Chapter 7B)
- [ ] Engine management system fault (Chapter 4A)

Note: There are many probable causes for the above problems, but diagnosing and correcting them is considered beyond the scope of this manual. Having checked the fluid level and all the wiring as far as possible, a dealer or transmission specialist should be consulted if the problem persists.

Driveshafts

Vibration when accelerating or decelerating

- [ ] Worn inner constant velocity joint (Chapter 8)
- [ ] Bent or distorted driveshaft (Chapter 8)
- [ ] Worn intermediate bearing (Chapter 8)

Clicking or knocking noise on turns (at slow speed on full-lock)

- [ ] Worn outer constant velocity joint (Chapter 8)
- [ ] Lack of constant velocity joint lubricant, possibly due to damaged gaiter (Chapter 8)
- [ ] Worn intermediate bearing (Chapter 8)

Braking system

Note: *Before assuming that a brake problem exists, make sure that the tyres are in good condition and correctly inflated, that the front wheel alignment is correct, and that the vehicle is not loaded with weight in an unequal manner. Apart from checking the condition of all pipe and hose connections, any faults occurring on the anti-lock braking system should be referred to a Volvo dealer or specialist for diagnosis.*

Vehicle pulls to one side under braking

- [ ] Worn, defective, damaged or contaminated brake pads on one side (Chapter 9)
- [ ] Seized or partially-seized brake caliper piston (Chapter 9)
- [ ] A mixture of brake pad lining materials fitted between sides (Chapter 9)
- [ ] Brake caliper mounting bolts loose (Chapter 9)
- [ ] Worn or damaged steering or suspension components (Chapter 1 or 10)

Noise (grinding or high-pitched squeal) when brakes applied

- [ ] Brake pad friction lining material worn down to metal backing (Chapter 9)
- [ ] Excessive corrosion of brake disc (may be apparent after the vehicle has been standing for some time (Chapter 9)
- [ ] Foreign object (stone chipping, etc) trapped between brake disc and shield (Chapter 9)

Excessive brake pedal travel

- [ ] Faulty master cylinder (Chapter 9)
- [ ] Air in hydraulic system (Chapter 6 or 9)
- [ ] Faulty vacuum servo unit (Chapter 9)

Brake pedal feels spongy when depressed

- [ ] Air in hydraulic system (Chapter 6 or 9)
- [ ] Deteriorated flexible rubber brake hoses (Chapter 1 or 9)
- [ ] Master cylinder mounting nuts loose (Chapter 9)
- [ ] Faulty master cylinder (Chapter 9)

Excessive brake pedal effort required to stop vehicle

- [ ] Faulty vacuum servo unit (Chapter 9)
- [ ] Faulty vacuum pump – diesel models (Chapter 9)
- [ ] Disconnected, damaged or insecure brake servo vacuum hose (Chapter 9)
- [ ] Primary or secondary hydraulic circuit failure (Chapter 9)
- [ ] Seized brake caliper piston (Chapter 9)
- [ ] Brake pads incorrectly fitted (Chapter 9)
- [ ] Incorrect grade of brake pads fitted (Chapter 9)
- [ ] Brake pad linings contaminated (Chapter 9)

Judder felt through brake pedal or steering wheel when braking

Note: *Under heavy braking on models equipped with ABS, vibration may be felt through the brake pedal. This is a normal feature of ABS operation, and does not constitute a fault*

- [ ] Excessive run-out or distortion of discs (Chapter 9)
- [ ] Brake pad linings worn (Chapter 1 or 9)
- [ ] Brake caliper mounting bolts loose (Chapter 9)
- [ ] Wear in suspension or steering components or mountings (Chapter 1 or 10)
- [ ] Front wheels out of balance (see *Weekly checks*)

Brakes binding

- [ ] Seized brake caliper piston (Chapter 9)
- [ ] Faulty handbrake mechanism (Chapter 9)
- [ ] Faulty master cylinder (Chapter 9)

Rear wheels locking under normal braking

- [ ] Rear brake pad linings contaminated or damaged (Chapter 9)
- [ ] Rear brake discs warped (Chapter 9)

Suspension and steering

Note: *Before diagnosing suspension or steering faults, be sure that the trouble is not due to incorrect tyre pressures, mixtures of tyre types, or binding brakes.*

Vehicle pulls to one side

☐ Defective tyre (see *Weekly checks*)
☐ Excessive wear in suspension or steering components (Chapter 1or 10)
☐ Incorrect front wheel alignment (Chapter 10)
☐ Accident damage to steering or suspension components

Wheel wobble and vibration

☐ Front wheels out of balance (vibration felt mainly through the steering wheel) (see *Weekly checks*)
☐ Rear wheels out of balance (vibration felt throughout the vehicle) (see *Weekly checks*)
☐ Roadwheels damaged or distorted (see *Weekly checks*)
☐ Faulty or damaged tyre (see *Weekly checks*)
☐ Worn steering or suspension joints, bushes or components (Chapter 1 or 10)
☐ Wheel bolts loose (Chapter 1)

Excessive pitching and/or rolling around corners, or during braking

☐ Defective shock absorbers (Chapter 10)
☐ Broken or weak spring and/or suspension component (Chapter 10)
☐ Worn or damaged anti-roll bar or mountings (Chapter 10)

Wandering or general instability

☐ Incorrect front wheel alignment (Chapter 10)
☐ Worn steering or suspension joints, bushes or components (Chapter 1or 10)
☐ Roadwheels out of balance (see *Weekly checks*)
☐ Faulty or damaged tyre (see *Weekly checks*)
☐ Wheel bolts loose (Chapter 1)
☐ Defective shock absorbers (Chapter 10)

Excessively-stiff steering

☐ Seized steering linkage balljoint or suspension balljoint (Chapter 1or 10)

☐ Broken or incorrectly-adjusted auxiliary drivebelt (Chapter 1)
☐ Incorrect front wheel alignment (Chapter 10)
☐ Steering rack damaged (Chapter 10)

Excessive play in steering

☐ Worn steering column/intermediate shaft joints (Chapter 10)
☐ Worn track rod balljoints (Chapter 1 or 10)
☐ Worn steering rack (Chapter 10)
☐ Worn steering or suspension joints, bushes or components (Chapter 1or 10)

Lack of power assistance

☐ Broken or incorrectly-adjusted auxiliary drivebelt (Chapter 1)
☐ Incorrect power steering fluid level (see *Weekly checks*)
☐ Restriction in power steering fluid hoses (Chapter 1)
☐ Faulty power steering pump (Chapter 10)
☐ Faulty steering rack (Chapter 10)

Tyre wear excessive

Tyres worn on inside or outside edges

☐ Tyres under-inflated (wear on both edges) (see *Weekly checks*)
☐ Incorrect camber or castor angles (wear on one edge only) (Chapter 10)
☐ Worn steering or suspension joints, bushes or components (Chapter 1 or 10)
☐ Excessively-hard cornering or braking
☐ Accident damage

Tyre treads exhibit feathered edges

☐ Incorrect toe-setting (Chapter 10)

Tyres worn in centre of tread

☐ Tyres over-inflated (see *Weekly checks*)

Tyres worn on inside and outside edges

☐ Tyres under-inflated (see *Weekly checks*)

Tyres worn unevenly

☐ Tyres/wheels out of balance (see *Weekly checks*)
☐ Excessive wheel or tyre run-out
☐ Worn shock absorbers (Chapter 10)
☐ Faulty tyre (see *Weekly checks*)

Electrical system

Note: *For problems associated with the starting system, refer to the faults listed under 'Engine' earlier in this Section.*

Battery will not hold a charge for more than a few days

☐ Battery defective internally (Chapter 5A)
☐ Battery terminal connections loose or corroded (see *Weekly checks*)
☐ Auxiliary drivebelt worn or incorrectly adjusted (Chapter 1)
☐ Alternator not charging at correct output (Chapter 5A)
☐ Alternator or voltage regulator faulty (Chapter 5A)
☐ Short-circuit causing continual battery drain (Chapter 5A or 12)

Ignition/no-charge warning light remains illuminated with engine running

☐ Auxiliary drivebelt broken, worn, or incorrectly adjusted (Chapter 1)
☐ Internal fault in alternator or voltage regulator (Chapter 5A)
☐ Broken, disconnected, or loose wiring in charging circuit (Chapter 5A or 12)

Ignition/no-charge warning light fails to come on

☐ Warning light bulb blown (Chapter 12)
☐ Broken, disconnected, or loose wiring in warning light circuit (Chapter 5A or 12)
☐ Alternator faulty (Chapter 5A)

Electrical system (continued)

Lights inoperative

- ☐ Bulb blown (Chapter 12)
- ☐ Corrosion of bulb or bulbholder contacts (Chapter 12)
- ☐ Blown fuse (Chapter 12)
- ☐ Faulty relay (Chapter 12)
- ☐ Broken, loose, or disconnected wiring (Chapter 12)
- ☐ Faulty switch (Chapter 12)

Instrument readings inaccurate or erratic

Fuel or temperature gauges give no reading

- ☐ Faulty gauge sender unit (Chapter 3 or 4A)
- ☐ Wiring open-circuit (Chapter 12)
- ☐ Faulty instrument cluster (Chapter 12)

Fuel or temperature gauges give continuous maximum reading

- ☐ Faulty gauge sender unit (Chapter 3 or 4A)
- ☐ Wiring short-circuit (Chapter 12)
- ☐ Faulty instrument cluster (Chapter 12)

Horn inoperative, or unsatisfactory in operation

Horn operates all the time

- ☐ Horn push either earthed or stuck down (Chapter 12)
- ☐ Horn cable-to-horn push earthed (Chapter 12)

Horn fails to operate

- ☐ Blown fuse (Chapter 12)
- ☐ Cable or connections loose, broken or disconnected (Chapter 12)
- ☐ Faulty horn (Chapter 12)

Horn emits intermittent or unsatisfactory sound

- ☐ Cable connections loose (Chapter 12)
- ☐ Horn mountings loose (Chapter 12)
- ☐ Faulty horn (Chapter 12)

Windscreen wipers inoperative, or unsatisfactory in operation

Wipers fail to operate, or operate very slowly

- ☐ Wiper blades stuck to screen, or linkage seized or binding (Chapter 12)
- ☐ Blown fuse (Chapter 12)
- ☐ Battery discharged (Chapter 5A)
- ☐ Cable or connections loose, broken or disconnected (Chapter 12)
- ☐ Faulty wiper motor (Chapter 12)

Wiper blades sweep over too large or too small an area of the glass

- ☐ Wiper blades incorrectly fitted, or wrong size used (see *Weekly checks*)
- ☐ Wiper arms incorrectly positioned on spindles (Chapter 12)
- ☐ Excessive wear of wiper linkage (Chapter 12)
- ☐ Wiper motor or linkage mountings loose or insecure (Chapter 12)

Wiper blades fail to clean the glass effectively

- ☐ Wiper blade rubbers dirty, worn or perished (see *Weekly checks*)
- ☐ Wiper blades incorrectly fitted, or wrong size used (see *Weekly checks*)
- ☐ Wiper arm tension springs broken, or arm pivots seized (Chapter 12)
- ☐ Insufficient windscreen washer additive to adequately remove road film (see *Weekly checks*)

Windscreen washers inoperative, or unsatisfactory in operation

One or more washer jets inoperative

- ☐ Blocked washer jet
- ☐ Disconnected, kinked or restricted fluid hose (Chapter 12)
- ☐ Insufficient fluid in washer reservoir (see *Weekly checks*)

Washer pump fails to operate

- ☐ Broken or disconnected wiring or connections (Chapter 12)
- ☐ Blown fuse (Chapter 12)
- ☐ Faulty washer switch (Chapter 12)
- ☐ Faulty washer pump (Chapter 12)

Washer pump runs for some time before fluid is emitted from jets

- ☐ Faulty one-way valve in fluid supply hose (Chapter 12)

Electric windows inoperative, or unsatisfactory in operation

Window glass will only move in one direction

- ☐ Faulty switch (Chapter 12)

Window glass slow to move

- ☐ Battery discharged (Chapter 5A)
- ☐ Regulator seized or damaged, or in need of lubrication (Chapter 11)
- ☐ Door internal components or trim fouling regulator (Chapter 11)
- ☐ Faulty motor (Chapter 11)

Window glass fails to move

- ☐ Blown fuse (Chapter 12)
- ☐ Faulty relay (Chapter 12)
- ☐ Broken or disconnected wiring or connections (Chapter 12)
- ☐ Faulty motor (Chapter 11)
- ☐ Faulty control module (Chapter 11)

Central locking system inoperative, or unsatisfactory in operation

Complete system failure

- ☐ Remote handset battery discharged, where applicable
- ☐ Blown fuse (Chapter 12)
- ☐ Defective control module (Chapter 12)
- ☐ Broken or disconnected wiring or connections (Chapter 12)
- ☐ Faulty motor (Chapter 11)

Latch locks but will not unlock, or unlocks but will not lock

- ☐ Remote handset battery discharged, where applicable
- ☐ Faulty master switch (Chapter 12)
- ☐ Broken or disconnected latch operating rods or levers (Chapter 11)
- ☐ Faulty control module (Chapter 12)
- ☐ Faulty motor (Chapter 11)

One solenoid/motor fails to operate

- ☐ Broken or disconnected wiring or connections (Chapter 12)
- ☐ Faulty operating assembly (Chapter 11)
- ☐ Broken, binding or disconnected latch operating rods or levers (Chapter 11)
- ☐ Fault in door latch (Chapter 11)

A

ABS (Anti-lock brake system) A system, usually electronically controlled, that senses incipient wheel lockup during braking and relieves hydraulic pressure at wheels that are about to skid.

Air bag An inflatable bag hidden in the steering wheel (driver's side) or the dash or glovebox (passenger side). In a head-on collision, the bags inflate, preventing the driver and front passenger from being thrown forward into the steering wheel or windscreen.

Air cleaner A metal or plastic housing, containing a filter element, which removes dust and dirt from the air being drawn into the engine.

Air filter element The actual filter in an air cleaner system, usually manufactured from pleated paper and requiring renewal at regular intervals.

Air filter

Allen key A hexagonal wrench which fits into a recessed hexagonal hole.

Alligator clip A long-nosed spring-loaded metal clip with meshing teeth. Used to make temporary electrical connections.

Alternator A component in the electrical system which converts mechanical energy from a drivebelt into electrical energy to charge the battery and to operate the starting system, ignition system and electrical accessories.

Alternator (exploded view)

Ampere (amp) A unit of measurement for the flow of electric current. One amp is the amount of current produced by one volt acting through a resistance of one ohm.

Anaerobic sealer A substance used to prevent bolts and screws from loosening. Anaerobic means that it does not require oxygen for activation. The Loctite brand is widely used.

Antifreeze A substance (usually ethylene glycol) mixed with water, and added to a vehicle's cooling system, to prevent freezing of the coolant in winter. Antifreeze also contains chemicals to inhibit corrosion and the formation of rust and other deposits that would tend to clog the radiator and coolant passages and reduce cooling efficiency.

Anti-seize compound A coating that reduces the risk of seizing on fasteners that are subjected to high temperatures, such as exhaust manifold bolts and nuts.

Anti-seize compound

Asbestos A natural fibrous mineral with great heat resistance, commonly used in the composition of brake friction materials. Asbestos is a health hazard and the dust created by brake systems should never be inhaled or ingested.

Axle A shaft on which a wheel revolves, or which revolves with a wheel. Also, a solid beam that connects the two wheels at one end of the vehicle. An axle which also transmits power to the wheels is known as a live axle.

Axle assembly

Axleshaft A single rotating shaft, on either side of the differential, which delivers power from the final drive assembly to the drive wheels. Also called a driveshaft or a halfshaft.

B

Ball bearing An anti-friction bearing consisting of a hardened inner and outer race with hardened steel balls between two races.

Bearing

Bearing The curved surface on a shaft or in a bore, or the part assembled into either, that permits relative motion between them with minimum wear and friction.

Big-end bearing The bearing in the end of the connecting rod that's attached to the crankshaft.

Bleed nipple A valve on a brake wheel cylinder, caliper or other hydraulic component that is opened to purge the hydraulic system of air. Also called a bleed screw.

Brake bleeding

Brake bleeding Procedure for removing air from lines of a hydraulic brake system.

Brake disc The component of a disc brake that rotates with the wheels.

Brake drum The component of a drum brake that rotates with the wheels.

Brake linings The friction material which contacts the brake disc or drum to retard the vehicle's speed. The linings are bonded or riveted to the brake pads or shoes.

Brake pads The replaceable friction pads that pinch the brake disc when the brakes are applied. Brake pads consist of a friction material bonded or riveted to a rigid backing plate.

Brake shoe The crescent-shaped carrier to which the brake linings are mounted and which forces the lining against the rotating drum during braking.

Braking systems For more information on braking systems, consult the *Haynes Automotive Brake Manual*.

Breaker bar A long socket wrench handle providing greater leverage.

Bulkhead The insulated partition between the engine and the passenger compartment.

C

Caliper The non-rotating part of a disc-brake assembly that straddles the disc and carries the brake pads. The caliper also contains the hydraulic components that cause the pads to pinch the disc when the brakes are applied. A caliper is also a measuring tool that can be set to measure inside or outside dimensions of an object.

Camshaft A rotating shaft on which a series of cam lobes operate the valve mechanisms. The camshaft may be driven by gears, by sprockets and chain or by sprockets and a belt.

Canister A container in an evaporative emission control system; contains activated charcoal granules to trap vapours from the fuel system.

Canister

Carburettor A device which mixes fuel with air in the proper proportions to provide a desired power output from a spark ignition internal combustion engine.

Carburettor

Castellated Resembling the parapets along the top of a castle wall. For example, a castellated balljoint stud nut.

Castellated nut

Castor In wheel alignment, the backward or forward tilt of the steering axis. Castor is positive when the steering axis is inclined rearward at the top.

Catalytic converter A silencer-like device in the exhaust system which converts certain pollutants in the exhaust gases into less harmful substances.

Catalytic converter

Circlip A ring-shaped clip used to prevent endwise movement of cylindrical parts and shafts. An internal circlip is installed in a groove in a housing; an external circlip fits into a groove on the outside of a cylindrical piece such as a shaft.

Clearance The amount of space between two parts. For example, between a piston and a cylinder, between a bearing and a journal, etc.

Coil spring A spiral of elastic steel found in various sizes throughout a vehicle, for example as a springing medium in the suspension and in the valve train.

Compression Reduction in volume, and increase in pressure and temperature, of a gas, caused by squeezing it into a smaller space.

Compression ratio The relationship between cylinder volume when the piston is at top dead centre and cylinder volume when the piston is at bottom dead centre.

Constant velocity (CV) joint A type of universal joint that cancels out vibrations caused by driving power being transmitted through an angle.

Core plug A disc or cup-shaped metal device inserted in a hole in a casting through which core was removed when the casting was formed. Also known as a freeze plug or expansion plug.

Crankcase The lower part of the engine block in which the crankshaft rotates.

Crankshaft The main rotating member, or shaft, running the length of the crankcase, with offset "throws" to which the connecting rods are attached.

Crankshaft assembly

Crocodile clip See Alligator clip

D

Diagnostic code Code numbers obtained by accessing the diagnostic mode of an engine management computer. This code can be used to determine the area in the system where a malfunction may be located.

Disc brake A brake design incorporating a rotating disc onto which brake pads are squeezed. The resulting friction converts the energy of a moving vehicle into heat.

Double-overhead cam (DOHC) An engine that uses two overhead camshafts, usually one for the intake valves and one for the exhaust valves.

Drivebelt(s) The belt(s) used to drive accessories such as the alternator, water pump, power steering pump, air conditioning compressor, etc. off the crankshaft pulley.

Accessory drivebelts

Driveshaft Any shaft used to transmit motion. Commonly used when referring to the axleshafts on a front wheel drive vehicle.

Driveshaft

Drum brake A type of brake using a drum-shaped metal cylinder attached to the inner surface of the wheel. When the brake pedal is pressed, curved brake shoes with friction linings press against the inside of the drum to slow or stop the vehicle.

Drum brake assembly

E

EGR valve A valve used to introduce exhaust gases into the intake air stream.

EGR valve

Electronic control unit (ECU) A computer which controls (for instance) ignition and fuel injection systems, or an anti-lock braking system. For more information refer to the Haynes Automotive Electrical and Electronic Systems Manual.

Electronic Fuel Injection (EFI) A computer controlled fuel system that distributes fuel through an injector located in each intake port of the engine.

Emergency brake A braking system, independent of the main hydraulic system, that can be used to slow or stop the vehicle if the primary brakes fail, or to hold the vehicle stationary even though the brake pedal isn't depressed. It usually consists of a hand lever that actuates either front or rear brakes mechanically through a series of cables and linkages. Also known as a handbrake or parking brake.

Endfloat The amount of lengthwise movement between two parts. As applied to a crankshaft, the distance that the crankshaft can move forward and back in the cylinder block.

Engine management system (EMS) A computer controlled system which manages the fuel injection and the ignition systems in an integrated fashion.

Exhaust manifold A part with several passages through which exhaust gases leave the engine combustion chambers and enter the exhaust pipe.

Exhaust manifold

F

Fan clutch A viscous (fluid) drive coupling device which permits variable engine fan speeds in relation to engine speeds.

Feeler blade A thin strip or blade of hardened steel, ground to an exact thickness, used to check or measure clearances between parts.

Feeler blade

Firing order The order in which the engine cylinders fire, or deliver their power strokes, beginning with the number one cylinder.

Flywheel A heavy spinning wheel in which energy is absorbed and stored by means of momentum. On cars, the flywheel is attached to the crankshaft to smooth out firing impulses.

Free play The amount of travel before any action takes place. The "looseness" in a linkage, or an assembly of parts, between the initial application of force and actual movement. For example, the distance the brake pedal moves before the pistons in the master cylinder are actuated.

Fuse An electrical device which protects a circuit against accidental overload. The typical fuse contains a soft piece of metal which is calibrated to melt at a predetermined current flow (expressed as amps) and break the circuit.

Fusible link A circuit protection device consisting of a conductor surrounded by heat-resistant insulation. The conductor is smaller than the wire it protects, so it acts as the weakest link in the circuit. Unlike a blown fuse, a failed fusible link must frequently be cut from the wire for replacement.

G

Gap The distance the spark must travel in jumping from the centre electrode to the

Adjusting spark plug gap

side electrode in a spark plug. Also refers to the spacing between the points in a contact breaker assembly in a conventional points-type ignition, or to the distance between the reluctor or rotor and the pickup coil in an electronic ignition.

Gasket Any thin, soft material - usually cork, cardboard, asbestos or soft metal - installed between two metal surfaces to ensure a good seal. For instance, the cylinder head gasket seals the joint between the block and the cylinder head.

Gasket

Gauge An instrument panel display used to monitor engine conditions. A gauge with a movable pointer on a dial or a fixed scale is an analogue gauge. A gauge with a numerical readout is called a digital gauge.

H

Halfshaft A rotating shaft that transmits power from the final drive unit to a drive wheel, usually when referring to a live rear axle.

Harmonic balancer A device designed to reduce torsion or twisting vibration in the crankshaft. May be incorporated in the crankshaft pulley. Also known as a vibration damper.

Hone An abrasive tool for correcting small irregularities or differences in diameter in an engine cylinder, brake cylinder, etc.

Hydraulic tappet A tappet that utilises hydraulic pressure from the engine's lubrication system to maintain zero clearance (constant contact with both camshaft and valve stem). Automatically adjusts to variation in valve stem length. Hydraulic tappets also reduce valve noise.

I

Ignition timing The moment at which the spark plug fires, usually expressed in the number of crankshaft degrees before the piston reaches the top of its stroke.

Inlet manifold A tube or housing with passages through which flows the air-fuel mixture (carburettor vehicles and vehicles with throttle body injection) or air only (port fuel-injected vehicles) to the port openings in the cylinder head.

J

Jump start Starting the engine of a vehicle with a discharged or weak battery by attaching jump leads from the weak battery to a charged or helper battery.

L

Load Sensing Proportioning Valve (LSPV) A brake hydraulic system control valve that works like a proportioning valve, but also takes into consideration the amount of weight carried by the rear axle.

Locknut A nut used to lock an adjustment nut, or other threaded component, in place. For example, a locknut is employed to keep the adjusting nut on the rocker arm in position.

Lockwasher A form of washer designed to prevent an attaching nut from working loose.

M

MacPherson strut A type of front suspension system devised by Earle MacPherson at Ford of England. In its original form, a simple lateral link with the anti-roll bar creates the lower control arm. A long strut - an integral coil spring and shock absorber - is mounted between the body and the steering knuckle. Many modern so-called MacPherson strut systems use a conventional lower A-arm and don't rely on the anti-roll bar for location.

Multimeter An electrical test instrument with the capability to measure voltage, current and resistance.

N

NOx Oxides of Nitrogen. A common toxic pollutant emitted by petrol and diesel engines at higher temperatures.

O

Ohm The unit of electrical resistance. One volt applied to a resistance of one ohm will produce a current of one amp.

Ohmmeter An instrument for measuring electrical resistance.

O-ring A type of sealing ring made of a special rubber-like material; in use, the O-ring is compressed into a groove to provide the sealing action.

O-ring

Overhead cam (ohc) engine An engine with the camshaft(s) located on top of the cylinder head(s).

Overhead valve (ohv) engine An engine with the valves located in the cylinder head, but with the camshaft located in the engine block.

Oxygen sensor A device installed in the engine exhaust manifold, which senses the oxygen content in the exhaust and converts this information into an electric current. Also called a Lambda sensor.

P

Phillips screw A type of screw head having a cross instead of a slot for a corresponding type of screwdriver.

Plastigage A thin strip of plastic thread, available in different sizes, used for measuring clearances. For example, a strip of Plastigage is laid across a bearing journal. The parts are assembled and dismantled; the width of the crushed strip indicates the clearance between journal and bearing.

Plastigage

Propeller shaft The long hollow tube with universal joints at both ends that carries power from the transmission to the differential on front-engined rear wheel drive vehicles.

Proportioning valve A hydraulic control valve which limits the amount of pressure to the rear brakes during panic stops to prevent wheel lock-up.

R

Rack-and-pinion steering A steering system with a pinion gear on the end of the steering shaft that mates with a rack (think of a geared wheel opened up and laid flat). When the steering wheel is turned, the pinion turns, moving the rack to the left or right. This movement is transmitted through the track rods to the steering arms at the wheels.

Radiator A liquid-to-air heat transfer device designed to reduce the temperature of the coolant in an internal combustion engine cooling system.

Refrigerant Any substance used as a heat transfer agent in an air-conditioning system. R-12 has been the principle refrigerant for many years; recently, however, manufacturers have begun using R-134a, a non-CFC substance that is considered less harmful to the ozone in the upper atmosphere.

Rocker arm A lever arm that rocks on a shaft or pivots on a stud. In an overhead valve engine, the rocker arm converts the upward movement of the pushrod into a downward movement to open a valve.

Rotor In a distributor, the rotating device inside the cap that connects the centre electrode and the outer terminals as it turns, distributing the high voltage from the coil secondary winding to the proper spark plug. Also, that part of an alternator which rotates inside the stator. Also, the rotating assembly of a turbocharger, including the compressor wheel, shaft and turbine wheel.

Runout The amount of wobble (in-and-out movement) of a gear or wheel as it's rotated. The amount a shaft rotates "out-of-true." The out-of-round condition of a rotating part.

S

Sealant A liquid or paste used to prevent leakage at a joint. Sometimes used in conjunction with a gasket.

Sealed beam lamp An older headlight design which integrates the reflector, lens and filaments into a hermetically-sealed one-piece unit. When a filament burns out or the lens cracks, the entire unit is simply replaced.

Serpentine drivebelt A single, long, wide accessory drivebelt that's used on some newer vehicles to drive all the accessories, instead of a series of smaller, shorter belts. Serpentine drivebelts are usually tensioned by an automatic tensioner.

Serpentine drivebelt

Shim Thin spacer, commonly used to adjust the clearance or relative positions between two parts. For example, shims inserted into or under bucket tappets control valve clearances. Clearance is adjusted by changing the thickness of the shim.

Slide hammer A special puller that screws into or hooks onto a component such as a shaft or bearing; a heavy sliding handle on the shaft bottoms against the end of the shaft to knock the component free.

Sprocket A tooth or projection on the periphery of a wheel, shaped to engage with a chain or drivebelt. Commonly used to refer to the sprocket wheel itself.

Starter inhibitor switch On vehicles with an automatic transmission, a switch that prevents starting if the vehicle is not in Neutral or Park.
Strut See MacPherson strut.

T

Tappet A cylindrical component which transmits motion from the cam to the valve stem, either directly or via a pushrod and rocker arm. Also called a cam follower.
Thermostat A heat-controlled valve that regulates the flow of coolant between the cylinder block and the radiator, so maintaining optimum engine operating temperature. A thermostat is also used in some air cleaners in which the temperature is regulated.
Thrust bearing The bearing in the clutch assembly that is moved in to the release levers by clutch pedal action to disengage the clutch. Also referred to as a release bearing.
Timing belt A toothed belt which drives the camshaft. Serious engine damage may result if it breaks in service.
Timing chain A chain which drives the camshaft.
Toe-in The amount the front wheels are closer together at the front than at the rear. On rear wheel drive vehicles, a slight amount of toe-in is usually specified to keep the front wheels running parallel on the road by offsetting other forces that tend to spread the wheels apart.

Toe-out The amount the front wheels are closer together at the rear than at the front. On front wheel drive vehicles, a slight amount of toe-out is usually specified.
Tools For full information on choosing and using tools, refer to the *Haynes Automotive Tools Manual*.
Tracer A stripe of a second colour applied to a wire insulator to distinguish that wire from another one with the same colour insulator.
Tune-up A process of accurate and careful adjustments and parts replacement to obtain the best possible engine performance.
Turbocharger A centrifugal device, driven by exhaust gases, that pressurises the intake air. Normally used to increase the power output from a given engine displacement, but can also be used primarily to reduce exhaust emissions (as on VW's "Umwelt" Diesel engine).

U

Universal joint or U-joint A double-pivoted connection for transmitting power from a driving to a driven shaft through an angle. A U-joint consists of two Y-shaped yokes and a cross-shaped member called the spider.

V

Valve A device through which the flow of liquid, gas, vacuum, or loose material in bulk may be started, stopped, or regulated by a movable part that opens, shuts, or partially obstructs one or more ports or passageways. A valve is also the movable part of such a device.
Valve clearance The clearance between the valve tip (the end of the valve stem) and the rocker arm or tappet. The valve clearance is measured when the valve is closed.
Vernier caliper A precision measuring instrument that measures inside and outside dimensions. Not quite as accurate as a micrometer, but more convenient.
Viscosity The thickness of a liquid or its resistance to flow.
Volt A unit for expressing electrical "pressure" in a circuit. One volt that will produce a current of one ampere through a resistance of one ohm.

W

Welding Various processes used to join metal items by heating the areas to be joined to a molten state and fusing them together. For more information refer to the *Haynes Automotive Welding Manual*.
Wiring diagram A drawing portraying the components and wires in a vehicle's electrical system, using standardised symbols. For more information refer to the *Haynes Automotive Electrical and Electronic Systems Manual*.

Note: *References throughout this index are in the form "**Chapter number**" • "**Page number**". So, for example, 2C•15 refers to page 15 of Chapter 2C.*

Note: *References throughout this index are in the form "Chapter number" • "Page number". So, for example, 2C•15 refers to page 15 of Chapter 2C.*

Note: *References throughout this index are in the form "Chapter number" • "Page number". So, for example, 2C•15 refers to page 15 of Chapter 2C.*

Haynes Manuals – The Complete UK Car List

Title	Book No.
ALFA ROMEO Alfasud/Sprint (74 - 88) up to F *	0292
Alfa Romeo Alfetta (73 - 87) up to E *	0531
AUDI 80, 90 & Coupe Petrol (79 - Nov 88) up to F	0605
Audi 80, 90 & Coupe Petrol (Oct 86 - 90) D to H	1491
Audi 100 & 200 Petrol (Oct 82 - 90) up to H	0907
Audi 100 & A6 Petrol & Diesel (May 91 - May 97) H to P	3504
Audi A3 Petrol & Diesel (96 - May 03) P to 03	4253
Audi A4 Petrol & Diesel (95 - 00) M to X	3575
Audi A4 Petrol & Diesel (01 - 04) X to 54	4609
AUSTIN A35 & A40 (56 - 67) up to F *	0118
Austin/MG/Rover Maestro 1.3 & 1.6 Petrol (83 - 95) up to M	0922
Austin/MG Metro (80 - May 90) up to G	0718
Austin/Rover Montego 1.3 & 1.6 Petrol (84 - 94) A to L	1066
Austin/MG/Rover Montego 2.0 Petrol (84 - 95) A to M	1067
Mini (59 - 69) up to H *	0527
Mini (69 - 01) up to X	0646
Austin/Rover 2.0 litre Diesel Engine (86 - 93) C to L	1857
Austin Healey 100/6 & 3000 (56 - 68) up to G *	0049
BEDFORD CF Petrol (69 - 87) up to E	0163
Bedford/Vauxhall Rascal & Suzuki Supercarry (86 - Oct 94) C to M	3015
BMW 316, 320 & 320i (4-cyl) (75 - Feb 83) up to Y *	0276
BMW 320, 320i, 323i & 325i (6-cyl) (Oct 77 - Sept 87) up to E	0815
BMW 3- & 5-Series Petrol (81 - 91) up to J	1948
BMW 3-Series Petrol (Apr 91 - 99) H to V	3210
BMW 3-Series Petrol (Sept 98 - 03) S to 53	4067
BMW 520i & 525e (Oct 81 - June 88) up to E	1560
BMW 525, 528 & 528i (73 - Sept 81) up to X *	0632
BMW 5-Series 6-cyl Petrol (April 96 - Aug 03) N to 03	4151
BMW 1500, 1502, 1600, 1602, 2000 & 2002 (59 - 77) up to S *	0240
CHRYSLER PT Cruiser Petrol (00 - 03) W to 53	4058
CITROËN 2CV, Ami & Dyane (67 - 90) up to H	0196
Citroën AX Petrol & Diesel (87 - 97) D to P	3014
Citroën Berlingo & Peugeot Partner Petrol & Diesel (96 - 05) P to 55	4281
Citroën BX Petrol (83 - 94) A to L	0908
Citroën C15 Van Petrol & Diesel (89 - Oct 98) F to S	3509
Citroën C3 Petrol & Diesel (02 - 05) 51 to 05	4197
Citroen C5 Petrol & Diesel (01-08) Y to 08	4745
Citroën CX Petrol (75 - 88) up to F	0528
Citroën Saxo Petrol & Diesel (96 - 04) N to 54	3506
Citroën Visa Petrol (79 - 88) up to F	0620
Citroën Xantia Petrol & Diesel (93 - 01) K to Y	3082
Citroën XM Petrol & Diesel (89 - 00) G to X	3451
Citroën Xsara Petrol & Diesel (97 - Sept 00) R to W	3751
Citroën Xsara Picasso Petrol & Diesel (00 - 02) W to 52	3944
Citroen Xsara Picasso (03-08)	4784
Citroën ZX Diesel (91 - 98) J to S	1922
Citroën ZX Petrol (91 - 98) H to S	1881
Citroën 1.7 & 1.9 litre Diesel Engine (84 - 96) A to N	1379
FIAT 126 (73 - 87) up to E *	0305
Fiat 500 (57 - 73) up to M *	0090
Fiat Bravo & Brava Petrol (95 - 00) N to W	3572
Fiat Cinquecento (93 - 98) K to R	3501
Fiat Panda (81 - 95) up to M	0793
Fiat Punto Petrol & Diesel (94 - Oct 99) L to V	3251
Fiat Punto Petrol (Oct 99 - July 03) V to 03	4066
Fiat Punto Petrol (03-07) 03 to 07	4746
Fiat Regata Petrol (84 - 88) A to F	1167
Fiat Tipo Petrol (88 - 91) E to J	1625
Fiat Uno Petrol (83 - 95) up to M	0923
Fiat X1/9 (74 - 89) up to G *	0273
FORD Anglia (59 - 68) up to G *	0001
Ford Capri II (& III) 1.6 & 2.0 (74 - 87) up to E *	0283
Ford Capri II (& III) 2.8 & 3.0 V6 (74 - 87) up to E	1309
Ford Cortina Mk I & Corsair 1500 ('62 - '66) up to D*	0214
Ford Cortina Mk III 1300 & 1600 (70 - 76) up to P *	0070
Ford Escort Mk I 1100 & 1300 (68 - 74) up to N *	0171
Ford Escort Mk I Mexico, RS 1600 & RS 2000 (70 - 74) up to N *	0139
Ford Escort Mk II Mexico, RS 1800 & RS 2000 (75 - 80) up to W *	0735
Ford Escort (75 - Aug 80) up to V *	0280
Ford Escort Petrol (Sept 80 - Sept 90) up to H	0686
Ford Escort & Orion Petrol (Sept 90 - 00) H to X	1737
Ford Escort & Orion Diesel (Sept 90 - 00) H to X	4081
Ford Fiesta (76 - Aug 83) up to Y	0334
Ford Fiesta Petrol (Aug 83 - Feb 89) A to F	1030
Ford Fiesta Petrol (Feb 89 - Oct 95) F to N	1595
Ford Fiesta Petrol & Diesel (Oct 95 - Mar 02) N to 02	3397
Ford Fiesta Petrol & Diesel (Apr 02 - 07) 02 to 57	4170
Ford Focus Petrol & Diesel (98 - 01) S to Y	3759
Ford Focus Petrol & Diesel (Oct 01 - 05) 51 to 05	4167
Ford Galaxy Petrol & Diesel (95 - Aug 00) M to W	3984
Ford Granada Petrol (Sept 77 - Feb 85) up to B *	0481
Ford Granada & Scorpio Petrol (Mar 85 - 94) B to M	1245
Ford Ka (96 - 02) P to 52	3570
Ford Mondeo Petrol (93 - Sept 00) K to X	1923
Ford Mondeo Petrol & Diesel (Oct 00 - Jul 03) X to 03	3990
Ford Mondeo Petrol & Diesel (July 03 - 07) 03 to 56	4619
Ford Mondeo Diesel (93 - 96) L to N	3465
Ford Orion Petrol (83 - Sept 90) up to H	1009
Ford Sierra 4-cyl Petrol (82 - 93) up to K	0903
Ford Sierra V6 Petrol (82 - 91) up to J	0904
Ford Transit Petrol (Mk 2) (78 - Jan 86) up to C	0719
Ford Transit Petrol (Mk 3) (Feb 86 - 89) C to G	1468
Ford Transit Diesel (Feb 86 - 99) C to T	3019
Ford Transit Diesel (00-06)	4775
Ford 1.6 & 1.8 litre Diesel Engine (84 - 96) A to N	1172
Ford 2.1, 2.3 & 2.5 litre Diesel Engine (77 - 90) up to H	1606
FREIGHT ROVER Sherpa Petrol (74 - 87) up to E	0463
HILLMAN Avenger (70 - 82) up to Y	0037
Hillman Imp (63 - 76) up to R *	0022
HONDA Civic (Feb 84 - Oct 87) A to E	1226
Honda Civic (Nov 91 - 96) J to N	3199
Honda Civic Petrol (Mar 95 - 00) M to X	4050
Honda Civic Petrol & Diesel (01 - 05) X to 55	4611
Honda CR-V Petrol & Diesel (01-06)	4747
Honda Jazz (01 - Feb 08) 51 - 57	4735
HYUNDAI Pony (85 - 94) C to M	3398
JAGUAR E Type (61 - 72) up to L *	0140
Jaguar MkI & II, 240 & 340 (55 - 69) up to H *	0098
Jaguar XJ6, XJ & Sovereign; Daimler Sovereign (68 - Oct 86) up to D	0242
Jaguar XJ6 & Sovereign (Oct 86 - Sept 94) D to M	3261
Jaguar XJ12, XJS & Sovereign; Daimler Double Six (72 - 88) up to F	0478
JEEP Cherokee Petrol (93 - 96) K to N	1943
LADA 1200, 1300, 1500 & 1600 (74 - 91) up to J	0413
Lada Samara (87 - 91) D to J	1610
LAND ROVER 90, 110 & Defender Diesel (83 - 07) up to 56	3017
Land Rover Discovery Petrol & Diesel (89 - 98) G to S	3016
Land Rover Discovery Diesel (Nov 98 - Jul 04) S to 04	4606
Land Rover Freelander Petrol & Diesel (97 - Sept 03) R to 53	3929
Land Rover Freelander Petrol & Diesel (Oct 03 - Oct 06) 53 to 56	4623
Land Rover Series IIA & III Diesel (58 - 85) up to C	0529
Land Rover Series II, IIA & III 4-cyl Petrol (58 - 85) up to C	0314
MAZDA 323 (Mar 81 - Oct 89) up to G	1608
Mazda 323 (Oct 89 - 98) G to R	3455
Mazda 626 (May 83 - Sept 87) up to E	0929
Mazda B1600, B1800 & B2000 Pick-up Petrol (72 - 88) up to F	0267
Mazda RX-7 (79 - 85) up to C *	0460
MERCEDES-BENZ 190, 190E & 190D Petrol & Diesel (83 - 93) A to L	3450
Mercedes-Benz 200D, 240D, 240TD, 300D & 300TD 123 Series Diesel (Oct 76 - 85)	1114
Mercedes-Benz 250 & 280 (68 - 72) up to L *	0346
Mercedes-Benz 250 & 280 123 Series Petrol (Oct 76 - 84) up to B *	0677
Mercedes-Benz 124 Series Petrol & Diesel (85 - Aug 93) C to K	3253
Mercedes-Benz A-Class Petrol & Diesel (98-04) S to 54	4748
Mercedes-Benz C-Class Petrol & Diesel (93 - Aug 00) L to W	3511
Mercedes-Benz C-Class (00-06)	4780
MGA (55 - 62) *	0475
MGB (62 - 80) up to W	0111
MG Midget & Austin-Healey Sprite (58 - 80) up to W *	0265
MINI Petrol (July 01 - 05) Y to 05	4273
MITSUBISHI Shogun & L200 Pick-Ups Petrol (83 - 94) up to M	1944
MORRIS Ital 1.3 (80 - 84) up to B	0705
Morris Minor 1000 (56 - 71) up to K	0024
NISSAN Almera Petrol (95 - Feb 00) N to V	4053
Nissan Almera & Tino Petrol (Feb 00 - 07) V to 56	4612
Nissan Bluebird (May 84 - Mar 86) A to C	1223
Nissan Bluebird Petrol (Mar 86 - 90) C to H	1473
Nissan Cherry (Sept 82 - 86) up to D	1031
Nissan Micra (83 - Jan 93) up to K	0931
Nissan Micra (93 - 02) K to 52	3254
Nissan Micra Petrol (03-07) 52 to 57	4734
Nissan Primera Petrol (90 - Aug 99) H to T	1851
Nissan Stanza (82 - 86) up to D	0824
Nissan Sunny Petrol (May 82 - Oct 86) up to D	0895
Nissan Sunny Petrol (Oct 86 - Mar 91) D to H	1378
Nissan Sunny Petrol (Apr 91 - 95) H to N	3219
OPEL Ascona & Manta (B Series) (Sept 75 - 88) up to F *	0316
Opel Ascona Petrol (81 - 88)	3215
Opel Astra Petrol (Oct 91 - Feb 98)	3156
Opel Corsa Petrol (83 - Mar 93)	3160
Opel Corsa Petrol (Mar 93 - 97)	3159
Opel Kadett Petrol (Nov 79 - Oct 84) up to B	0634
Opel Kadett Petrol (Oct 84 - Oct 91)	3196
Opel Omega & Senator Petrol (Nov 86 - 94)	3157
Opel Rekord Petrol (Feb 78 - Oct 86) up to D	0543
Opel Vectra Petrol (Oct 88 - Oct 95)	3158
PEUGEOT 106 Petrol & Diesel (91 - 04) J to 53	1882
Peugeot 205 Petrol (83 - 97) A to P	0932
Peugeot 206 Petrol & Diesel (98 - 01) S to X	3757
Peugeot 206 Petrol & Diesel (02 - 06) 51 to 06	4613
Peugeot 306 Petrol & Diesel (93 - 02) K to 02	3073
Peugeot 307 Petrol & Diesel (01 - 04) Y to 54	4147
Peugeot 309 Petrol (86 - 93) C to K	1266
Peugeot 405 Petrol (88 - 97) E to P	1559
Peugeot 405 Diesel (88 - 97) E to P	3198
Peugeot 406 Petrol & Diesel (96 - Mar 99) N to T	3394
Peugeot 406 Petrol & Diesel (Mar 99 - 02) T to 52	3982

* Classic reprint

CL24.08/09

Preserving Our Motoring Heritage

< The Model J Duesenberg
Derham Tourster.
Only eight of these
magnificent cars were
ever built – this is the
only example to be found
outside the United States
of America

Almost every car you've ever loved, loathed or desired is gathered under one roof at the Haynes Motor Museum. Over 300 immaculately presented cars and motorbikes represent every aspect of our motoring heritage, from elegant reminders of bygone days, such as the superb Model J Duesenberg to curiosities like the bug-eyed BMW Isetta. There are also many old friends and flames. Perhaps you remember the 1959 Ford Popular that you did your courting in? The magnificent 'Red Collection' is a spectacle of classic sports cars including AC, Alfa Romeo, Austin Healey, Ferrari, Lamborghini, Maserati, MG, Riley, Porsche and Triumph.

A Perfect Day Out

Each and every vehicle at the Haynes Motor Museum has played its part in the history and culture of Motoring. Today, they make a wonderful spectacle and a great day out for all the family. Bring the kids, bring Mum and Dad, but above all bring your camera to capture those golden memories for ever. You will also find an impressive array of motoring memorabilia, a comfortable 70 seat video cinema and one of the most extensive transport book shops in Britain. The Pit Stop Cafe serves everything from a cup of tea to wholesome, home-made meals or, if you prefer, you can enjoy the large picnic area nestled in the beautiful rural surroundings of Somerset.

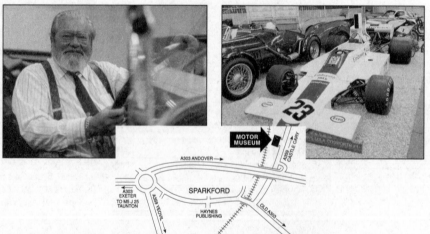

> John Haynes O.B.E.,
Founder and
Chairman of the
museum at the wheel
of a Haynes Light 12.

< Graham Hill's Lola
Cosworth Formula 1
car next to a 1934
Riley Sports.

The Museum is situated on the A359 Yeovil to Frome road at Sparkford, just off the A303 in Somerset. It is about 40 miles south of Bristol, and 25 minutes drive from the M5 intersection at Taunton.
Open 9.30am - 5.30pm (10.00am - 4.00pm Winter) 7 days a week, *except Christmas Day, Boxing Day and New Years Day*
Special rates available for schools, coach parties and outings Charitable Trust No. 292048